S

ARCHITECT'S SQUARE FOOT COSTBOOK 2014 EDITION

Architect's Square Foot Costbook 2014

ISBN 978-1-58855-145-0

Table of Contents

Tenant Build-Out and Healthcare Facilities

No matter what the economic conditions are, businesses will grow, change, and need updated facilities to perform their operations. With many areas of the country experiencing low-rent levels along with a large amount of vacancies, many businesses are choosing to move into larger, more modern facilities keeping the Tenant Build-Out market busy.

The *2014 Architect's Square Foot Costbook* focuses on Tenant Build-Outs and Hospital construction. Construction projects for the healthcare industry continue to move forward in the midst of this tough economic climate as large health care systems and regional hospitals build new facilities while modernizing existing facilities. These areas, along with commercial renovations, will be areas of growth for the next few years.

This manual will help you delve into the costs of these construction types with detailed square foot costs of hospitals, tenant build-outs, and renovations. Each of the 65 projects and their building systems are completely broken down so you can easily calculate the cost impact of modifications and enhancements to your projects.

This manual also features:

- Detailed costs for each of the case studies, enabling design professionals to "mix and match" components to more closely follow their own designs.
- Regional modifiers that can be used to adjust costs to local markets.
- An extensive index to assist in quickly finding every component related to your project.

Part One

Square Foot Costs

Every case study is described in a short summary. These summaries are given to provide insight into the circumstances and requirements behind the design. A building's function or location often influences the choice of building materials and thus the cost. Site limitations and local building and zoning codes are factors that have to be taken into consideration. Budget constraints, material availability and personal expertise of an individual builder all affect a project's outcome. Wherever appropriate, these types of issues are explained in the descriptions that accompany each case study. Further, when costs within one or more of the CSI divisions for the project are abnormally high or low, an explanation is usually provided.

Building Case Studies Included In This Edition

File 1:

J&S Construction recently completed work on the Stones River Manor Independent Living Facility located in Murfreesboro, Tenn. This $1.2 million addition to the faith-based, not-for-profit senior living organization was designed and built to be energy efficient and environmentally friendly. The project is the first LEED certified independent care facility in Tennessee.

J&S Construction designed and built the project to meet LEED for Homes requirements and received LEED Gold Certification June 2012. The 7,500 square-foot, nine-unit addition includes energy efficiencies such as spray foam insulation, Energy Star(R) windows, Energy Star(R) appliances, compact fluorescent lighting, reduced envelope leakage rates and insulated duct in unconditioned spaces. In addition to being LEED certified, all nine units are Energy Star(R) Certified.

"Stones River Manor is committed to excellence in the services we provide, a commitment that J&S shares, which is reflected in the quality of their work," said Kirkland Mason, CEO of Stones River Manor.

In addition to the energy savings, the project focused on water efficiency, indoor air quality, types of materials used, as well as thoughtful land use and landscaping. Other environmentally friendly features of the project include:

- 40% of the Construction Waste being diverted from landfill and was recycled;
- The utilization of drought-resistant plants for landscaping;
- The project being designed so that at least 70% of the buildable land, not including area under the roof, is permeable;
- The framing waste factor for this project being limited to less than 10;
- This project being located within ½ mile of 14 community resources.

As part of the LEED for Homes program, each unit was inspected and tested by independent third parties to ensure all requirements were met. The building committee for Stones River Manor originally requested LEED Silver Certification, but J&S Construction used its expertise in energy-efficient design and construction to build and certify the project as LEED Gold Certified with no additional costs to the owners.

"Energy savings was important to Stones River Manor," said Brad Leimer, project manager and LEED AP for J&S Construction. "This project was designed to be 29% more efficient than the current code requirements."

The project was also built with durability by focusing on reducing the effects of water and moisture, reducing air infiltration, reducing the risks from pests, reducing heat loss and ultraviolet radiation and reducing the effects of natural disasters. Some of these strategies included vapor retarder under the slab, exhausting fans in all bathrooms and kitchen to the exterior, foam being filled around exterior windows, exterior doors and other exterior building penetrations, separating all wood to concrete connections, and installing rafter tie hurricane clips at all wall to rafter connections.

Code	Division Name	%	Sq. Cost	Projected
01	General Requirements	12.03	20.80	156,982
03	Concrete	10.05	17.38	131,148
04	Masonry	8.48	14.66	110,661
06	Wood, Plastics, and Composites	7.25	12.53	94,613
07	Thermal and Moisture Protection	12.10	20.92	157,897
08	Openings	4.86	8.41	63,446
09	Finishes	16.37	28.31	213,650
10	Specialties	0.83	1.43	10,776
11	Equipment	2.49	4.31	32,557
21	Fire Suppression	3.40	5.87	44,341
22	Plumbing	9.69	16.75	126,449
23	HVAC	6.18	10.69	80,699
26	Electrical	6.28	10.85	81,898
	Total Building Costs	100.00	172.91	1,305,117

COST PER SQUARE FOOT = $172.91

File 2:

A number of creative, innovative and technologically advanced solutions were implemented to modernize Augusta-Richmond County's infrastructure. Over time, the government predicts many of those upgrades will deliver cost savings far greater than the original expenditure. Heery's role as lead adviser to the client on design and construction issues resulted not only in significant short-term cost savings across projects, but also in smart long-term recommendations.

The Reynolds Street parking garage was initially designed to provide parking for the Augusta Convention Center, which is being built across Reynolds Street. The 650-space, $12 million parking deck was paid for with a 3-cent local car rental tax and special-purpose local-option sales tax funds. Designed to respect the style of surrounding historic buildings and to blend in with the downtown's existing architecture, the parking garage is one of several building projects in the county either completed or in the works.

Facing a backlog of voter-approved Special Purpose Local Option Sales Tax (SPLOST) projects that needed to be guided to completion, Augusta-Richmond County selected Heery to oversee renovations to some of the consolidated city-county's most noteworthy structures, as well as several new construction projects. Projects include the expansion of the county jail, design and construction of a new main library, new judicial center, exhibition center and Sheriff's Administrative Headquarters; and renovations to the Municipal Building, and the Augusta Museum of History.

Code	Division Name	%	Sq. Cost	Projected
01	General Requirements	11.99	6.22	1,331,403
03	Concrete	58.87	30.54	6,536,144
04	Masonry	0.22	0.11	24,098
05	Metals	2.72	1.41	301,973
07	Thermal and Moisture Protection	2.29	1.19	253,778
08	Openings	8.66	4.49	961,908
09	Finishes	1.45	0.75	160,996
10	Specialties	1.24	0.64	137,489
11	Equipment	1.52	0.79	168,483
14	Conveying Systems	2.26	1.17	250,967
21	Fire Suppression	0.74	0.38	82,389
22	Plumbing	2.05	1.07	228,132
26	Electrical	5.53	2.87	613,610
28	Electronic Safety and Security	0.46	0.24	51,042
	Total Building Costs	100.00	51.88	11,102,411

COST PER SQUARE FOOT = $51.88

File 3:

Since 1959 the Patriarch of the Hicks family, Mr. Ed Hicks, has been affiliated with the automotive industry in one form or another. From owning a Phillips 66 gas station in Austin to working his way from salesman to manager at Patterson Chevrolet in Detroit. Less than a decade later Mr. Hicks moved the family from Michigan to Corpus Christi where he obtained his first Texas Auto Dealer License. That was the beginning of the Hicks family legacy of single and multi-franchise dealerships including Datsun, Volkswagen, Porsche, Audi, BMW, Nissan, Mercedes-Benz, and Infinity.

Seeing vibrant growth, the Hicks family began their extended relationship with the construction industry in 2004 when they broke ground on their Nissan facility. A few years later they expanded their operations with a stand-alone pre-owned facility. Fully accustomed to the benefits of global branding the family decided it was time to build a Mercedes-Benz Autohaus facility.

Design started after a thorough analysis of the program and the use of BIM software to create a 3D model of the proposed design was complete. On April 22, 2010 construction began on the 25,273-square-foot facility following a series of meetings with the family: Mr. Ed Hicks (Founder), Mrs. Gloria Hicks (Partner), Mr. Charles Hicks (Dealer Principal) and Mrs. Debbie Layton (Controller). The doors opened for business in June 2011.

The building features key design elements of the program that portray a sense of welcome, familiarity, transparency, openness, unencumbered product representation and customer convenience. Some of the key branding elements incorporated in the building include the triple-finned capital at the columns, entry portal, 45 degree angles at the exposed beams, signage, Autohaus furniture, lighting, colors and finishes throughout.

Once you enter the showroom doors you step into a two story space surrounded by full height glass. The "skeleton" of the building is exposed throughout the showroom. Surrounded by structural steel and glass the 6 display vehicles on the showroom floor stand out as the primary focal points. To your right you see a glass enclosed New Vehicle Delivery and to your left runs the "spine" of the building leading the customer from sales through a warm apricot enveloped customer lounge and boutique to the service department.

A delightful kid's play area is visible from both sales and service areas and directly across from Mrs. Gloria Hicks' office where she greets each customer with a warm smile. The lounge is equipped with business stations and a café. The openness of the plan extends further with a view into the service shop through a large window from the customer lounge. The enclosed service drive has visibility the length of the drive into the service writer's area and lounge.

The building shell is a combination of steel framing and concrete masonry units on a suspended concrete foundation. Behind the service shop is a freestanding car wash.

The site features concrete pavement with brick pavers at the sidewalk. Vehicle display pads showcase vehicles along the front of the property surrounded by coastal landscaping.

Code	Division Name	%	Sq. Cost	Projected
01	General Requirements	23.76	43.73	1,105,281
03	Concrete	13.31	24.50	619,260
04	Masonry	4.18	7.70	194,551
05	Metals	7.47	13.75	347,558
06	Wood, Plastics, and Composites	1.43	2.63	66,347
07	Thermal and Moisture Protection	8.38	15.41	389,549
08	Openings	9.97	18.35	463,811
09	Finishes	10.61	19.52	493,444
10	Specialties	0.39	0.71	18,055
22	Plumbing	3.79	6.97	176,258
23	HVAC	6.75	12.42	313,960
26	Electrical	9.62	17.71	447,632
28	Electronic Safety and Security	0.33	0.61	15,361
	Total Building Costs	100.00	184.03	4,651,067

COST PER SQUARE FOOT = $184.03

File 4:

The Beaumont Community Credit Union is a credit union serving the employees of the City of Beaumont, Texas. They represent a diverse group of citizens and wished to move and build a new credit union building, which represented their community and its heritage. The site is located along one of Beaumont's major streets, MLK Parkway. It was the former location of a large feed store and grain warehouse and adjacent to the railroad line, as were many of Beaumont's mercantile establishments which were built in the late 1800's and early 1900's. The warehouse had long been demolished prior to the purchase of the property by the Credit Union. Because of the site's history the exterior design is reminiscent of an early 1900's rail station. Exterior detailing follows a traditional Georgian style with its Doric columns and divided light windows.

The building is situated on the site for maximum visibility from the 5-lane MLK Parkway. The building tower, over 30 feet tall, contains the Credit Union logo and can be seen from a distance both north and south of the site. The site is entered from a city cross street because it is not directly accessible from MLK. The site plan is one of an organic layout of parking and drives which is in stark contrast to the strong lineal lines of the building. Customer and employee parking are located in front of the building while the Credit Union's three drive-thru windows are located at the rear of the building. The site is landscaped with native trees and flowering shrubs indicative of the site geographic location. Planting were designed so that the site always has seasonal color throughout the year.

The interior of the building is a traditional design, which reflects the exterior style of the building. Earth tone colors along with walnut stained cabinets, doors and wood moldings add to the rich feel of the interiors. The colors and furnishings invite customers in and give them the feeling of being at home. Light fixtures reflect a traditional setting and add to the richness of the furnishings. The interior spaces include union lobby, offices, teller areas, vault, conference rooms, restrooms and a break area. The building surrounds the lobby. The lobby provides a natural separation between private offices and more public spaces such as the conference and break areas.

Code	Division Name	%	Sq. Cost	Projected
01	General Requirements	11.17	27.59	90,149
03	Concrete	9.69	23.93	78,186
04	Masonry	8.47	20.94	68,398
06	Wood, Plastics, and Composites	9.18	22.69	74,126
07	Thermal and Moisture Protection	6.45	15.94	52,070
08	Openings	8.07	19.94	65,135
09	Finishes	4.63	11.44	37,379
10	Specialties	3.77	9.31	30,422
12	Furnishings	1.41	3.49	11,387
22	Plumbing	3.56	8.79	28,703
23	HVAC	7.40	18.29	59,757
26	Electrical	25.07	61.95	202,377
28	Electronic Safety and Security	1.12	2.76	9,003
	Total Building Costs	100.00	247.04	807,092

COST PER SQUARE FOOT = $247.04

File 5:

The Central Contra Costa Sanitary District (CCCSD) was formed in 1946, and currently serves a 146 mile area of Contra Costa County, in Northern California. Centrally located within the District, is the Collection System Operations (CSO) Department, responsible for the cleaning, maintenance, and repair of the District's 1,500 miles of underground pipeline.

The original CSO Facility was constructed in 1956. The 5.15 acre site, with a 70-foot elevation change, is bounded by the I-680/24 Highway Interchange, the Bay Area Rapid Transit (BART) District, and by Springbrook Road, a public street leading to a residential area. Overhead High Voltage transmission lines bisect the site east-to-west.

The facility includes Crew Operations, Warehousing, Administration, Training, and Lockers and Showers. The Secure Site includes Vehicle Storage, Covered Material Bins and Loading Area, Yard Storage, Fueling Stations, and Training areas. A separate, existing Vehicle Maintenance Facility shares the site. The original facilities no longer met the operational, spatial, and technological needs of the District and the CSO Department. A new CSO Facility was designed to accommodate present and future operations and technology needs, improved site circulation, training facilities, site storage, and a Secondary Emergency Operations Center (EOC) for the District.

The new CSO Facility consolidates the Crews, Administration, and Warehousing in a single, two-story building. Due to the topography of the site, the yard is divided into Lower, Middle, and Upper Yards; the new CSO Facility is nestled into the hillside separating the Lower and Middle Yards. A central Second Floor Crew Room, which also serves as Training Rooms and EOC, with adjoining Kitchen, provides a gathering place for the Crews to plan and collaborate on their daily work schedules, and opens onto the Middle Yard. Adjacent to the Crew Room are separate Workrooms for the Construction and Cleaning Crews, and the Technical Services support areas. Mud Rooms, Locker Rooms, and Showers are provided for the Crews returning at the end of the day. Administration Offices and the Warehouse are located on the First Floor, and opens onto the Lower Yard. Public Entry is situated mid-level between the two floors, due to the topography.

The CSO Facility utilizes a concrete slab with drilled pier and pad foundations, a 20-foot high Tie-Back Retaining Wall to retain the hillside, and structural steel framing with concrete and metal decks. Concrete Wall Panels envelope the Warehouse area. Roofing is a reflective SBS Membrane Roofing, with Metal Sunshades. The metal exterior cladding with the curtain wall and concrete invoke the clean lines of the building.

The CSO Facility is LEED-registered, and is pursuing LEED-Gold. Environment and Energy Planning includes High-Efficient HVAC Equipment, Hydronic Floor Heating and Low-Velocity Fan, Low-Flow Plumbing Fixtures, Site Stormwater Filtration through Pervious Pavement, Bio-Swales, and a Roof Garden. Windows are abundant throughout, with exterior Sunshades, and an automated interior Shading System, to provide views and daylighting, and are complimented by Energy-Efficient Light Fixtures, with motion sensors. Polished Concrete Floors and Recycled Countertops are used throughout the facility, and Low-emitting Materials on all interior finishes.

Code	Division Name	%	Sq. Cost	Projected
01	General Requirements	11.48	29.07	790,221
03	Concrete	13.49	34.15	928,206
04	Masonry	0.83	2.09	56,836
05	Metals	11.31	28.65	778,655
06	Wood, Plastics, and Composites	2.08	5.26	143,038
07	Thermal and Moisture Protection	6.44	16.31	443,322
08	Openings	6.98	17.67	480,266
09	Finishes	10.39	26.31	715,188
10	Specialties	1.95	4.95	134,512
11	Equipment	0.62	1.57	42,627
12	Furnishings	1.31	3.31	89,991
14	Conveying Systems	1.58	4.01	108,936
21	Fire Suppression	1.40	3.56	96,621
22	Plumbing	3.44	8.71	236,817
23	HVAC	13.76	34.85	947,269
26	Electrical	11.42	28.93	786,234
28	Electronic Safety and Security	1.51	3.83	104,200
	Total Building Costs	100.00	253.24	6,882,938

COST PER SQUARE FOOT = $253.24

File 6:

HMN Architects, Inc. recently finished work on the new, 112-bed Henry County Detention Center. The 29,000-square-foot facility includes Work Release, a kitchen, training room and a law enforcement center. The building has expansion capabilities giving Henry County the option to add courts in the future, if necessary.

In addition to designing the law enforcement and detention center, HMN was originally retained by the County to assist the Citizens' Jail Committee in assessing the need for a new Jail. After the need had been established, HMN aided the County in site selection, choosing an underutilized commercial site located near the historic courthouse. Later, HMN helped with the bond referendum process providing information concerning design, cost estimates and graphics and appearing at public hearings.

The County Commission used the innovative approach of dividing the bond referendum into three separate votes: a Detention Center, Justice Center and 911 expansion vote. The Detention Center proved popular, easily passing, while the Justice Center and 911 expansion did not. This allowed the much needed Detention Center project to go forward on the first vote.

HMN's design team faced a few challenges relating to the site's size. After reviewing the area needs, operational philosophy and staffing requirements, the team determined a single, enclosed control area would best meet the County's security needs. Security electronics and mechanical space were placed in a mezzanine above the control room providing maximum secure access and reducing the overall project footprint on the downtown site.

The Henry County Detention Center uses tilt-up concrete. Thin faced brick and "stone" accents were part of the system allowing the facility to integrate well with the adjacent historic downtown.

Skylights in the dayrooms provide natural light. A combined indoor/outdoor recreation yard offers minimum American Correctional Association (ACA) requirements for recreation in a shared space, while reducing overall construction cost. A single, indirect supervision control post allows 360° views to all inmate housing areas and recreation.

Code	Division Name	%	Sq. Cost	Projected
00	Procurement and Contracting Require	5.80	17.10	496,404
01	General Requirements	14.07	41.48	1,204,339
03	Concrete	22.24	65.57	1,903,531
08	Openings	0.21	0.63	18,162
09	Finishes	12.97	38.23	1,109,757
11	Equipment	8.22	24.24	703,661
12	Furnishings	3.62	10.67	309,672
21	Fire Suppression	1.07	3.16	91,637
22	Plumbing	7.24	21.33	619,330
23	HVAC	8.94	26.36	765,302
26	Electrical	15.61	46.01	1,335,718
	Total Building Costs	100.00	294.76	8,557,513

COST PER SQUARE FOOT = $294.76

File 7:

Auld & White Constructors completed the construction of Fire Station #40 as a design-build project along with Dasher Hurst Architects. The contract agreement with the City of Jacksonville was to construct a new two-story, free-standing Fire Station, consisting of structural steel, poured concrete, a composite deck 2nd floor, a bar joist and metal deck roof structure, and a 12-inch concrete tilt-panel wall system, designed to withstand 150 mph winds at 3 second gusts and the wave action created by a 14-foot storm surge. This unique building faces the beautiful St. Johns River and is located off of Heckscher Drive in Jacksonville, Fla. This land and marine based facility is anticipating LEED certification, and is used as a post storm operations/search and rescue center. Auld & White received a 2012 Excellence in Construction (Eagle) Award from the Associated Builders and Contractors (ABC) First Coast Chapter. The architect received a Merit Award from the American Institute of Architects (AIA) Jacksonville Chapter.

Code	Division Name	%	Sq. Cost	Projected
00	Procurement and Contracting Require	18.86	51.85	503,125
01	General Requirements	14.41	39.61	384,332
03	Concrete	21.51	59.14	573,880
04	Masonry	1.23	3.39	32,912
05	Metals	4.76	13.10	127,094
06	Wood, Plastics, and Composites	2.23	6.14	59,529
07	Thermal and Moisture Protection	2.01	5.53	53,679
08	Openings	5.92	16.26	157,806
09	Finishes	6.61	18.18	176,372
10	Specialties	3.24	8.91	86,466
12	Furnishings	0.20	0.54	5,265
14	Conveying Systems	1.23	3.39	32,912
21	Fire Suppression	0.67	1.84	17,842
22	Plumbing	2.46	6.75	65,518
23	HVAC	4.91	13.50	131,036
26	Electrical	6.95	19.09	185,272
27	Communications	1.56	4.30	41,687
28	Electronic Safety and Security	1.23	3.38	32,759
	Total Building Costs	100.00	274.91	2,667,485

COST PER SQUARE FOOT = $274.91

File 8:

Nestled into northern Indiana woods, Cameron Woods provides a new, supportive senior living facility for the Angola area. Sponsored by Cameron Woods Hospital of Angola, the project is a first venture for the hospital into outpatient, extended care and is proving quite successful.

Visitors approaching Cameron Woods get their first glimpse of the facility as a grand lodge set into a park-like wooded setting - both tranquil and welcoming. The site also offers relaxed dining overlooking one of Indiana's few remaining undeveloped lakes. Several wetland areas on the thirteen acre site created challenges - both in finding ways to preserve those areas and in situating the building in a reasonable fashion to respect the wetlands. With the site being heavily wooded, another goal was to preserve as many of the natural amenities as possible.

The broad expanse of the covered front entrance welcomes residents and visitors alike, while providing protection from the elements and a great place for warm-weather chats with friends after supper. The timed lighting controls provide secure entering and leaving after dark.

Cameron Woods offers 48 assisted living units of varying sizes - from studio apartments to one-and two-bedroom units, many with dens. Bay windows and walk-in closets add to the overall appeal of the units.

While the apartments have cooking facilities, the main dining room provides a place for residents to meet and enjoy dinner together. There is even a jigsaw puzzle waiting on one table for someone ambitious. Food preparation is handled in the full-service commercial kitchen.

Other amenities include a large multipurpose room for community interaction and "theme lounges" for TV and board games, for baking, and for reading. The library offers computers for research, writing, and the Internet. Another popular place is the "Cafe", a great place to meet before or after dinner and to enjoy popcorn or an occasional wine-tasting. Easy access to both floors is achieved by the centrally-located elevator.

Tranquil blues and greens create a relaxing interior - enhanced by the warm gleam of brass accents. Outside relaxation opportunities include walking paths to explore the woods, a screened porch, and raised planter boxes for hands-on, close-to-nature "growing opportunities".

The site is near the city limits of Angola, and city services were extended to serve the Cameron Woods site. Many specific design features of the project were with the needs of seniors in mind, not the least of which was accessibility. The structure was stick-built construction, and there was not a prevailing wage scale on the job as it was not required.

The owner was quite involved in all stages of the project - from initial exploration into ways to achieve the greatest value for their investment to selection of the exterior color scheme. Their involvement and interest helped create a cohesive working team for the project. Offering both independence and security to residents attractively inside and out, Cameron Woods has provided a welcomed addition to the Angola area.

Code	Division Name	%	Sq. Cost	Projected
00	Bidding Requirements	4.22	5.00	248,070
01	General Requirements	3.36	3.98	197,329
03	Concrete	5.01	5.94	294,677
04	Masonry	0.67	0.80	39,466
05	Metals	0.16	0.19	9,397
06	Wood & Plastics	18.13	21.48	1,065,950
07	Thermal & Moisture Protection	6.35	7.53	373,421
08	Doors & Windows	10.94	12.96	643,103
09	Finishes	15.91	18.85	935,150
10	Specialties	2.01	2.38	118,209
12	Furnishing	0.81	0.96	47,547
14	Conveying Systems	0.97	1.15	57,131
15	Mechanical	21.61	25.60	1,270,232
16	Electrical	9.85	11.67	579,018
	Total Building Costs	100.00	118.48	5,878,701

COST PER SQUARE FOOT = $118.48

File 9:

The owner/developer, KJV Development Corporation, envisioned Autumn Woods Assisted Living with a building design that included generously sized residential units and varied types and sizes of common use areas. The aim was to create an assisted living residence which truly provided all the comforts of home. These goals, as well as the desire to position this building competitively in the rental market, were the main tasks facing Dahn & Krieger Architects Planners PC upon beginning the project.

The site is located within an existing business park, and the site backs up to a stream, making the usable shape of the site rather long and narrow. The building form responds to the shape of the site while still presenting a residential type front porch entry sequence. The site was developed to provide for varying types of exterior spaces at several locations around the building.

The structural system consists of metal stud bearing walls with concrete plank floors. Structural steel framing is minimal, occurring only in the large first floor public space. Exterior walls are framed with a metal stud curtainwall system. The pitched roof is built with fire treated wood trusses. This system allows for prefabrication of nearly all the major building components, greatly condensing the construction phase and allowing for a speedy enclosure of the building shell.

Exterior finish materials are residential in scale and character, including brick, vinyl siding, wood trim and vinyl double-hung windows with insulating glass. Interior finishes include wood base, trim and moldings, vinyl wall covering and carpet. Finishes are varied from floor to floor, giving each area its own identity and aiding in way finding by the residents.

Residential units are heated and cooled by through-wall heating and cooling units, giving residents total control of their own unit's environment. Public spaces and corridors are treated by small packaged heating and cooling units disbursed throughout the building, eliminating the need for a large central mechanical plant as well as providing for individual control of spaces depending on usage.

The building is organized around a central activities core at the first and second floors. Public use spaces at the first floor include a hair salon, library, wellness center, exercise room, country kitchen, multipurpose room and residents' store. Connecting these two activity areas is a traditional open wood stair, which contributes to the residential feel of the space. Additional smaller scale living room areas are disbursed on each floor, providing residents with varied opportunities for interaction.

One wing of the first floor is designed as a self-contained unit of 13 units for residents with early stage Alzheimer's disease. This unit includes a dining area, residential-type kitchen, activity area and a secure exterior garden area, providing these special needs residents with a contained and safe living environment.

Residential units vary in size from basic studio units of 360-square-feet to large one-bedroom units of 700-square-feet. All units have large closet areas, fully accessible bathrooms and kitchenettes with a small refrigerator-freezer unit and microwaves. Oversized windows maximize natural daylight and connect the residents to the building surroundings.

Code	Division Name	%	Sq. Cost	Projected
00	Bidding Requirements	9.22	15.20	1,016,530
03	Concrete	10.07	16.61	1,110,337
04	Masonry	2.64	4.35	290,726
05	Metals	7.05	11.63	777,848
06	Wood & Plastics	8.75	14.43	964,514
07	Thermal & Moisture Protection	4.30	7.10	474,700
08	Doors & Windows	5.31	8.75	585,286
09	Finishes	17.69	29.18	1,950,715
10	Specialties	1.30	2.15	143,917
11	Equipment	2.79	4.60	307,649
14	Conveying Systems	1.57	2.60	173,568
15	Mechanical	19.37	31.95	2,136,116
16	Electrical	9.94	16.40	1,096,371
	Total Building Costs	100.00	164.94	11,028,276

COST PER SQUARE FOOT = $164.94

File 10:

Grand Meadows Glen is a 12-unit Congregate Housing unit that follows a prototypical design created by The Evangelical Lutheran Good Samaritan Society.

Since the intended use is to provide housing for the area seniors, the building has two different unit styles.

Built on an average sized site adjacent to the existing nursing facility, it offers 2, two-bedroom units and 10, one-bedroom units. Each unit contains a full bath which is fully accessible along with a shower, a full kitchen with cabinets, over the range microwave/hood, refrigerator, stove and pantry. The kitchens adjoin the living rooms which contain a bay window for a spacious feel. The bedrooms contain large closets and a window. All windows are operable.

Units are cooled by individual units and they are heated by hot water heat. Unit baths are exhausted by individual fans. Common areas are heated by hot water heat and cooled by a central HVAC unit. The building is fully protected by an automatic sprinkler system.

This unit along with others is designed to provide a warm and friendly place to enjoy companionship while receiving moderate supportive services. This is ideal for a person who likes more company, and who can benefit from some assistance.

This Congregate Community has a large common dining room with outdoor patio accessibility, kitchen and a laundry facility. The services and social areas in the residence are the main difference between congregate living and senior living. The services usually include one or more meals every day, 2 hours of house keeping each month, accessible call system for emergency services and scheduled transportation.

The Good Samaritan Society began serving the community in the early 1920's with $2,000 and a mission to help others in need. The first center opened in a six-room home in Arthur, North Dakota in 1923. The Society later grew from providing services to physically and mentally handicap persons to providing services to elders and others with special needs.

Today the Society operates facilities in 25 states, employs 21,000 staff members and serves more than 28,000 residents.

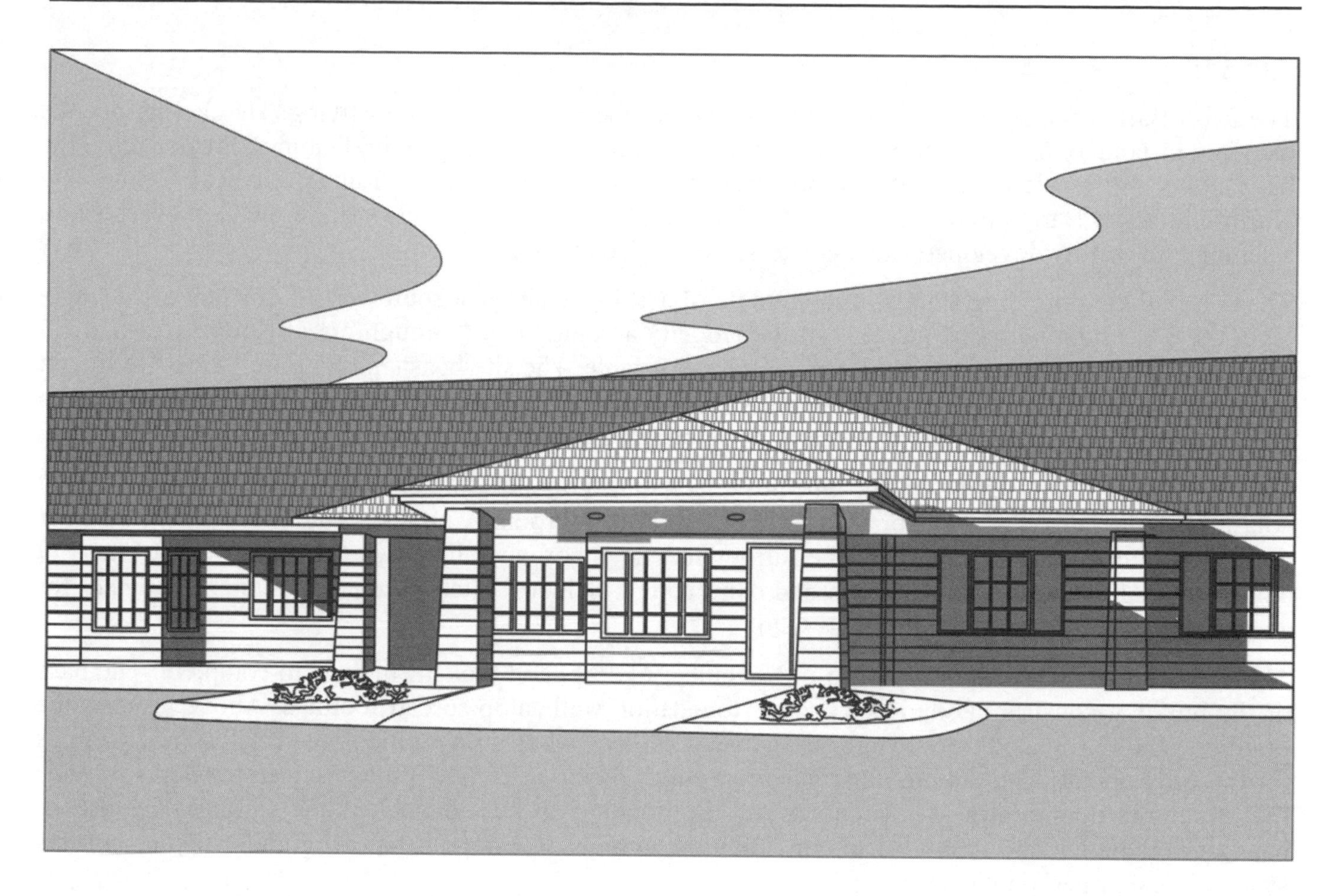

Code	Division Name	%	Sq. Cost	Projected
00	Bidding Requirements	6.11	7.70	96,242
01	General Requirements	6.11	7.70	96,242
03	Concrete	11.00	13.86	173,236
04	Masonry	0.18	0.23	2,887
05	Metals	0.27	0.34	4,235
06	Wood & Plastics	21.73	27.38	342,237
07	Thermal & Moisture Protection	5.90	7.44	92,970
08	Doors & Windows	6.75	8.50	106,251
09	Finishes	10.05	12.66	158,222
10	Specialties	1.08	1.36	16,939
11	Equipment	3.85	4.85	60,633
12	Furnishings	0.37	0.46	5,775
15	Mechanical	17.43	21.96	274,483
16	Electrical	9.18	11.56	144,556
	Total Building Costs	100.00	125.99	1,574,907

COST PER SQUARE FOOT = $125.99

File 11:

The Rush Barton Supportive Living Facility embodies the forefront of senior living. The facility opened its doors in January of 2001. Designed by the architectural firm of Mann, Gin, Dubin & Frazier, Ltd., the building is the result of a joint venture between Rush-Presbyterian-St. Luke's Medical Center and Northfield based Barton Senior Care L.L.C. This residence is the first of its kind in the City of Chicago; a senior care facility developed expressly to serve low income seniors.

The solid looking building stands in the middle of a 1.5 acre site just southwest of downtown Chicago. With the CTA running trains just east of the property and the main thoroughfare of Roosevelt Road 1.5 blocks north, transportation to and from is easily navigable. The site boasts parking for 38 cars, wrought iron and masonry fencing surrounding fully landscaped grounds, and a quarter acre courtyard with concrete patios and a gazebo to allow early morning sun gazing.

On the interior, the facility offers amenities including complete kitchen and dining room, a skylit solarium, four TV lounges, a library, a chapel, and activity room, wellness center, hair salon, 24-hour security services, and great views of the surrounding neighborhood and downtown area. Each of the 139 apartments (133 studios and 6 two-bedroom units) includes kitchenette, bathrooms designed for accessibility, and an emergency alert system.

The construction of this facility began in November of 1999 and took 14 months to complete. The base of the building consists of shallow concrete foundation walls atop spread footings. Above ground, the building's bulk is created from load bearing masonry block walls with multicolored brick skin. Openings for the fully operational, double-hung windows punch the brick facade. Precast concrete planks provide the structural floor plates. The majority of the building is heated and cooled through the use of baseboard radiation and through-wall air conditioning units. Rooftop air handling units supplement this system in the larger, public spaces.

This project highlights BABCO Construction's devotion to the senior care/living industry, and illustrates their ability and continued success in providing unique facilities in a wide range of markets.

Code	Division Name	%	Sq. Cost	Projected
00	Bidding Requirements	1.66	2.59	214,363
01	General Requirements	11.41	17.79	1,469,550
03	Concrete	11.18	17.42	1,439,664
04	Masonry	12.64	19.70	1,627,611
05	Metals	1.78	2.77	229,234
06	Wood & Plastics	4.87	7.59	627,125
07	Thermal & Moisture Protection	1.77	2.75	227,349
08	Doors & Windows	5.15	8.03	663,244
09	Finishes	9.66	15.06	1,244,105
10	Specialties	0.51	0.79	65,674
11	Equipment	3.60	5.62	464,096
14	Conveying Systems	1.25	1.95	160,960
15	Mechanical	21.74	33.89	2,799,826
16	Electrical	12.78	19.93	1,646,438
	Total Building Costs	100.00	155.88	12,879,241

COST PER SQUARE FOOT = $155.88

File 12:

Oak Terrace is a 54 unit assisted living and memory care facility, with 38 assisted and 16 Alzheimer units. Only the lower level of one half of the building encompasses the memory care facility and is kept separate from the assisted living facility for security purposes.

The entire design of Oak Terrace's interior decor portrays a warm, inviting, home-like atmosphere for the residents who live there. Some key features of the interior include decorative oak moldings, French doors, custom wood casework, and special woodcarvings throughout. A double-sided, field stone fireplace serves the library and the living room simultaneously. A curved grand staircase leading to the second floor includes a finely detailed curved oak railing with carved wood pedestals. A built-in glass waterfall adds acoustic ambiance to the atrium space and provides a focal point while ascending the curved stairs to the next level.

The main entrance to the building is enhanced with the inclusion of a large drive under canopy constructed to compliment the exterior of the building while providing much needed function for protected drop offs of the residents. As one enters the facility you are met with an inviting and comfortable sitting area. The main office is centrally located nearest the primary entrance and has large windows allowing clear view of all whom enter or leave the facility. The first floor utilizes a kitchen that is centrally located to serve separate dining rooms for the assisted living and the Alzheimer's residents independently. In addition, there is also a small secluded dining area available for residents and family members who wish to have private dining events with their loved ones.

The floor plan of the facility allows for support services to be shared in the building. This simple yet commonly overlooked design feature allows both the Alzheimer's and assisted living buildings to conveniently use the services of the common areas, yet remain separated and secured. Security is always paramount when designing memory care facilities. A security system, with Wanderguard(R) protection, was designed to provide both the tenant and staff with the necessary required levels of security found in memory care facilities. The Alzheimer wing also includes a beautiful outdoor fenced-in courtyard complete with a gazebo, walking paths, and beautiful gardens. Looking out onto the courtyard spaces is a large multipurpose dining room and half of the resident rooms.

The exterior of the building is detailed with traditional design elements that make use of brick masonry, vinyl windows with integral mullions, permanent siding, stone details, crown moldings, and asphalt shingles. The stone keystones provide a decorative accent to the face of the building giving it a truly high-end residential appeal.

Code	Division Name	%	Sq. Cost	Projected
01	General Requirements	11.80	12.58	563,042
03	Concrete	7.57	8.06	360,939
05	Metals	5.93	6.32	283,085
06	Wood, Plastics, and Composites	13.92	14.83	663,808
07	Thermal and Moisture Protection	3.72	3.97	177,637
08	Openings	8.67	9.24	413,397
09	Finishes	12.02	12.81	573,548
10	Specialties	1.10	1.18	52,630
11	Equipment	2.85	3.04	135,977
12	Furnishings	1.63	1.74	77,739
14	Conveying Systems	1.13	1.21	54,136
22	Plumbing	16.21	17.27	773,115
23	HVAC	2.80	2.98	133,373
26	Electrical	7.74	8.25	369,138
27	Communications	0.22	0.23	10,486
28	Electronic Safety and Security	2.69	2.87	128,353
	Total Building Costs	100.00	106.57	4,770,404

COST PER SQUARE FOOT = $106.57

File 13:

The site for the Greater Nashua YMCA was a City owned parcel adjacent to a community hockey rink, community football/soccer stadium and historic public park with walking trails. Part of the site was over a former landfill that had to be monitored while appropriately removed. The site was then capped and vented under the slab on grade building. The site was at the edge of an existing parking lot that is shared with the other community recreational facilities.

The site suggested a long, thin building plan organized along a double loaded spine with an aquatics facility on the south side, the gymnasium at the other end with the locker rooms and studios in between. A conference/lounge overlooks the aquatics facility. The kids' spaces have direct access to the fenced playground. The fitness area is on the second level overlooking the pool with a walking track that circles the gym. The building is designed to accept a second floor addition of approximately 5,600 square feet over the Kid Stop and multi-purpose spaces that would expand the second floor fitness capacity and provide additional offices.

The open concept is an effort to maximize natural light and to encourage the users to be aware of all the activities available at the facility while still creating a sense of place for each activity. Lighting, materials, and colors are used to enhance this concept. The building provides a high performance envelope. The HVAC system includes natural gas fired high performance boilers with water source heat pumps, cooling tower and remote ERV ventilation. The aquatics center is treated with a dehumidifier and large ceiling fan.

Code	Division Name	%	Sq. Cost	Projected
00	Procurement and Contracting Require	2.92	4.66	233,035
01	General Requirements	5.50	8.78	438,757
03	Concrete	4.60	7.35	367,303
04	Masonry	6.35	10.14	506,656
05	Metals	10.89	17.38	868,538
06	Wood, Plastics, and Composites	4.52	7.21	360,278
07	Thermal and Moisture Protection	11.75	18.76	937,691
08	Openings	6.49	10.35	517,494
09	Finishes	11.07	17.68	883,461
10	Specialties	1.15	1.84	92,082
11	Equipment	0.56	0.89	44,471
12	Furnishings	0.13	0.20	10,040
13	Special Construction	9.31	14.85	742,406
14	Conveying Systems	0.71	1.13	56,664
23	HVAC	16.64	26.56	1,327,313
26	Electrical	7.41	11.82	591,009
	Total Building Costs	100.00	159.61	7,977,197

COST PER SQUARE FOOT = $159.61

File 14:

The opportunity to serve Our Lady of Lourdes Regional Medical Center, create a new health center for the people of Lafayette, and continue the relationship with our friends there, has been a joy. Our Lady of Lourdes Regional Medical Center (OLOL), located in Lafayette, Louisiana resulted from exceptional collaboration and vision of the clinical teams and the designers of the new replacement campus.

Blending the clinical vision with global strategic objectives for the health system with a design that achieved thousands of functional and clinical objectives into an efficient, flexible and technologically advanced campus was the primary goal of this three-year effort.

Goal achieved. The Art and Science of Health Care Planning and Design relies upon transforming thousands of ideas into a vision that achieves clinical goals and functional objectives and conveys a commitment to faith, healing and compassion. OLOL is a product of this philosophy.

This project provided a procedural platform that allows the staff to be highly efficient in the treatment of patients. The procedural platform is located on the second floor, with an ambulance ramp to the Emergency Department, in order for the Emergency Department to remain adjacent to the Surgery and Imaging Departments. All patient rooms are same-handed and private with large windows overlooking the grounds. Green roofs and exterior respite areas are incorporated so that the staff and patients can enjoy the outdoor environment adjacent to the patient floors.

The six-floor, 410,273-square-foot facility houses all acute-care clinical services, has 192 private patient rooms and rests on a 45-acre Greenfield site in a growing area of Lafayette. This state-of-the-art acute care hospital has 1,500 parking spaces and a 16,000-square-foot Central Energy Plant designed for future growth. The hospital is also structurally engineered for the future expansion of two additional floors.

The Replacement Hospital will be the epicenter of the OLOL campus, which will additionally include a Cancer Center, Heart Hospital, Ambulatory Surgery Center, Convent, Spa/Fitness Center, and an Outpatient Clinic and MOB.

TEG's "Efficient Design+ Productive Care" Design Strategy allowed OLOL to incorporate innovative and efficient clinical features and relationships that are based on EBD findings from TEG Health Research.

Code	Division Name	%	Sq. Cost	Projected
01	General Requirements	20.65	87.76	36,003,966
03	Concrete	5.93	25.22	10,347,117
04	Masonry	1.90	8.09	3,319,178
05	Metals	9.03	38.38	15,745,562
06	Wood & Plastics	2.32	9.85	4,042,750
07	Thermal & Moisture Protection	5.17	21.97	9,014,257
08	Doors & Windows	1.86	7.91	3,245,024
09	Finishes	10.82	45.99	18,866,425
10	Specialties	0.23	0.98	403,896
11	Equipment	0.84	3.56	1,459,107
12	Furnishings	0.13	0.54	223,509
13	Special Construction	0.17	0.72	295,005
14	Conveying Systems	2.07	8.80	3,608,459
15	Mechanical	25.15	106.92	43,865,645
16	Electrical	13.73	58.38	23,950,276
	Total Building Costs	100.00	425.06	174,390,176

COST PER SQUARE FOOT = $425.06

File 15:

West Calcasieu Cameron Hospital located in Sulphur, Louisiana is a part of the southwestern Louisiana Gulf Coast region for the past 57 years. The hospital was established as a community hospital in 1953 in which the hospital has provided experienced physicians, skilled health care professionals, state of the art medical technology and a great reputation for caring for their patients. Their primary market includes Calcasieu and northern Cameron parishes, but patients come as far as Southeast Texas for medical care.

West Calcasieu Cameron Hospital is a 101-bed hospital in which this is the second major addition in its history. Construction for the Radiology and ICU expansion project began in early 2008 and was funded by the taxpayer approved $25 million capital bond issue of 2006. This addition is part of a three phase construction project in which this is phase one. Phase one includes the following:

The First Floor has the Diagnostic Imaging with an MRI, Nuclear Medicine, CT, Ultrasound, Mammography, X-Ray Rooms and a Cath Lab. This addition is now the new front door for the hospital with plenty of parking for patients, drop off canopy and four private registration booths. The Diagnostic Imaging Department is adjacent to the Emergency Department.

The Second Floor has the Intensive Care Unit with twelve new beds, large waiting room for ICU patients, waiting room for Surgery patient families and Respiratory Therapy. ICU is adjacent to the Surgery Department.

The Third Floor is a mechanical Penthouse and will be used as a connection to the patient tower that will be constructed in a later phase.

There are two remaining phases in the master plan, phase two will feature a new patient tower with outpatient services on the ground level and phase three will expand the laboratory, dietary and materials management departments. When all three phases are complete this will be considered a replacement hospital on the existing site.

Code	Division Name	%	Sq. Cost	Projected
00	Procurement and Contracting Require	8.98	22.05	1,086,784
03	Concrete	9.52	23.38	1,152,366
04	Masonry	3.76	9.23	455,018
05	Metals	10.83	26.61	1,311,503
06	Wood, Plastics, and Composites	4.14	10.17	501,416
07	Thermal and Moisture Protection	7.18	17.63	868,824
08	Openings	6.38	15.67	772,338
09	Finishes	13.42	32.97	1,625,079
10	Specialties	1.30	3.18	156,892
11	Equipment	0.81	2.00	98,481
13	Special Construction	0.25	0.60	29,763
14	Conveying Systems	2.08	5.10	251,541
23	HVAC	21.36	52.47	2,585,850
26	Electrical	10.01	24.59	1,211,908
	Total Building Costs	100.00	245.67	12,107,764

COST PER SQUARE FOOT = $245.67

File 16:

Union Hospital is a not-for-profit health care system that was established in 1892. In April of 2007 Union Hospital began planning for a major addition to their hospital in hopes that they could redefine healthcare delivery for Terre Haute and West Central Indiana.

Union Hospital was uniquely designed to incorporate a four-story atrium with a sloping glass curtain wall system as the building's central unifying element. The atrium extends from the lower level to the third-floor and injects natural daylight into the building. Within the atrium are two major feature walls, which playfully highlight solid and void forms to create a dynamic space. The 492,348-square-foot facility has four floors above grade with a lower level that houses dietary, chapel, meeting and waiting spaces. The atrium acts as public circulation and access to all of the building's outpatient functions.

In addition to the atrium, the remainder of the building's exterior skin is primarily composed of brick veneer and architectural precast concrete with metal stud back up. The palette of materials and colors unifies the building with the previously established campus aesthetic.

The first floor becomes a procedural platform where co-located functions will improve staff efficiency and patient experience. The hospital's major ancillary functions including Emergency Department, Diagnostic Imaging, and Surgery are located here with shell space for future cath labs.

The second, third and fourth floors house the nursing units of this new addition. These floors utilize a combination of centralized and decentralized nursing work areas, a concept that was a part of a specific planning effort that focused on reducing nursing travel distances. Evidence based design suggests that moving the care giver closer to the patient will improve clinical outcomes. The core support spaces are arranged so that the travel time from supply areas to patient care areas is minimized. A staff only internal corridor reduces traffic and noise in the patient corridors to enhance the patient experience and promote healing. Patient rooms face either the exterior or the atrium to provide visually stimulating views for both patients and visitors that helps enhance comfort and well being.

A strong emphasis was placed on staff and patient safety. This resulted in a design that embraces a consistent patient room layout as well as patient rooms and patient restrooms designed specifically to accommodate bariatric patients. Bariatric patient lifts and other design features were incorporated to ensure the optimum safety of the staff and comfort for the patient.

The building's natural daylight, open public spaces, warm and inviting finishes and well designed patient areas have made Union Hospital a truly distinct healthcare provider. This new addition will ensure that Union Hospital is able to continue providing efficient and highly functional healthcare for West Central Indiana.

Code	Division Name	%	Sq. Cost	Projected
00	Procurement and Contracting Require	6.73	17.89	8,807,002
01	General Requirements	5.89	15.66	7,709,194
03	Concrete	7.84	20.84	10,261,405
04	Masonry	2.26	6.00	2,955,391
05	Metals	9.24	24.55	12,085,205
06	Wood, Plastics, and Composites	2.03	5.39	2,653,695
07	Thermal and Moisture Protection	3.50	9.30	4,577,841
08	Openings	4.11	10.93	5,381,706
09	Finishes	12.01	31.91	15,709,961
10	Specialties	1.03	2.74	1,351,076
11	Equipment	0.13	0.33	164,622
13	Special Construction	0.77	2.05	1,007,246
14	Conveying Systems	1.80	4.78	2,354,250
21	Fire Suppression	1.28	3.40	1,673,373
22	Plumbing	16.81	44.69	22,002,402
23	HVAC	6.68	17.76	8,742,087
26	Electrical	17.89	47.56	23,413,766
	Total Building Costs	100.00	265.77	130,850,221

COST PER SQUARE FOOT = $265.77

File 17:

In 2006, Hoefer Wysocki Architects (HWA) was selected to master plan, design and construct a replacement hospital for Cass County. As there was no sufficient space available at the current site, the Board of Trustees purchased 81 acres of land to build a new hospital which allowed them to create a new identity and recapture markets lost due to the perception of care the existing facility had on the county.

HWA created an interior rotunda as a wayfinding element where patients and visitors can see to every major department in the hospital. The replacement hospital was built to house a 21-bed medical/surgical unit, a 4-bed intensive care unit and a 10-bed behavioral health unit plus all outpatient services currently offered. The ability to expand the four main hospital zones for future services was an important element in the design. The design accommodates existing and future patient and staff needs, consolidates specialty clinics and physical therapies on campus, and creates a more efficient, flexible and functional floor plan that supports patient dignity and personhood. The design emphasizes domestic aesthetics, art and warm home-like, non-institutional environments and incorporated natural light and elements of nature to improve the healing process for patients. Healing gardens in the front and back of the hospital allow a view from all areas of the hospital. The concept of bringing the “outdoors inside” was integral in shaping the overall design of the new medical center.

HWA also provided a phased construction and financial plan to meet the goals of the master plan to be completed as one project that is separated into two phases. Multiple schemes, layouts and budgets were also provided giving Cass Regional Medical Center several options to choose from while trying to remain within budget. In addition, HWA addressed three other significant secondary priorities within the plan. First, the new hospital image along the Highway 71 was enhanced by the massing of the new structures, and separate entrances, parking and traffic were provided for Outpatient clinics, Emergency, Admitting and the main hospital, in-patient and same day surgery and the staff and loading dock. Second, the plan provided for the separation of staff and public corridors and ease of wayfinding for the public by identifying a new public image. Also, the basement and loading dock provide vertical access to the patient.

Code	Division Name	%	Sq. Cost	Projected
01	General Requirements	8.44	24.78	3,407,652
03	Concrete	10.64	31.24	4,296,936
04	Masonry	1.95	5.72	786,084
05	Metals	7.10	20.83	2,865,125
06	Wood, Plastics, and Composites	7.13	20.92	2,877,610
07	Thermal and Moisture Protection	5.03	14.77	2,031,802
08	Openings	2.16	6.34	871,258
09	Finishes	11.23	32.99	4,536,724
10	Specialties	0.34	1.01	138,489
11	Equipment	0.88	2.57	354,098
14	Conveying Systems	1.05	3.07	422,088
21	Fire Suppression	0.80	2.36	324,185
23	HVAC	24.47	71.85	9,880,497
26	Electrical	18.79	55.17	7,587,858
	Total Building Costs	100.00	293.62	40,380,405

COST PER SQUARE FOOT = $293.62

File 18:

Coordinated Health has been providing orthopedic surgery and physical therapy to its patients since 1987 when they moved into their first 10,000-square-foot facility. Having provided Coordinated Health with their first successful 20 bed Orthopedic Hospital and Ambulatory Surgical Center in Bethlehem in 2006, Bonsall Shafferman Architects began the design of another facility in nearby Allentown consisting of 79,800 square feet on three floors. This building incorporates an Imaging Center, a Physical Therapy Suite and Orthopedic and Podiatric Offices as well as the Hospital.

An existing three-story office building in the right location was found and work began. All exterior materials were removed. In order to accommodate the extra height needed for the hospital, the third floor was removed. New steel and an EDPM roof were installed along with a new exterior envelope of insulated glass and EIFS meeting the new Energy Code.

In order to extend the necessary services to patients undergoing significant orthopedic and podiatric procedures such as joint replacements, it was necessary to combine the Ambulatory Surgical Center with a new 22 bed short-stay orthopedic hospital. This permits post-operative observation and rehabilitation for a period up to 96 hours. Three 400 square foot and one 600 square foot operatories were constructed on the Third Floor providing a “tree-top” view of the neighboring countryside.

EIFS was chosen for the infill panels around the windows as well as the “brick work”, saving weight and providing great insulation values along with a surprising look and feel. The mandatory entrance canopy for the hospital entrance was constructed using the same materials. Extensive use of bronze glass set into “champagne” bronze aluminum storefront and window components satisfy the owner's desire for a bright and cheery environment, while complimenting the rich brown “brick” and siding; simple, yet elegant. Inside, soft warm neutral tones greet patients, families and staff alike.

Construction of the steel frame building and the interior fit-out, under the direction of North Star Construction Management, Inc., was started in late Summer of 2008 and was completed some ten months later in June of 2009.

Code	Division Name	%	Sq. Cost	Projected
01	General Requirements	3.70	6.21	495,633
03	Concrete	0.47	0.79	62,720
04	Masonry	1.53	2.57	205,306
05	Metals	8.18	13.72	1,094,592
06	Wood, Plastics, and Composites	3.12	5.24	417,959
07	Thermal and Moisture Protection	9.61	16.12	1,286,578
08	Openings	5.94	9.96	794,997
09	Finishes	18.07	30.30	2,417,996
10	Specialties	3.76	6.30	502,762
21	Fire Suppression	2.64	4.43	353,646
22	Plumbing	9.47	15.89	1,267,933
23	HVAC	17.49	29.33	2,340,842
26	Electrical	16.02	26.86	2,143,529
	Total Building Costs	100.00	167.71	13,384,494

COST PER SQUARE FOOT = $167.71

File 19:

Hoefer Wysocki Architects (HWA) designed a 25-bed critical access replacement hospital for Barton County. As there was not sufficient space at the current site, the Board of Trustees purchased 50 acres of land to build a new hospital which allowed them to create a new identity and recapture markets lost due to the perception of care the existing facility had on the county. The site is accessible via a frontage road from US highway 71 and is located within the city limits of Lamar. The replacement hospital was built to house 25 beds plus all outpatient services currently offered. The ability to expand the four main hospital zones for future services to be offered was an important element in the design.

The design accommodates existing and future patient and staff needs, consolidates specialty clinics and physical therapies on campus, and creates a more efficient, flexible and functional floor plan that supports patient dignity and personhood. Our design emphasizes domestic aesthetics, art and warm home-like, non-institutional environments. The goal of the exterior design and interior lobbies was to create a landmark on the highway that captures the “Great Lodge” feeling of southern Missouri.

From the sound of music in the comfortable atrium and the smell of fresh baked cookies to serving healthy nutritious foods, the experience is at Barton County Memorial Hospital is an enjoyable one. Spacious private rooms, along with supportive caregivers trained to make your stay as pleasant as possible; focusing on the individual patient's needs.

Project Highlights: 25-bed patient wing; 14 exam rooms; 6 emergency exam rooms; 2 operating rooms and support space; physical and cardiac therapy services; lab and radiology services; and medical department support services.

Code	Division Name	%	Sq. Cost	Projected
01	General Requirements	14.24	37.92	2,256,347
03	Concrete	6.15	16.38	974,590
04	Masonry	2.91	7.76	461,509
05	Metals	5.69	15.16	902,029
06	Wood, Plastics, and Composites	8.86	23.60	1,404,468
07	Thermal and Moisture Protection	5.90	15.71	934,813
08	Openings	1.63	4.34	258,472
09	Finishes	13.47	35.88	2,134,565
11	Equipment	2.91	7.75	461,266
21	Fire Suppression	0.96	2.55	151,748
22	Plumbing	10.36	27.59	1,641,871
23	HVAC	14.21	37.86	2,252,614
26	Electrical	12.71	33.86	2,014,407
	Total Building Costs	100.00	266.36	15,848,699

COST PER SQUARE FOOT = $266.36

File 20:

Conversations initially began with the McCune-Brooks Regional Hospital's team on how to best continue the McCune-Brooks mission and vision while providing a healing and restorative environment for patients, families, visitors and staff. By working with the themes of water, natural light and the environment as traditional sources of healing, the team began to reinvent the hospital's internal culture and operations, integrating nature as part of the healing process. The result is a facility that is a cultural center for the community, a healthcare resource for the whole person and integrates the latest technology available in patient care.

Patient rooms were designed and constructed for families to effectively participate in the patients' care. The orientation of the bed and locations of furnishings, artwork and other room amenities were carefully crafted with family participation in mind. Each room is equipped with a flat screen television and space for a small refrigerator, so families feel welcome, making their stay less stressful. Several other major design elements throughout the hospital provide patients with a restorative environment with the incorporation of natural daylight and views to nature from the facility, which aid in the reduction of stress. The windows in each patient room are large enough to provide sufficient daylight, even in winter months, with portions of the window sills extending down to the floor, to allow the patients to see the courtyard stream and pond from their bed.

The facility is organized along a central circulation, which fronts a large central courtyard. This space is more than sixty feet in width in response to behavioral studies indicating that courtyards of fewer dimensions limit daylight and is minimally effective in relieving stress. Each patient care area can be expanded, or modified, to suit changing needs. For instance, each clinical department can expand independently into either interior "soft" space or into a defined exterior zone. The location of future stairs and elevators were carefully planned, so that nursing units can expand not only horizontally, but also vertically.

The nursing units are arranged on the south side of the courtyard and are grouped into three pods: the Birthing Center, with four LDRP rooms; the Medical/Surgical Unit; and the shared Rehabilitation and Geri-Psych pod. The nursing concept is based on decentralized patient care with shared staff support spaces. Each patient room has been designed for ADA accessibility and ease of staff assistance to patients. The intensive care rooms were planned to allow for multi-acuity patient care needs. Additional flexibility has been planned in the patient room design, so that medical, surgical and rehabilitation patients may be accommodated in a variety of ways. In addition, each of the psychiatric rooms may be converted to medical, surgical or rehabilitation rooms in the future.

The hospital actively reaches out to the community in a number of ways. The City of Carthage lacks civic facilities where citizens can meet. Part of the new hospital's focus from day one was the incorporation of community rooms, which can be used for community-wide gatherings, health fairs and staff training, as well as a cafeteria that will be an inviting locale for the public. Additionally, the Cardiac Rehabilitation and Physical Therapy Center is planned to be a public amenity, featuring a glass-walled facade facing the water feature and a soaring roof that can be seen from a distance.

McCune-Brooks' mission and vision is strong in Carthage, Missouri. The facility continues to provide state of the art healthcare services by working with the themes of water, natural light and the environment, as traditional sources of healing continuing the legacy of care McCune-Brooks offers.

Code	Division Name	%	Sq. Cost	Projected
01	General Requirements	16.53	51.07	7,300,514
03	Concrete	6.32	19.53	2,791,931
04	Masonry	3.69	11.41	1,631,703
05	Metals	8.86	27.36	3,911,356
06	Wood, Plastics, and Composites	8.55	26.41	3,775,111
07	Thermal and Moisture Protection	5.74	17.73	2,534,324
08	Openings	3.93	12.15	1,736,577
09	Finishes	9.81	30.32	4,334,522
10	Specialties	0.24	0.74	105,999
11	Equipment	0.01	0.04	5,828
21	Fire Suppression	0.90	2.79	398,756
22	Plumbing	7.66	23.66	3,382,808
23	HVAC	12.27	37.90	5,417,555
26	Electrical	15.49	47.86	6,842,064
	Total Building Costs	100.00	308.96	44,169,048

COST PER SQUARE FOOT = $308.96

File 21:

Fitzgibbon Hospital's history dates back to the 1800's, when John Fitzgibbon, an Irish immigrant, settled in Saline County and saw the rising need for healthcare in mid-Missouri. Mr. Fitzgibbon set up a trust to build a hospital upon his death; the hospital was to operate as a private, not-for-profit corporation under a board of directors. Fitzgibbon's estate paid for the construction of the original hospital, which began in March 1922 with the first patient being admitted in April 1923.

Over time, as the healthcare needs of area residents continued to change, the Fitzgibbon Hospital Board decided they could not adequately address the concerns shown in the local community. As a solution to this the Board decided to expand services and recruit additional physicians by constructing a new building. In 1987 they chose a 73- acre site west of Highway 65, across from the Saline County Fairgrounds. The new Fitzgibbon Hospital opened in July of 1991.

HMN Architects, Inc. was retained by Fitzgibbon Hospital in early 2005 to expand the facility to grow selected service lines. This was accomplished with two new additions to the existing hospital totaling 27,000 square feet and a renovation of 12,000 existing square feet. The first addition was a 1-story main entrance to the hospital, which included a new lobby, concierge desk, privatized registration bays, and a gift shop. The second project was a 2-story clinical services addition, which included a new radiology department, sleep labs, clinic space, an education center, as well as new administrative space. The renovated area included an expansion of Women's Center, Emergency Department and the creation of a new Pre-Admission Testing and Ambulatory Care department.

Several principles guided the flow and organization of the newly created and renovated departments including; maximizing separation of inpatient and outpatient traffic through the use of separate corridors; increasing patient privacy through the use of private registration and pre/post operation bays; and providing more appropriately sized staff support and work areas in each department.

The exterior design of the new additions had to incorporate the existing hospitals' distinctive green mansard roof and pitched canopies, which had become the symbol of the hospital within the community, providing an identifiable image, as well as greater visibility from the adjacent roadways. The incorporation of this design was achieved by relocating the existing pitched canopies to the new entrance drive and relocating the second canopy to a newly created outdoor picnic area. The green mansard roof was incorporated into the design with vertical massing elements providing relief from the continuous green band of metal. In addition these massing elements allowed for greater building height, better roadway visibility and signage opportunities for the Hospital.

With the opening of the expansion, Fitzgibbon Hospital will be poised to continue to provide state-of-the-art, compassionate care for many more years to come.

Code	Division Name	%	Sq. Cost	Projected
00	Procurement and Contracting Require	5.80	16.97	661,636
01	General Requirements	10.17	29.72	1,159,022
03	Concrete	3.84	11.23	438,089
04	Masonry	3.34	9.77	381,117
05	Metals	7.79	22.78	888,525
06	Wood, Plastics, and Composites	11.00	32.16	1,254,062
07	Thermal and Moisture Protection	4.40	12.86	501,670
08	Openings	4.26	12.46	485,810
09	Finishes	15.02	43.90	1,712,037
10	Specialties	0.56	1.63	63,653
14	Conveying Systems	0.94	2.74	106,665
21	Fire Suppression	1.31	3.83	149,250
23	HVAC	19.35	56.58	2,206,511
26	Electrical	12.22	35.72	1,393,140
	Total Building Costs	100.00	292.34	11,401,187

COST PER SQUARE FOOT = $292.34

File 22:

In the spring of 2001, Lancaster General Hospital (LGH) concluded that they could improve patient care and outcomes for orthopedic surgery patients if that service line was moved into a separate, yet co-joined facility. The decision to create a new orthopedic hospital integral with the existing campus challenged many longstanding assumptions about the facility; provided a way to fundamentally change the organization of the campus and aligned it with this new vision as LGH moves into the new century.

The project includes a four-story orthopedic hospital, new main entrance atrium building, screen for an existing parking garage, and a 5 ½ story vertical expansion of an existing building for new bed tower.

The new four-story building reestablishes the sidewalk boundary and garden yard for the neighborhood. The new facade presents a studied scale that is sympathetic to the neighboring row houses. The entrance retreats from the street as a concave motor court inviting both vehicles and pedestrians through an elegant walled garden approach to the building. The existing garage has a new screen wall that mimics the exterior language of the Orthopedic Center and extends the new unifying architecture across the south end of the campus.

The entrance atrium has a bridge that sweeps through a stand of structural column trees, connecting the Orthopedic Center with the Existing Hospital. Opposite the front door, an interior water wall offers allure and retreat as a separating screen for the new Chapel area. Other amenities include concierge, gift shop, reception desk, grand piano lounge, patient resource center, and gourmet cafe.

Two second floor waiting areas serve the Perioperative Services. Each is set in the atrium and is designed to make the family time for surgical patients more relaxed. Features of these lounges include seating to accommodate laptops, wireless connections for the public, and family sized, “Romeo & Juliet” balconies to accommodate larger extended families in Lancaster County. The noise of children's play and television viewing has been managed by providing areas for these activities, leaving the lounges free for social conversation.

The new 10 Operating Room Suite is organized with 5 rooms on either side of a sterile core providing better infection control and a location where case carts are staged, to facilitating room turnaround. The operating rooms are identical and fully digitized. The multi-boomed 720 square foot rooms have cameras in the light heads as well as throughout the room giving complete visual access of the surgical field to remote locations. The information management system allows for automated room set-ups as well as the ability to send still and video images to all web enabled locations for instruction and consultation.

The project also built 5½ floors for patient unit expansion including a vertical transportation core for patient circulation. This dedicated patient transport core allows for the movement of inpatients without overlapping public and staff circulation.

After surgery, the patient is moved to one of two orthopedic units on the fourth floor. Two nursing units, an 18 bed total joint unit and a 24 bed general orthopedic unit, share this floor with a dedicated physical and occupational therapy suite. Hospitality sensibilities have been designed into the private patient rooms providing for family/caregiver, patient, and staff. Patient rooms array around the perimeter with a central nursing/support core. Nursing care is delivered using a hybridized model. A primary team station is near the unit entrance and supports the work of the Unit Clerk. Physician consults and dictation occur in a discreet room off of this station. Other nurse work areas are distributed through the core.

The success of this project is tied to the client's desire to be the undisputed leader for orthopedic care in the community. Careful planning and standards of excellence have been applied in detail to this project, leading to a clear increase in patient satisfaction and physician loyalty. The new Orthopedic Hospital and associated additions for Lancaster General have placed it on solid foundations to face the competitive healthcare environment of the new century.

Code	Division Name	%	Sq. Cost	Projected
01	General Requirements	10.08	28.19	9,219,042
03	Concrete	4.34	12.14	3,969,833
04	Masonry	6.19	17.32	5,662,468
05	Metals	9.58	26.79	8,761,920
06	Wood, Plastics, and Composites	1.11	3.11	1,016,689
07	Thermal and Moisture Protection	3.70	10.34	3,382,520
08	Openings	15.39	43.04	14,075,699
09	Finishes	7.36	20.60	6,735,631
10	Specialties	0.55	1.55	505,873
11	Equipment	9.24	25.84	8,450,941
12	Furnishings	1.25	3.49	1,140,201
14	Conveying Systems	2.04	5.71	1,866,455
21	Fire Suppression	1.52	4.26	1,392,499
22	Plumbing	0.01	0.03	10,973
23	HVAC	19.21	53.73	17,569,820
26	Electrical	8.43	23.57	7,706,606
	Total Building Costs	100.00	279.72	91,467,170

COST PER SQUARE FOOT = $279.72

File 23:

Oktibbeha County Hospital is a medical center experiencing significant growth as a result of its position in a dynamic community. Located in Starkville, Mississippi, the medical center is the only hospital in a county that is also home to Mississippi State University. Strong community support coupled with an experienced and highly respected medical staff has pushed Oktibbeha County Hospital forward as one of Mississippi's premier health care leaders.

The multi-phased, $24 million project completed in 2006 focused on dramatic expansion of outpatient surgery and surgery. The project also included new emergency services, laboratory, pharmacy, imaging, and central sterile supply. Other new and expanded services include a new central plant, materials management facility, financial services, and a new staff parking deck.

The primary design challenge of the project involved staging the expansion in a manner to ensure that existing clinical functions continued while new construction and renovation work progressed. The project was organized into four (4) distinct phases and each phase was further subdivided to minimize disruptions of ongoing medical center operations. Phase IV, the South Tower Expansion included several departments. The new construction and renovation included expansion of the Emergency Room, Radiology, Lab, Respiratory Therapy, Pharmacy, Surgery, Central Sterile Supply, and Outpatient Surgery. Outpatient Surgery had the most significant expansion from 1,239 square feet to 14,801 square feet.

The primary construction system of the facility is cast-in-place concrete with a concrete pan-joint floor structural system. Exterior cladding systems include curtainwall, drainable EIFS and face brick. Cast-in-place concrete elevator shafts and stairway shafts provide lateral support of the overall structural system. All mechanical air-handling units are located in rooftop penthouses and each floor is served by mechanical chases that extend from the ground floor to the fourth floor mechanical penthouses.

The construction delivery method of the project was the Construction Management process. The Construction Manager, White Construction Company, was commissioned during the Design Development Phase of the project and worked with the design team to craft bid packages and to coordinate the work of the multiple phases. Ultimately, the bids received on the four phases of the project were below budget; the savings were utilized by the hospital to expand the scope of the project.

Code	Division Name	%	Sq. Cost	Projected
01	General Requirements	3.82	8.22	1,194,647
03	Concrete	13.07	28.16	4,090,882
04	Masonry	0.86	1.84	267,986
05	Metals	3.59	7.74	1,124,350
06	Wood, Plastics, and Composites	1.22	2.62	380,682
07	Thermal and Moisture Protection	3.97	8.56	1,242,788
08	Openings	3.08	6.65	965,459
09	Finishes	12.49	26.92	3,910,309
10	Specialties	0.97	2.08	302,785
11	Equipment	37.33	80.43	11,682,731
22	Plumbing	5.05	10.89	1,581,513
23	HVAC	7.90	17.02	2,472,177
26	Electrical	6.64	14.31	2,079,176
	Total Building Costs	100.00	215.46	31,295,485

COST PER SQUARE FOOT = $215.46

File 24:

The Baylor Regional Medical Center at Plano was constructed on a 21-acre site and consisted of a hospital of 354,400 square feet; a medical office building of 195,000 square feet; a six-level, 1,080 vehicle parking garage; a central plant; and surface parking. Baylor Plano's goal was to first understand the hospital experience from the patient's point of view and second, based on this understanding, to create an environment that eases worries and focuses on health. Every detail of Baylor Plano is part of a healing environment designed to nurture and patient comfort abounds, from the private, well-appointed patient rooms, to the nearby visitors' lounge where family and friends can prepare a meal, socialize or just relax.

The hospital's first phase has inpatient units with 96 beds and a 40 bed day-patient unit. Patient diagnostic and treatment areas include urgent care, imaging, women's health, endoscopy, surgical procedures, catheterization lab, and physical medicine. Hospital support areas are business office, medical records, administration, dietary, laboratory, pharmacy, central processing, materials management, maintenance, security, housekeeping and biomedical engineering. Functionally, hospital diagnostic and treatment activities are located in the lower three stories, including the below grade garden level. Above this base structure is a five-story patient/nursing tower that together provides an impressive and highly visible seven-story facility.

At the lower level, a terraced garden and outdoor courtyard are located outside the cafe, where light filters into the area through the chapel's stained-glass windows, which is the perfect place to enjoy a meal and peaceful surroundings.

On the main floor, access is provided to outpatient care and centralized registration. Additionally, a Concierge Desk for arriving patients, visitors, or conference center attendees along with a cyber cafe and coffee shop bistro are available.

Thanks to a floor plan that puts each nursing station close to the patient rooms as well as a low patient-to-nurse ratio, nurses are never more than 25 steps away. The carpeted patient care floors utilize personal touches and soothing colors in the patient rooms to make recovery as pleasant as possible.

A seven-story medical office building is located across the medical boulevard from the hospital with an enclosed bridge connecting the two. For patient and staff convenience, a six-level, 1,080 vehicle parking structure is situated near the professional office building and main hospital entrance.

Code	Division Name	%	Sq. Cost	Projected
01	General Requirements	9.30	33.37	11,443,527
03	Concrete	19.61	70.38	24,137,405
04	Masonry	2.18	7.82	2,680,387
05	Metals	3.61	12.95	4,442,926
06	Wood & Plastics	3.42	12.26	4,203,516
07	Thermal & Moisture Protection	3.58	12.84	4,404,941
08	Doors & Windows	5.98	21.45	7,356,444
09	Finishes	10.08	36.16	12,402,685
10	Specialties	1.70	6.11	2,096,378
11	Equipment	0.90	3.23	1,106,155
12	Furnishings	0.36	1.30	445,108
13	Special Construction	0.22	0.77	264,755
14	Conveying Systems	2.22	7.98	2,737,900
15	Mechanical	23.44	84.13	28,851,452
16	Electrical	13.40	48.09	16,493,983
	Total Building Costs	100.00	358.84	123,067,562

COST PER SQUARE FOOT = $358.84

File 25:

Somerset Medical Center's new Emergency Department has revolutionized the delivery of emergency care. At 40,000 square feet, the new facility is nearly four times the size of its former quarters, making it one of the largest, best-equipped emergency departments in the state. The new facility is designed to serve 46,000 patient visits/year. Supported by a new 633-space parking garage, the new ED provides 16 triage/fast track exam rooms, 25 private exam rooms, 2 major resuscitation rooms, 2 digital radiographic rooms, a CT room and a self-contained psychiatric evaluation center. Separate ambulance and walk-up patient entrances are provided, along with a large open public waiting area complete with amenities.

The Emergency Department provides direct support to the 70-bed medical/surgical floor above it. The building is designed to support three additional medical/ surgical floors.

The new Medical/Surgical Pavilion is divided into two 35-bed suites; one serves traditional medical/surgical patients while the second suite is dedicated to oncology patients. All rooms are primarily used as single-patient rooms, however; 20 of the rooms (10 in each suite) are designed to have the flexibility to accommodate two patients, when demand for beds is high. The two suites have distinct finish palettes so that each suite has its own identity. In honor of a significant donor, the oncology rooms have a special graphic of the phrase “Carpe Diem” applied to the footwall. This phase is said to embody the attitudes of this special donor.

In order to improve patient service, pairs of rooms are provided with a nurse substation located between the rooms for enhanced access to patient information and amenities. The entrance to each pair of rooms is highlighted through the use of applied materials and colors so as to enliven the rooms with a more “hotel-like” quality. The patient rooms are provided with other amenities, such as flat panel TVs, writing surfaces with Internet connections for the patient and family, in-room refrigerators, enlarged showers, wood and wood accents, vinyl wallcovering and wood plank-like vinyl flooring. In order to reduce the potential institutionalism of the patient rooms, medical gases and services are provided within a wall-mounted wood-finished headwall unit, and behind wall-mounted artwork in the case of the semi-private rooms. All of these features are provided to ensure that the quality of the hospital stay is maximized, while the sense of institution is reduced.

This major expansion, as well as the new Cancer Center being constructed on campus, is part of the reason Somerset was recently recognized by Solucient as one of the top 100 performance improvement leaders in the country. Solucient is an independent health care information company that ranks the nation's best-performing hospitals.

Array Healthcare Facilities Solutions has provided planning, architectural and interior design services to Somerset Medical Center for over 20 years. In addition to the recently completed Emergency Department & Medical Surgical Pavilion, Array is currently designing the Cancer Center. Other recent projects include a new Arrivals Pavilion, Surgical Suite Expansion and Catheterization Lab Expansion.

Code	Division Name	%	Sq. Cost	Projected
00	Bidding Requirements	9.79	33.79	3,779,834
01	General Requirements	8.45	29.16	3,261,688
03	Concrete	4.36	15.04	1,682,731
04	Masonry	1.32	4.56	510,277
05	Metals	5.39	18.61	2,081,937
06	Wood & Plastics	4.21	14.53	1,625,882
07	Thermal & Moisture Protection	8.19	28.24	3,159,606
08	Doors & Windows	4.28	14.75	1,650,327
09	Finishes	12.52	43.21	4,833,491
10	Specialties	0.41	1.40	156,758
14	Conveying Systems	1.23	4.25	475,005
15	Mechanical	27.37	94.45	10,566,176
16	Electrical	12.48	43.06	4,817,322
	Total Building Costs	100.00	345.05	38,601,031

COST PER SQUARE FOOT = $345.05

File 26:

Stormont-Vail HealthCare in Topeka, Kansas, a long-time partner with HMN Architects, Inc. in Overland Park, Kansas, had outgrown their surgery department and was in need of an entirely new unit. After working with the hospital and conducting meetings and interviews with the surgery department, the team developed a plan that accommodated both the hospital's and the community's growing needs.

The replacement surgery and central sterile addition includes 18 new spacious operating rooms, 15 of which were entirely built-out and equipped. The remaining three are shelled space for future expansion. The new department also houses 25 new Pre/Post-Op rooms and a new 19-bay post anesthesia care unit (PACU). A new large central sterile/decontamination unit with sterilization, prep-pack, and clean storage supports the sizable department.

The expansion and renovation also called for a new hospital entry and lobby, because the hospital wanted an atmosphere that was more inviting for patients and their families and other visitors, as well as the staff. A large contemporary canopy identifies the new entry, complimenting the exterior of the existing facility, while giving it more of a modern and innovative look.

Warm tones utilized throughout the new lobby, waiting areas, and surgery registration area create a comforting and healing environment, so that patients and family members can feel more at ease. Special rooms in the waiting areas designated for children allow them to keep busy while they wait. Family rooms adjacent to the waiting areas provide a quiet environment to allow for discussions between physicians and family, as well as provide privacy.

Other features of the expansion project include a new distribution warehouse, receiving area, and three-bay loading dock; an expanded CCU waiting room; and staff support area including generously sized locker rooms, offices, and conference rooms.

SURGERY CENTER ADDITION & RENOVATION

Code	Division Name	%	Sq. Cost	Projected
01	General Requirements	5.46	14.92	2,444,180
03	Concrete	9.05	24.74	4,052,337
04	Masonry	4.76	13.02	2,132,532
05	Metals	8.61	23.55	3,858,693
06	Wood, Plastics, and Composites	4.53	12.39	2,029,201
07	Thermal and Moisture Protection	10.05	27.47	4,500,973
08	Openings	3.48	9.52	1,559,296
09	Finishes	8.82	24.12	3,951,668
10	Specialties	0.49	1.34	219,395
12	Furnishings	0.15	0.40	65,176
14	Conveying Systems	2.48	6.77	1,109,493
21	Fire Suppression	1.10	3.00	491,598
22	Plumbing	27.01	73.87	12,101,303
23	HVAC	1.56	4.25	696,743
26	Electrical	11.82	32.33	5,296,429
28	Electronic Safety and Security	0.65	1.77	289,723
	Total Building Costs	100.00	273.45	44,798,743

COST PER SQUARE FOOT = $273.45

File 27:

The Hoeger House is a two-phase project designed for short-term rehabilitation, as an alternative for patients to receiving rehabilitation in a hospital or nursing home. A residential feel was incorporated throughout the design to begin the separation of the residents from the institutional environment. A communal kitchen, along with private bedrooms and bathrooms assists the patients and therapists in practicing the everyday motions needed to live independently. The Hoeger House is part of a larger expansion of a growing healthcare and retirement community.

Phase I of the Hoeger House project opened in October 2006 and received a Leading Edge in Care and Services Award in May 2007 from the Kansas Association of Homcs and Services for the Aging (Phase I published in the May/June 2008 Design Cost Data). This award is given annually to recognize innovative programs and services focused on the well being of the elderly.

Phase II was completed in 2010. The addition brings the number of private rooms from 19 to 34. It also offers a larger centralized kitchen and improved laundry facilities. The expansion has allowed the hospital to add new services that enhance the short-term rehabilitation experience.

Code	Division Name	%	Sq. Cost	Projected
00	Procurement and Contracting Require	6.56	13.29	183,420
01	General Requirements	11.78	23.88	329,519
03	Concrete	4.69	9.51	131,280
04	Masonry	2.85	5.78	79,732
05	Metals	1.44	2.91	40,177
06	Wood, Plastics, and Composites	17.15	34.77	479,878
07	Thermal and Moisture Protection	5.24	10.62	146,620
08	Openings	6.36	12.90	178,040
09	Finishes	12.37	25.08	346,079
10	Specialties	0.34	0.70	9,646
11	Equipment	0.10	0.19	2,672
12	Furnishings	0.06	0.13	1,743
21	Fire Suppression	1.97	4.00	55,184
22	Plumbing	7.27	14.73	203,305
23	HVAC	9.34	18.93	261,230
26	Electrical	12.49	25.33	349,577
	Total Building Costs	100.00	202.76	2,798,102

COST PER SQUARE FOOT = $202.76

File 28:

Cochise Oncology is a 15,000 square foot, state-of-the-art cancer center located in Sierra Vista, Arizona. Completed in October 2006 the facility was conceived by Dr. Janet Nettleton, a radiation oncologist whose treatment philosophy is based on total patient care. Cochise Oncology offers patients a comfortable and respectful experience in a soothing environment while they receive the latest cancer treatments available. Having comprehensive and innovative cancer services in this growing community allows patients to elect to receive treatment in Sierra Vista rather than travel to Tucson or Phoenix.

The building elevations distinguish it from a traditional hospital - multiple parapet heights and facade depths, interesting angles and a variety of building materials and colors supplant the characteristic broad massing of a traditional hospital. Conveying warmth and human scale, the building also exudes the confidence of the staff members to provide the highest quality services.

Resident doctors requested that their individual practice spaces read more as private entities than as parts of a clinic. Each space functions independently and has its own identity within the facility. Interior design of the building fosters a friendly, home-like atmosphere. The flow of the center, with its warm Southwestern colors, inviting reception area and abundant natural light throughout the building, immerses patients in peaceful surroundings. The mechanical systems are designed using highly effective sound attenuation technologies. Sub-waiting areas for radiation patients as well as the chemotherapy suite open into enclosed landscaped courtyards, connecting visitors to the out-of-doors during their stay. Private, quiet areas are provided for patients and families to gather in.

Cochise Oncology is using the latest technology in radiation therapy, an advanced treatment system called TomoTherapy. There are currently 109 TomoTherapy machines worldwide; Cochise Oncology's unit is the only one in Southern Arizona. Inspectors of the installed equipment found the end result of the installation to be the best they had observed to date. Thoughtful placement of TomoTherapy, HDR therapy and CT Scan equipment allows staff to operate efficiently, provides easy access to operators and maintenance providers, affords privacy and focus for patients and staff.

The facility features radiation therapy and chemotherapy suites, supported by three nurses stations, several exam rooms, a consulting room where doctors meet with patients and family members, a staff area and a spacious reception area. Conference rooms are provided for community support groups; space is also provided for support staff such as counseling, nutritionist, massage therapy and pastoral care specialists.

Code	Division Name	%	Sq. Cost	Projected
00	Procurement and Contracting Require	14.56	54.67	826,982
01	General Requirements	11.00	41.32	624,981
03	Concrete	23.05	86.56	1,309,349
04	Masonry	0.07	0.25	3,769
05	Metals	2.14	8.02	121,327
06	Wood, Plastics, and Composites	6.54	24.56	371,439
07	Thermal and Moisture Protection	4.36	16.38	247,776
08	Openings	4.64	17.44	263,835
09	Finishes	9.93	37.27	563,802
10	Specialties	0.46	1.74	26,294
11	Equipment	0.20	0.74	11,185
12	Furnishings	0.14	0.51	7,778
13	Special Construction	0.32	1.19	18,069
21	Fire Suppression	1.42	5.33	80,690
22	Plumbing	10.14	38.07	575,774
26	Electrical	11.04	41.46	627,072
	Total Building Costs	100.00	375.52	5,680,123

COST PER SQUARE FOOT = $375.52

File 29:

This 88,483 square foot cancer center was designed to provide complete services from radiation oncology to chemotherapy to specialized women's services.

The foundation is cast-in-place reinforced concrete. Exterior walls are metal panels with a brick veneer finish. The building utilizes a membrane roofing system. The exterior features extensive curtainwall recessed beneath concrete overhangs to provide both natural daylight and natural shading into the interior. The exterior design is highlighted by a 3-story entry atrium and sloped curtainwall on the west side of the building.

Interior walls on the second and third floors are gypsum drywall over metal studs. The first floor features 4-10 foot thick concrete walls to accommodate the technical needs of a CT scanner and two linear accelerators. The floor is also of concrete, with tile and terrazzo flooring throughout. The interior also features acoustical ceilings, metal vault and access doors, and wall and corner guards.

The center is a 3-story facility with a fully utilized basement. The basement serves as conference space, storage, and mechanical space. The first floor houses a radiation oncology suite that includes the CT scanner and two linear accelerators, with the expansion capabilities to add a third. Continuing the theme of complete patient care, the first floor also has a reflection room and an enclosed garden available for patient and family use. The second floor is dedicated to chemotherapy oncology suites and specialty care. Additional chemotherapy and women's health suites are on the third floor. The facility is equipped with radiation and lead shielding, as well as a water-based fire suppression system.

Code	Division Name	%	Sq. Cost	Projected
00	Bidding Requirements	1.14	2.40	212,764
01	General Requirements	11.45	24.25	2,145,711
03	Concrete	13.16	27.86	2,464,959
04	Masonry	5.32	11.26	996,417
05	Metals	10.23	21.65	1,915,654
06	Wood, Plastics, and Composites	2.42	5.11	452,554
07	Thermal and Moisture Protection	5.76	12.19	1,078,265
08	Openings	7.80	16.52	1,461,477
09	Finishes	11.32	23.98	2,121,481
10	Specialties	0.39	0.83	73,185
12	Furnishings	0.01	0.03	2,736
13	Special Construction	0.61	1.28	113,573
14	Conveying Systems	1.05	2.21	195,950
21	Fire Suppression	1.64	3.47	307,156
23	HVAC	16.30	34.52	3,054,481
26	Electrical	11.41	24.17	2,138,447
	Total Building Costs	100.00	211.73	18,734,810

COST PER SQUARE FOOT = $211.73

File 30:

Modesto Radiological Institute is a medical imaging group in the central valley of California. The home office in Modesto serves medical groups and hospitals.

Since the population in the area had expanded, business grew; and with many patients traveling from surrounding towns to visit the clinic, there came an opportunity to expand. Modesto Radiological Institute decided to open another facility in the town of Turlock, a half hour drive down the valley.

After a qualifications-based interview, Nacht & Lewis was awarded the contract. The delivery method suggested by the architect was Design-Assist. Cameron Builders, Inc., the general contractor, was brought into the project at the beginning to review drawings and provide cost control during design and documentation. The major trades were competitively bid and the result was faster delivery to the permit phase with no delays for value engineering and a smoother construction process.

The program was for 20,000 square feet of building space with 10,000 square feet for multi-modality imaging in the first phase. The second phase was identified as future lease space for related medical services. The imaging modalities selected were MRI, PET/CT, rad/fluoro, ultrasound, dexa scanner, and required support spaces.

In the initial goal-setting meeting, the client defined patient comfort as their major concern, emphasizing that the path the patient takes should be clear and smooth. A second goal was to achieve comfort and efficiency in work flow for the staff. As a third goal, the client wished to be a part of and serve the local community.

With the three goals in mind, the team came up with a design to accommodate those goals:

- The project is a two-story building. The first phase imaging, located on the ground floor, accommodates the heavy equipment and provides ease of patient access. A two-story lobby space accommodates the entry and waiting rooms, and is easily recognizable from the exterior. Internal circulation was designed around the idea of providing views to the exterior from all staff spaces and one end of all corridors.
- A large part of Turlock's population comes from an Assyrian background. Building forms and landscaping features were designed as gestures to honor the Assyrian population's historic architecture. Stone is used as the major accent material with sloping walls on the east and west ends. The second accent material is zinc, which clads an exit staircase and feature wall at the entry. The fenestration on the lower floor is function-specific.
- The upper floor has horizontal windows with sunscreens to provide flexibility for future tenants. The imaging rooms have windows screened for privacy. Screen walls of landscaping draped over a metal frame will allow for added privacy and solar control when the plants mature. Each corner of the building is treated differently and the waiting room has a large expanse of two-story glazing facing the parking lot. A second wall provides a visual barrier to the parking area and has a horizontal strip of glazing between it and the slab. The feature wall appears to float and has a prominent opening for artwork, to draw attention to the interior and away from the parking outside.

Code	Division Name	%	Sq. Cost	Projected
01	General Requirements	20.00	56.49	1,183,190
03	Concrete	9.16	25.88	542,070
04	Masonry	1.70	4.81	100,777
05	Metals	10.86	30.68	642,551
06	Wood, Plastics, and Composites	2.10	5.93	124,179
07	Thermal and Moisture Protection	3.23	9.14	191,342
08	Openings	7.45	21.06	441,058
09	Finishes	16.69	47.16	987,709
10	Specialties	0.66	1.86	39,031
11	Equipment	2.34	6.61	138,544
12	Furnishings	0.14	0.41	8,537
13	Special Construction	2.63	7.43	155,551
14	Conveying Systems	1.41	3.98	83,288
21	Fire Suppression	0.89	2.51	52,538
22	Plumbing	3.47	9.81	205,473
23	HVAC	10.93	30.87	646,552
26	Electrical	5.86	16.54	346,492
28	Electronic Safety and Security	0.47	1.34	28,060
	Total Building Costs	100.00	282.50	5,916,940

COST PER SQUARE FOOT = $282.50

File 31:

This new Cancer Center unites two previously separate buildings under one roof to provide the public with not only complete clinical services, which range from testing and diagnostics to treatment, but also with a resource for support and learning.

The Cancer Center broke ground in August and the doors were opened to the public 17 months later. Complete outpatient services are provided at the Center for the two major components of the clinical process: radiology/diagnostics and treatment/therapy. The building's floor plan reflects this; you enter at the central lobby space with radiology to your right and medical oncology to your left. This layout allows for more customized patient care; because everything is happening in a single, united center, the entire process is streamlined. The center contains a fully electronic medical records system, which assists not only in registration, but also in generating increased efficiency in communication between the radiology, radiation therapy and oncology departments.

On the diagnostics side, the Cotton O'Neil Cancer Center is truly state-of-the-art, with the only PET/CT scanner in a 13-county region of Kansas. The PET/CT combines both types of scans in one piece of equipment. This makes it one of the most effective tools in cancer diagnosis and staging. The center is also equipped with the second Trilogy Image-Guided Radiotherapy Linear Accelerator within the state of Kansas. This piece of equipment is used to fight cancer, while causing minimal damage to a patient's healthy tissue. The Linear Accelerator sits in a vault made with 15,000 tons of concrete and has a shielded door weighting approximately 5,000 pounds, separating it from the rest of the building. Once inside the vault, patients discover a space that was designed to calm them during the tensest of times. Muted finishes are used throughout, and a dome above the Accelerator uses fiber-optic lighting to portray a starry Kansas night sky.

In keeping with the spirit of customized patient care, the center offers the choice of chemotherapy treatment in three distinct areas. There are six totally private, two family, and eight open chemotherapy treatment areas in the facility. These choices allow the patient to be treated in an environment where they can feel comfortable. In all instances throughout the building there is an emphasis on natural materials and light. Stone, brick and wood are used extensively throughout both the exterior and interior of the Cancer Center and artwork is placed extensively inside to soothe and inspire, rather than overwhelm. A large central area in chemotherapy treatment gives the nursing staff easy access to facilitate the needs of the patients and is comprised of an abundance of natural light.

In addition to diagnosing and treating the disease, the Cancer Center has phlebotomy and clinical services available, equipped with wireless technology to maintain accurate patient records. An impressive clinical research program with 80 to 90 open research trials is also offered at the center. Currently there are 30 to 40 research patients undergoing active treatments and 300 to 400 patients in the follow-up stage of research. A library is located right off the lobby at the building for easy access for both patients and the public. Not only does it offer patients and their families a resource facility where they can gain knowledge of cancer issues, but it also serves as a space where education programs can be held.

Cancer is a disease that affects everyone and The Cotton-O'Neil Cancer Center at Stormont-Vail HealthCare was designed with that in mind. From education to diagnostics to treatment and from staff to patients to visitors, a holistic approach has been taken and improved with the latest technology to create a single place that the community can utilize to increase both their health and awareness.

Code	Division Name	%	Sq. Cost	Projected
01	General Requirements	7.58	17.84	562,401
03	Concrete	9.02	21.24	669,379
04	Masonry	4.26	10.04	316,417
05	Metals	7.39	17.39	548,036
06	Wood & Plastics	8.67	20.42	643,730
07	Thermal & Moisture Protection	5.11	12.03	379,332
08	Doors & Windows	5.42	12.76	402,275
09	Finishes	17.58	41.39	1,304,711
10	Specialties	0.66	1.55	48,856
11	Equipment	0.02	0.04	1,416
15	Mechanical	21.06	49.59	1,563,014
16	Electrical	13.22	31.13	981,276
	Total Building Costs	100.00	235.43	7,420,845

COST PER SQUARE FOOT = $235.43

File 32:

The Center for Total Cancer Care located in Macon, the heart of Georgia and a historical crossroads of the South, stands as a proud beacon of both the city's progressive movement and historical foundation. This shining jewel, easily recognizable by its signature clock tower, is a bold statement of modern composition with conservative materials. Traditional red brick meshes beautifully with brushed aluminum panels. The original building slides into the new addition with ease. The interior provokes a sense of awe as you look up three stories to the exposed structure, yet feel cozy with the orange and brown stained concrete at your feet, brick on the wall, and light pouring in from the signature stairs. Environmentally conscious sunscreens, covered canopy and dramatic day lighting contemporize a traditionally institutional space while embracing the city's natural architectural beauty.

Designed for convenience, this multiuse facility houses all aspects of holistic, patient centered cancer care. The concept was to bring targeted cancer therapy to communities in Macon and Middle Georgia. The goal is to provide comprehensive treatment in one location that can meet the total needs of all cancer care patients in the region.

As an addition and renovation to an existing shell, special care was taken to ensure no interruption to the existing patients' continuing care at the facility. Because of the specific nature of the services provided at this building, and how they integrate with each other for the patients, consideration was given to each doctor, treatments and the patient's path of travel.

With the intention to create an all-encompassing cancer care facility, while backing onto the existing municipal Coliseum, the site posed considerable challenges. These challenges were resolved by utilizing the site to advantage. Underground parking facilities for staff, extensive landscaping to maintain a park-like setting, and using the clock tower as a landmark turned this difficult site from disadvantage to advantage.

An architecturally expressive dialogue exists in a melding of conservative and progressive materials to create a hospitality-like interior. The intent is to distract and inspire the mind and capture natural light into medical spaces that traditionally have none. Capitalizing on the natural soothing qualities of nature and light, a glass shell encapsulates the prominent stairwell and transcends the barrier between interior and exterior environments.

The goal for this project was not to build the most inexpensive medical space; the goal was to build the best medical space possible to provide the convenience of everything a patient needs in one place. The materials used in this building were selected for aesthetics, life-cycle benefits and stellar performance. The combined efforts of all involved parties produced a beautiful and functional solution for both the community and individual patients.

Code	Division Name	%	Sq. Cost	Projected
01	General Requirements	23.40	28.80	1,353,548
03	Concrete	7.21	8.88	417,187
04	Masonry	1.71	2.10	98,825
05	Metals	12.10	14.89	699,924
06	Wood, Plastics, and Composites	4.25	5.23	245,904
07	Thermal and Moisture Protection	6.20	7.63	358,352
08	Openings	6.90	8.50	399,273
09	Finishes	12.52	15.41	724,314
10	Specialties	3.32	4.08	191,970
12	Furnishings	0.24	0.30	14,056
13	Special Construction	0.03	0.04	1,978
14	Conveying Systems	1.40	1.73	81,114
21	Fire Suppression	1.31	1.61	75,567
22	Plumbing	5.13	6.31	296,430
23	HVAC	6.67	8.21	385,961
26	Electrical	7.59	9.34	438,873
	Total Building Costs	100.00	123.06	5,783,277

COST PER SQUARE FOOT = $123.06

File 33:

The Cancer Treatment Center at Union General Hospital emphasizes both therapy and patient/physician education in Blairsville, Georgia, a mountain town on the Georgia-North Carolina border. The Center is a unique collaboration of dedicated radiation and medical oncologists, and two small, rural northeast Georgia hospitals.

Prior to the opening of this facility, patients were required to travel more than 55 miles over steep mountain roads, to receive treatment. The availability of comprehensive cancer treatment encourages more patients to remain in their hometown for services, thus increasing the utilization of the existing hospital.

Based on the nature of cancer detection, and the typical physician referral process, the architecture of the building was intended to be civic and noticeable. When a referring physician directs his patient to the "cancer center behind the hospital", the patient should find more than "the behind of the hospital".

The soaring clock tower slab and lightning rod provide a landmark of distinction. Referring physicians now cite the clock tower as the locating feature. The exterior walls are made of brick and cast stone with large areas of glass. The traditional materials are composed in a somewhat more modern style of clean, sharp lines.

The extensive use of glass storefront with high performance glazing filters light into all parts of the building radiating light throughout, illuminating the open plan.

The curb-less entry and automatic doors of the Center remove any accessible barrier, as many visitors use walkers, wheel chairs, and are typically elderly. The plan is organized around a simple central core, between radiation oncology on the right, medical oncology on the left with the lounge and doctor's offices in the rear.

The Center has a full range of waiting and sub-waiting areas, exam rooms, physician offices, chemotherapy laboratory and infusion area, CT-simulator, radiation treatment vault, physics laboratory and shielding room.

The Center with its simple lines, warm colors, and traditional materials creates a peaceful environment helping patients and their families understand the course of their treatment. Although the design is clean, it is not sterile. The result is a one-of-kind patient-centered design that provides care, comfort, and hope under the pressures of a managed-care environment.

Code	Division Name	%	Sq. Cost	Projected
00	Procurement and Contracting Require	4.44	11.73	119,577
01	General Requirements	18.53	48.92	498,784
03	Concrete	14.03	37.03	377,517
04	Masonry	9.03	23.85	243,117
05	Metals	5.83	15.40	157,016
06	Wood, Plastics, and Composites	4.58	12.08	123,144
07	Thermal and Moisture Protection	4.69	12.39	126,284
08	Openings	5.22	13.78	140,439
09	Finishes	12.35	32.60	332,328
10	Specialties	0.93	2.45	25,013
12	Furnishings	0.26	0.69	7,003
13	Special Construction	0.57	1.51	15,378
21	Fire Suppression	1.46	3.85	39,242
22	Plumbing	3.65	9.63	98,135
23	HVAC	5.32	14.03	143,081
26	Electrical	9.12	24.06	245,337
	Total Building Costs	100.00	263.99	2,691,393

COST PER SQUARE FOOT = $263.99

File 34:

What began, as an adaptive reuse of a turn-of-the-century bank building quickly became a complex architectural project involving rehabilitation, preservation and building addition. The bank was once a cornerstone of a busy commercial street, which fell victim to decline and abandonment in the decades following the sixties. The project is designed to provide 27,000 square feet of class “A” office space for use as corporate headquarters.

The project addresses the issues of scale, connection and style that are inherent in an addition to an early American, Romanesque style bank building. The grandeur of a traditional banking floor is recreated by leaving a double height lobby space, and by inserting a mezzanine floor separated from the adjoining walls. The sense of drama and visual delight enhance the architectural quality of the existing structure. The building addition creates an entrance court, which is located between the renovated bank building and new office space. The entrance court provides a formal entrance, and gives the project a monumental presence, emphasizing its open, community based function. Two vertical elements in the entrance court, reinforce the sense of entry, provide a setting for local artists to display their art work, act as skylights for lower level offices, and provide fresh air intake for building's air conditioning system. The recessed façade of the entrance court is designed to be transparent as against the solid surface of the bank building. The height and façade treatment are designed to be sympathetic to the architectural characteristics of the bank building, without imitating them.

A monumental stairway connects the street level and the lower level. This stairway, together with a variety of skylights and areaways along the perimeter enhance the quality and feel of the lower level. Third floor, which rises above the original parapet of the bank building, is setback from the building line, and provides spaces for educational and community meeting facilities. There is a greenhouse, computer and other training labs, and a multi-purpose meeting room on the third floor as well. A rear courtyard provides a setting for informal outdoor meetings and recreation.

The project respects the scale and quality of the original structure, and allows integration of new architectural elements and volumes. The addition seeks to harmonize the existing building through its scale and architectural features without attempting a literal imitation of materials or form. It attempts to establish a formal vocabulary, which complements the original structure and at the same time creates a new identity for the project.

The program called for a building designed for not only today's technology needs but for future needs as well. The flexible arrangement of office spaces would permit a variety of configurations for tenant spaces of varying sizes. Fiber optics and high-tech electrical systems would allow voice, data and video transmissions as well as video conferencing to and from the building. The mechanical system has been designed with multiple HVAC systems per floor to provide flexibility and energy efficiency. To coincide with the building's exterior, the interior has been designed to be upscale. Interior finishes include granite flooring in the main lobby, with glass and steel railing along the monumental stairway, and recessed gypsum board ceiling with cove lighting. The ceiling system creates an illusion of a skylight and suggests a much greater ceiling height. The mezzanine floor in the original structure has been designed to maximize the use of rentable square footage, without sacrificing the architectural quality of a traditional banking floor.

Code	Division Name	%	Sq. Cost	Projected
00	Bidding Requirements	2.18	4.06	110,309
01	General Requirements	14.38	26.73	726,942
03	Concrete	7.33	13.63	370,692
04	Masonry	6.32	11.75	319,692
05	Metals	11.83	21.99	598,114
06	Wood & Plastics	1.98	3.68	100,101
07	Thermal & Moisture Protection	3.43	6.38	173,607
08	Doors & Windows	11.36	21.11	574,184
09	Finishes	13.75	25.57	695,416
10	Specialties	3.60	6.70	182,216
11	Equipment	0.52	0.97	26,289
12	Furnishings	0.46	0.85	23,090
14	Conveying Systems	4.95	9.21	250,373
15	Mechanical	9.63	17.90	486,837
16	Electrical	8.27	15.37	417,955
	Total Building Costs	100.00	185.88	5,055,818

COST PER SQUARE FOOT = $185.88

File 35:

Constructed in 1908, the Alliance Center (formerly the Otero Building) has seen many uses over the years. In its hey-day, the Lower Downtown District (LoDo) in Denver, Colorado had 80 trains arriving every day to nearby Union Station. As time passed, fewer than five trains stopped in LoDo, and the area became known as "Skid Row."

Recently, LoDo has experienced revitalization and has been recognized for its characteristic historic buildings with new uses. In the 1990's the Otero building was purchased by the neighboring Tattered Cover bookstore and was used primarily as a shipping and receiving warehouse. Then the Alliance for Sustainable Colorado purchased the Otero Building in 2004 and began renovating and creating the Alliance Center-with the goal of creating one of the nation's greenest office buildings and a center for innovation in the Rockies.

The renovation comprised of the reconfiguration of interior spaces, repairing and updating building HVAC, telecom, and electrical systems, and new finishes. The Architects - ShearsAdkins, LLC - worked with the Alliance to preserve the historic integrity of the building, while pursuing sustainable strategies to promote building health, energy and water efficiencies.

Interior spaces were reconfigured based upon the relationship between the existing elevator and stairwell core and the large windows on three sides of the building. This strategy succeeded in providing natural daylight to over 75% of spaces and maintains an open floor plan - an important feature helping to reduce waste during tenant turnover.

With no process water used on site, the Alliance focused on updating its water fixtures to water-free urinals, 1.0 gallon flush toilets, and high-efficiency faucets. As a result, the Alliance Center cut its water use by 90% and its water bills by 75%.

In an effort to create this high performance building from renewable or recycled resources, the Alliance used a variety of green materials. For example, natural cotton-based fiber insulation, made from old blue jeans, was used as a direct substitute for fiberglass batting. Bamboo, wheat board, and reclaimed wood products were used wherever possible and drywall was secured from a local source.

For energy efficiency, the Alliance worked with Ecube for retro-commissioning and upgraded its HVAC system to digital controls. With mechanical plans showing a boiler in the basement - which wasn't there - all HVAC and commissioning was on-site discovery, complicating the job. Finally, the Alliance participated in the utility's Demand Side Management program to upgrade all lighting ballasts and bulbs and independently installed daylight harvesting Axis Ballasts. Despite doubling the building population, this work resulted in a 14% energy reduction and a 10% drop in energy bills.

The Alliance Center achieved two LEED(R) Certifications (Existing Buildings-Gold; Commercial Interiors-Silver), one of only two buildings in the world to achieve this dual distinction. More unique than this pairing of LEED Certifications is the Alliance Center's development as a Multi-Tenant Non-Profit Center. The high-performance building practices mimic the mission of the building's 27 non-profit tenants - promoting sustainability. Further, every dollar tenants save on reduced utility bills is money put toward renewable energy, government ethics, conservation, and healthcare. The Alliance Center has served as the headquarters for the Colorado Smoking Ban, Colorado High Performance Buildings Bill, and the Colorado Renewable Energy Act - taking sustainability beyond the brick.

Code	Division Name	%	Sq. Cost	Projected
01	General Requirements	22.57	6.05	233,537
03	Concrete	0.31	0.08	3,251
04	Masonry	0.21	0.06	2,217
06	Wood, Plastics, and Composites	9.17	2.46	94,869
07	Thermal and Moisture Protection	0.24	0.07	2,512
08	Openings	5.07	1.36	52,432
09	Finishes	22.57	6.05	233,486
10	Specialties	3.58	0.96	37,040
21	Fire Suppression	1.63	0.44	16,817
22	Plumbing	2.69	0.72	27,870
23	HVAC	10.48	2.81	108,392
25	Integrated Automation	6.29	1.69	65,094
26	Electrical	11.13	2.98	115,142
27	Communications	4.06	1.09	41,970
	Total Building Costs	100.00	26.80	1,034,630

COST PER SQUARE FOOT = $26.80

File 36:

This 25,000 square foot corporate facility is located in a 332 acre master-planned office park. The park's management group required an exterior of red brick, a sloped green metal roof and white trimmed, metal, ribbon-type windows. A drainage easement in the middle of the site and jurisdictional wetlands to the north of the site were further complications.

The exterior surface uses contrasting volumetric shapes within the façade. The main entrance is a two-story space with slanted full height glass panels that frame a hollowed cube cut at a diagonal. The narrow end of the building has an arrow-shaped profile accentuated by a two-story aluminum and glass curtain wall.

Significant portions of the building are located in the building's corners. In one corner, the lobby features amber and green geometric Italian tile. Opposite the lobby is a square-shaped room projecting into the main façade and separated from it by two slanted glass saddle panels. The other corner houses meeting rooms which are transparent behind the glass curtain wall. Indirect pendant linear light fixtures illuminate the interior.

Code	Division Name	%	Sq. Cost	Projected
00	Bidding Requirements	10.29	14.99	354,573
01	General Requirements	12.33	17.96	424,857
03	Concrete	6.07	8.84	209,259
04	Masonry	8.31	12.11	286,375
05	Metals	12.72	18.52	438,154
06	Wood & Plastics	2.61	3.81	90,003
07	Thermal & Moisture Protection	5.31	7.74	183,075
08	Doors & Windows	6.86	10.00	236,361
09	Finishes	17.69	25.76	609,365
10	Specialties	1.09	1.60	37,638
12	Furnishings	0.33	0.47	11,251
14	Conveying Systems	1.68	2.45	57,889
15	Mechanical	9.50	13.84	327,285
16	Electrical	5.20	7.57	178,984
	Total Building Costs	100.00	145.67	3,445,069

COST PER SQUARE FOOT = $145.67

File 37:

The CHA Angiogram Imaging Suite recently reopened at CHA Hollywood Presbyterian Medical Center in Hollywood, California. An international client purchased the hospital two years ago and is embarking on a journey to bring patients from around the world to Southern California for a premiere boutique medical care experience. Kluger Architects, Inc. is the project architect for this multi-phased, multi-year transformation process.

At a cost of $917,103, the 981-square-foot suite is outfitted with the most modern angiographic equipment allowing the hospital to provide invasive procedures to its patients. The program consisted of the control room, procedure room, equipment room, scrub room, and workroom. A challenge to the design included installation of a ceiling mounted air handling unit, due to the lack of air volume for the required air changes.

The suite is part of the future CHA Cardiac Institute. Therefore finish materials were selected from the hospital's new overall interior master materials, a color palette offering all patrons a fresh and spa-like atmosphere. Careful logistical planning allows the renovations to occur while the hospital continues to operate. From commencement the project took two months for construction documents, three months in OSHPD review, and six months for construction including OSHPD approvals to complete. This project completed on time and on budget.

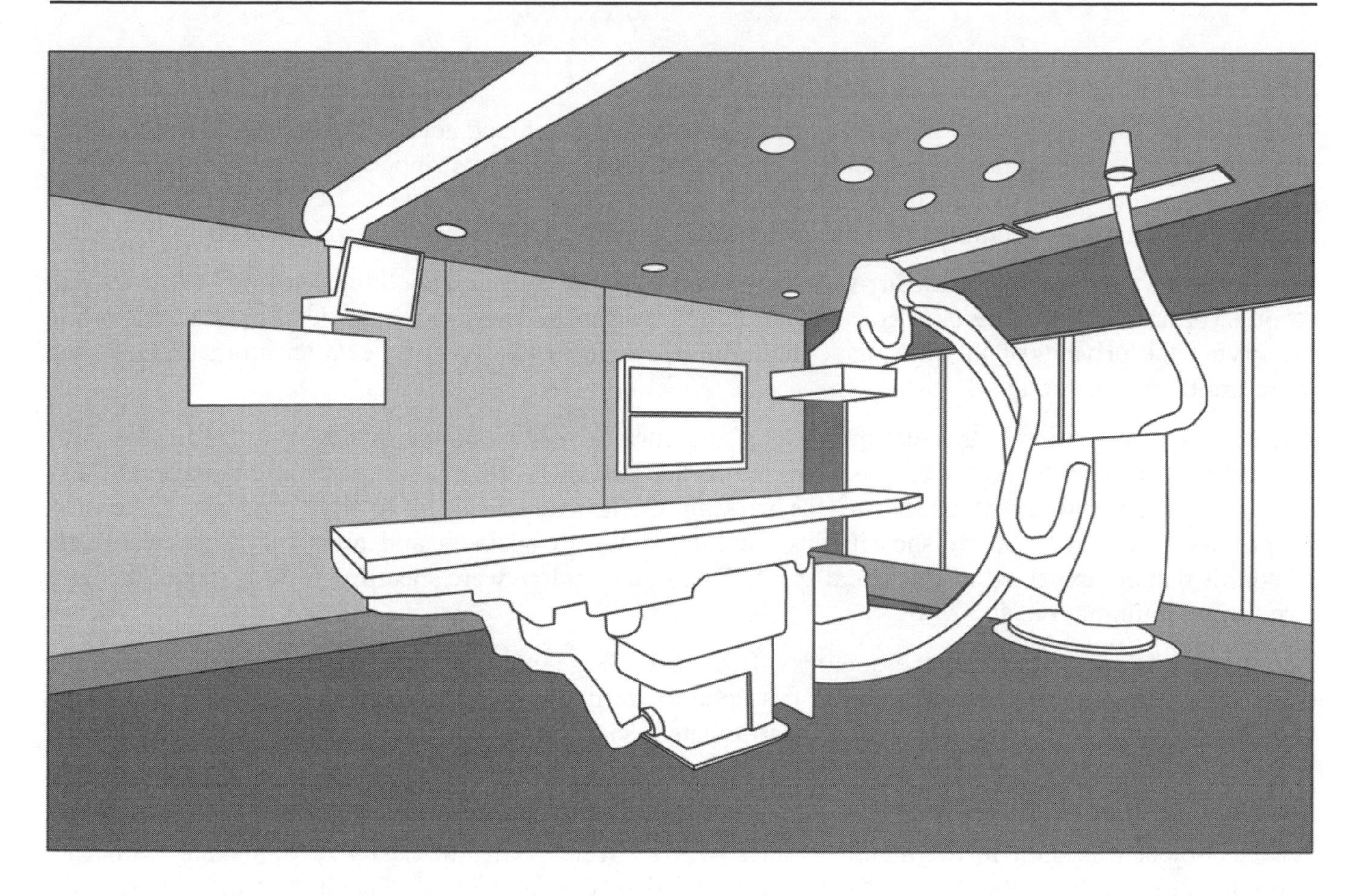

Code	Division Name	%	Sq. Cost	Projected
01	General Requirements	29.15	285.29	279,868
03	Concrete	1.14	11.19	10,982
05	Metals	9.56	93.57	91,792
06	Wood, Plastics, and Composites	0.05	0.53	519
07	Thermal and Moisture Protection	1.03	10.06	9,866
08	Openings	3.49	34.15	33,500
09	Finishes	3.46	33.86	33,219
12	Furnishings	2.32	22.70	22,265
13	Special Construction	0.46	4.55	4,461
23	HVAC	15.47	151.38	148,499
25	Integrated Automation	5.52	54.05	53,021
26	Electrical	28.21	276.12	270,873
27	Communications	0.13	1.29	1,261
	Total Building Costs	100.00	978.72	960,125

COST PER SQUARE FOOT = $978.72

File 38:

The formation of a brand new partnership required the gutting of, and addition to an existing building to create a new maxillofacial surgical center. The existing building was stripped down to the studs and the spaces were reconfigured to create the best possible surgical experience. Because of the specific requirements of this particular dental specialty the building is divided into three programmatic zones.

The first zone accommodates the arriving patients in a comfortable and soothing reception area. Patient records, billing, the initial exam, consultation and x-ray capabilities are all provided in this area, while preserving the privacy of the patients. The interior design in this zone reflects an intimate, cozy and more traditional aesthetic.

The second zone satisfies the requirements of the surgical nature of this practice with four spacious surgery rooms. Convenient access is provided to the lab and sterilization areas. A generous and airy recovery room with direct access to the parking lot is also provided to give patients the easiest experience possible. The finishes in this zone are down to business and meet the high cleanliness standards that are expected of a surgical space. The lighter colors were specified to help reflect the light to improve illumination.

The third zone accommodates the doctor's offices and a large employee lounge and seminar area. The color scheme was drastically changed in this zone to warmer colors as a way to encourage interaction and the exchange of ideas. As the doctors participate in community education relating to dental care and other topics, this area was given a separate entrance. This entry provides public access while keeping the practice and its activities private.

As the project was built in the medical center of town it needed to be easily recognizable, while not overwhelming the neighbors. So a curve was added to the front of the facade and the signage was updated and moved to a more prominent location. As the parking needed to be maintained, and more accessibility was needed since most patients are under the effects of anesthesia as they leave, generous curb cuts and new sidewalks were poured.

To revitalize the tired and diseased plantings on the site and to provide some solar shading new plantings were established. A stand of bamboo was added on the backside of the property. New healthy trees and shrubs were planted to bring new color and life to the project.

This successful venture revitalizes an old building, elevates the dental care of the region, and provides continuing education seminar space, much needed in this highly concentrated area of medical providers.

Code	Division Name	%	Sq. Cost	Projected
01	General Requirements	24.34	111.05	245,855
04	Masonry	6.62	30.22	66,899
06	Wood, Plastics, and Composites	13.24	60.43	133,799
07	Thermal and Moisture Protection	3.56	16.26	35,992
08	Openings	6.79	30.97	68,572
09	Finishes	13.33	60.81	134,635
12	Furnishings	11.59	52.88	117,074
22	Plumbing	6.29	28.71	63,554
23	HVAC	5.96	27.19	60,209
26	Electrical	8.28	37.77	83,624
	Total Building Costs	100.00	456.28	1,010,215

COST PER SQUARE FOOT = $456.28

File 39:

To meet the aggressive project schedule, a design/build approach rather than the traditional design-bid-build process was chosen. By overlapping the design and construction, BLM was able to pre-order long-lead items. To realize the client's vision for an efficient and modern facility BLM was also able to assign separate interior design and architectural teams to plan and design the interior and exterior renovations.

BLM's designers selected tinted glass and a standing-seam metal roof, as well as tower elements and a canopied entrance to complete the transformation from colonial to contemporary. An EIFS system manufactured by Dryvit Systems, Inc. contributed to construction-cost efficiency-permitting BLM's designers to develop a high-tech, precast appearance (using color, texture and a geometric pattern), and acting as the necessary exterior wall insulation for the building. Additionally, Dryvit's ease of application, done on-site, facilitated the compressed construction schedule.

Patient registration, information and nine exam rooms are located on the first floor. The Outpatient Surgery area, Cataract Operating Room and two Laser Surgery Rooms are located on the second floor. Office space, billing and records, and staff facilities are located in the renovated lower level. To provide patient and staff access to all levels, the building's points-of-egress and interior plan in compliance with present-day ADA requirements, including a front entrance ramp and a five-stop elevator.

The interiors team selected a palette of teal and blue with magenta accents for the interior space, and dark teal-green, grey and salmon for the exterior.

Code	Division Name	%	Sq. Cost	Projected
00	Bidding Requirements	2.89	4.11	65,418
01	General Requirements	1.62	2.30	36,603
03	Concrete	2.41	3.43	54,515
04	Masonry	1.79	2.55	40,497
05	Metals	2.92	4.16	66,197
06	Wood & Plastics	5.31	7.57	120,400
07	Thermal & Moisture Protection	11.03	15.72	249,989
08	Doors & Windows	6.74	9.60	152,641
09	Finishes	10.86	15.48	246,095
10	Specialties	1.81	2.58	40,964
12	Furnishings	8.35	11.90	189,244
13	Special Construction	5.84	8.33	132,393
14	Conveying Systems	3.44	4.90	77,878
15	Mechanical	21.07	30.02	477,394
16	Electrical	13.92	19.84	315,407
	Total Building Costs	100.00	142.72	2,265,634

COST PER SQUARE FOOT = $142.72

File 40:

Cedar Hills Crossing Business Park was in need of a major facelift to bring it into the competitive marketplace. This former warehouse building sits on a 6-acre site in Beaverton, Oregon, central to the cities office and industrial high tech business core. The scope of work for this project aimed to address the building's lack of curb appeal as well as improve the site's landscaping. Prior to renovation, the property was typical of all industrial projects built in the late 1960's, where asphalt ruled the development. The lack of landscaping on the site was overwhelming and put the property in a competitive disadvantage in today's leasing environment. The parking lot and building perimeter were both redesigned to reduce the amount of asphalt present by adding 15% more landscaped area to the site. In conjunction with the new landscaping reducing storm water runoff, new catch basins were installed to filter the remaining storm water before entering the public sewer system.

From an architectural standpoint, it was important that the building establish visual points of entry. Three new identification pieces were created to direct visitors to the businesses within. New storefronts were cut out of the tilt panel concrete walls

These entrances were visually built up using products from Trex decking. The decking was installed horizontally on the walls around the storefronts to resemble the look of wood siding without the associated maintenance. It was then trimmed with prefinished metal surrounds in order to finish the look and anchor the design. The entire building was also repainted using low VOC paint.

Exterior lighting for the building and parking lot was also upgraded with low energy use fluorescent and metal halide fixtures. Energy efficient lighting replacement will occur throughout the project as new tenants occupy the building. Cobalt Blue resin panels from 3Form were installed to provide a strong color accent on the sconces flanking the main entry points. This splash of color helps define the new entries into each suite.

Topping off this remodel project, is a new white, reflective, single ply roofing system over rigid insulation.

Code	Division Name	%	Sq. Cost	Projected
01	General Requirements	23.80	0.87	92,143
03	Concrete	0.35	0.01	1,373
04	Masonry	1.32	0.05	5,127
05	Metals	4.81	0.18	18,612
06	Wood, Plastics, and Composites	18.56	0.68	71,842
07	Thermal and Moisture Protection	7.17	0.26	27,753
08	Openings	5.46	0.20	21,127
09	Finishes	17.01	0.62	65,835
21	Fire Suppression	1.09	0.04	4,202
26	Electrical	20.44	0.75	79,136
	Total Building Costs	100.00	3.67	387,151

COST PER SQUARE FOOT = $3.67

File 41:

The new Waverly Public Library, which is located on one of the two main highways that go through this town of 7,500 people, was a long time in coming. The existing library building was a combination of construction time periods built on five different levels, in a building without any historical significance what so ever. The final site that was chosen for the new building after many false starts was 1-1/2 miles from downtown on the major north-south street through town.

The site housed the Rural Electric Cooperative in a building that was constructed in 1947. The library board was given the building site in a trade for the existing library building. Since a building existed on the site, the architects reviewed its condition for possible use in housing the new 21,000-square-foot building. There was an existing concrete basement of 2,000-square-feet below the original one-story building. The eventual result of the review was to attempt to reuse the existing columns and foundations since, in some locations, the floor slab was five feet thick. It created an irregular structural bay which altered the stack layout to some extent, but the main irregularities were masked by a new super structure.

The exterior walls of the previous site structure were removed so that a more contextual design could be created. The existing column locations were used to create a center open space which is illuminated by clerestory windows on all sides which bathe the interior in natural light. A series of arched windows in the exterior walls also allow natural light to penetrate all areas of the new library.

A new floor slab was poured over the top of the existing rough concrete slab in order to allow for the placement of a flexible electrical power network over the main areas of the library. The indirect lighting system provides an effective distribution of light at work surfaces and stack areas and is complemented by the natural light produced by the continuous clerestory windows.

The interior environment is warm and inviting with the use of natural oak as trim on columns and walls and also in the entry ways. Earth tones are combined with reds and blues to create a pleasant interior space. These colors occur in the carpet, furniture fabrics and in some cases on drywall ceilings.

The program called for two meeting rooms to be positioned so that they could operate beyond normal library hours and a drive-up materials handling window to facilitate usage in all kinds of weather.

The general floor plan layout is influenced by the library board's desire to provide a book pick-up area that could be served from the general work room area and be in constant view of the staff at all times. The large meeting room is divisible and easily accessible from the children's area without crossing through adult space.

The imprint of the existing electrical power plant has been replaced by a new community cultural resource built over an existing structural skeleton. An abandoned building on an existing site has been given new meaning for a 21st century use of a major cultural facility.

Code	Division Name	%	Sq. Cost	Projected
00	Bidding Requirements	1.80	3.17	84,938
01	General Requirements	4.05	7.13	190,804
03	Concrete	6.43	11.33	303,074
04	Masonry	8.23	14.51	388,283
05	Metals	1.61	2.84	75,991
06	Wood & Plastics	11.56	20.37	545,095
07	Thermal & Moisture Protection	11.99	21.13	565,506
08	Doors & Windows	8.74	15.41	412,391
09	Finishes	14.49	25.53	683,295
10	Specialties	1.10	1.93	51,659
11	Equipment	0.26	0.45	12,174
12	Furnishings	0.42	0.74	19,803
15	Mechanical	17.17	30.26	809,667
16	Electrical	12.16	21.43	573,485
	Total Building Costs	100.00	176.24	4,716,164

COST PER SQUARE FOOT = $176.24

File 42:

The Coro Center for Civic Leadership contributes to Pittsburgh's success at recycling its existing building stock. Coro Center for Civic Leadership's decision to establish residence at a location so intrinsically tied to Pittsburgh's industrial past, validates its commitment to recycling land for progress and change. The building owner, Pittsburgh Terminal Properties, has utilized this historic area, originally built as a warehouse. It is currently being transformed into a vibrant office complex. Its location takes advantage of the views across the river to downtown Pittsburgh, the infrastructure of the neighboring Southside, and its proximity to Station Square and the central business district of Pittsburgh.

Coro occupies eight bays on the fourth floor of the Terminal Way Properties. During the programming and schematic design process it was determined that Coro required a potentially flexible, open space plan for their main business function. Demountable fiberglass partitions and a raised floor system for mechanical and electrical distribution allow for the reconfiguration of office space and other functions. The main conference or training room serves as a more permanent function at the heart of the Coro space.

Renaissance 3 Architects was brought on board for the project by the Contractor, Jendoco Corporation in a design-build arrangement. The project team made a commitment to follow the guidelines set forth under LEED(R) for Commercial Interiors and served as a pilot project under this program. The building owner, encouraged by the tenant's commitment to sustainability, will be establishing future bicycle storage racks, showers and a building recycling collection area. In the overall process, the project team has succeeded in providing Coro with sustainable features reflective of their community involvement and corporate image.

Code	Division Name	%	Sq. Cost	Projected
00	Bidding Requirements	1.39	0.95	9,837
01	General Requirements	27.33	18.73	193,356
03	Concrete	0.66	0.45	4,638
04	Masonry	0.46	0.32	3,259
06	Wood, Plastics, and Composites	4.14	2.84	29,316
07	Thermal and Moisture Protection	0.25	0.17	1,784
08	Openings	2.15	1.47	15,190
09	Finishes	13.74	9.41	97,179
10	Specialties	5.84	4.00	41,342
21	Fire Suppression	0.98	0.67	6,930
22	Plumbing	0.58	0.40	4,117
23	HVAC	26.18	17.94	185,249
26	Electrical	16.29	11.16	115,266
	Total Building Costs	100.00	68.52	707,465

COST PER SQUARE FOOT = $68.52

File 43:

The Ribault Club is a two-story Colonial Revival public facility with Georgian architectural features. The facility has an "H" shaped form that overlooks the Ft. George River northeast of downtown Jacksonville, Florida. Designed by architect Maurice Fatio and constructed under the direction of architect Mellon Greeley in 1928, the Club served an elite membership of businessmen, financiers, and industrialists.

Organized in the roaring 1920s, the Ribault Club's membership was eclipsed by the stock market crash in 1929 and later by World War II. Over the years, however, club members enjoyed golf, croquet, boating, fishing, socializing and fine dining in the clubhouse.

During successive ownerships by developers, the building suffered from the ravages of fire, decay and termite damage. The State of Florida acquired most of Ft. George Island in 1989 as part of Ft. George Island Cultural State Park.

In 1996, the Florida Park Service initiated a preservation planning study, funded in part from a preservation grant awarded by the Department of State.

In 1998, with the support of Jacksonville's City Council, the Historic Jacksonville Preservation Commission, and the National Park Service to save the structure, the Florida Park Service appointed local citizens to a "Ribault Clubhouse Task Force" to identify and recommend to FPS the highest and best uses for the clubhouse. During this time the Ribault Club was nominated and listed on the National Register of Historic Places.

The Task Force recommended that a mixed use of recreation, including interpreting natural and cultural resources, public meetings and social events, and educational and research opportunities for local public schools and area universities' could be offered at a well managed public facility. The Ribault Club has today become the gateway to the Timucuan Trail State & National Parks.

A condition assessment of the Ribault Club revealed that the building suffered considerable termite damage concealed in exterior load-bearing walls. Water damage had contributed to wood rot and deterioration of the chimneys. Differential settling of terrazzo floors where foundations were absent had caused floor cracking that was repaired by hydraulically injecting concrete to raise and realign floors. Insufficient roof ventilation was corrected to meet code, and building modifications were made to meet accessibility codes appropriate for historic buildings. Fire-damaged floor, wall and roof structures in the northwest wing were repaired. Windows and many of the French doors damaged by vandals were repaired or replaced. All electrical service was upgraded, deteriorated plumbing was repaired, and HVAC mechanical equipment was installed. An elevator to new upstairs offices and bridal changing room was installed to maximize use of the facility.

The cost of rehabilitating the Ribault Club, with furnishings and site improvements, was less than projected costs.

The Ribault Club held its grand reopening in December 2003, exactly 75 years to the day after the original grand opening. In the several months since the reopening, the Club has been steadily booked for meetings, non-profit events, weddings and corporate retreats. The Club has hosted researchers studying archaeology, and a stream of day-use visitors who enjoy the grounds, visitor center and educational book store.

Code	Division Name	%	Sq. Cost	Projected
01	General Requirements	16.92	51.28	1,041,084
03	Concrete	0.22	0.68	13,792
04	Masonry	0.06	0.18	3,569
05	Metals	0.10	0.30	6,061
06	Wood, Plastics, and Composites	13.34	40.45	821,088
07	Thermal and Moisture Protection	4.73	14.34	291,042
08	Openings	13.04	39.52	802,315
09	Finishes	13.50	40.94	831,013
10	Specialties	0.28	0.85	17,254
11	Equipment	1.40	4.24	86,171
14	Conveying Systems	1.63	4.93	100,119
21	Fire Suppression	2.76	8.38	170,061
22	Plumbing	3.97	12.04	244,361
23	HVAC	11.04	33.47	679,380
26	Electrical	17.02	51.59	1,047,358
	Total Building Costs	100.00	303.19	6,154,669

COST PER SQUARE FOOT = $303.19

File 44:

What do you do with an abandoned senior high school building that is slowly disintegrating? The community of Mt. Pleasant retained the Howard R. Green Company to see whether this building could become a civic center or remain a civic disaster. The original structure was built in 1932 with subsequent additions in 1948, 1955 and 1973. The building had eight different levels with four of them being in the part of the building that the public library would eventually be located in. The existing building contained 70,000 square feet on three floors and the new program for the public library required 23,000 square feet of that space on one floor.

The restored building has become the Mt. Pleasant Civic Center with the one space added to the exterior being the new lobby entrance to the public library. All of the existing windows which were a combination of prefinished metal panel and glass, have been replaced with an all glass configuration similar to the original building design. The original brick diapering has also been restored and repaired where additional windows were added later and changed the original pattern.

The four floor levels in the library area were reduced to just two by raising and lowering adjacent areas. The entire adult collection is now at one level with the new lobby. The children's area and the periodicals section are two feet higher and are connected by a ramp and steps. The new raised floor in the main part of the library area now serves as a plenum to carry air ducts and electrical raceways to the entire space. The center part of the building that now houses the library is located in the original gym of the 1932 portion of the building. The tile ceiling has been removed, the structure exposed, and north facing clerestories have been added to capture daylight.

The library now exists in a 28-foot high space, bathed in natural light, surrounded by perimeter spaces where reading areas are located next to windows. New overhead ductwork is exposed and painted a metallic color to blend with new aluminum light fixtures. Open grille screens serve as low barriers to maintain openness for air circulation and to maintain sightlines. Sheet aluminum and granite are used on the main circulation desk to continue the theme of exposed, simple materials in the main public areas.

A new elevator in the building provides access to offices on the 2nd floor for the school district, light and sound booths that serve a refurbished auditorium, and a 150 seat community meeting room for the library.

The old high school auditorium has been returned to its former glory and now serves as a second meeting room for the library and a performance space for the community theatre organization seating 350. Dressing rooms, a green room, storage and a scene shop have been created in other spaces of the building. A lower level has been created out of the basement shop areas and now houses the office location of the Area Education Agency. New window areas and an at-grade entrance to a parking area now allow this space to function independently of the rest of the building.

The remainder of the building houses the existing gymnasium and wrestling room that was added in 1973, which has been converted to a community recreation center with three classroom spaces created and new shower and toilet facilities for the gym.

The new mechanical heart of the building is housed in the old coal room of the high school. All of the previous space of the building has been used in an efficient manner with 5 separate occupants now housed there.

Code	Division Name	%	Sq. Cost	Projected
01	General Requirements	7.61	8.77	668,883
03	Concrete	6.32	7.29	555,934
06	Wood & Plastics	2.16	2.50	190,386
07	Thermal & Moisture Protection	4.57	5.27	401,641
08	Doors & Windows	7.32	8.44	643,833
09	Finishes	26.86	30.98	2,362,416
12	Furnishings	1.41	1.63	124,384
14	Conveying Systems	0.82	0.94	71,738
15	Mechanical	31.99	36.89	2,813,081
16	Electrical	10.94	12.62	962,529
	Total Building Costs	100.00	115.34	8,794,825

COST PER SQUARE FOOT = $115.34

File 45:

Recent scholarship has uncovered documentation indicating that the second building of Wilkes-Barre's First Presbyterian Church was a “mail-order” project of New York City Architect James Renwick, Jr. Renwick (1818-1895) was Architect of New York's St. Patrick's Cathedral (1853-1887) and the original Castle building (1846) of the Smithsonian in Washington, D.C. Records show that Renwick was paid for plans sent to the First Presbyterian Church in Wilkes-Barre, but no record exists of his visiting Wilkes-Barre prior to submitting his design. Numerous architectural details of this church building bear an uncanny resemblance to Renwick's 1850 Oak Hill Cemetery Chapel in Georgetown, D.C. Construction began in 1849 on the First Presbyterian Church, it was dedicated in December 1851 and built at a cost of $15,000.

Except for the Church Bell Tower on the south corner, the original building remained unaltered for many years. An early rendering, as well as a pre-1890 photograph, show a tall tapered spire of approximately the same height as the brick tower on which it rests. Photographs from the early history of the OFL (c.1900±) show a pyramid shaped roof (of approximately a 12/12 pitch) resting on top of the original brick Bell Tower. At some unknown later date (estimated to be c.1908) this roof was removed, and the crenellated terra cotta, brick parapet wall, and flat roof (which resembles the tower at the Smithsonian) was built.

In the early 20th century, the OFL continued to expand, and the first of several additions was begun. In 1906 Wilkes-Barre Architectural firm of Welsh & Sturdevant was hired to design a 3-story Stack Wing Addition on the south side of the original building. The similarity in the Terra Cotta trim on this addition to the Terra Cotta coping on top of the Bell Tower, leads this writer to believe that the pyramid shaped Bell Tower roof was removed at this time. Also containing a catalog room and a repair room, this addition is noteworthy for its 32 stained/leaded glass windows. Designed by the second head librarian, Miss Myra Poland, the windows were executed by the H.J. Smith & Sons Co. of Philadelphia and completed in 1908.

Two modest office additions on the backside of the Library were completed in 1954 and 1964. The Ken Pollack Children's Wing on the front (South) corner was designed by this firm in 1982.

By the beginning of the 21st Century, the original Church Building, as well as the 1908 Stack Wing, were exhibiting signs of “old age.” After receiving reports from roof and masonry consultants, the Architect was hired to perform a comprehensive analysis of the OFL facility. The result of this study was the recommendation of a 5-Phase renovation program. In 2006 the OFL applied for and received substantial renovation grants from the Keystone Grant Program of the Commonwealth Libraries and from Luzerne County.

The Architect was authorized in April 2007 to begin Construction Documents on the first 3 phases of OFL's exterior renovations, which included complete masonry restoration of the 1849 former Church, the “Unknown” Addition and 1908 Stack Wing, as well as the complete rebuilding (with salvaged brick & terra cotta) of the top 15-feet± of the Bell Tower. New wood and aluminum louvers were replicated to replace the deteriorated louvers in the Bell Tower. Stained glass windows in both portions were removed, restored and reinstalled with new vented protective storm windows.

A new flat seam copper roof was installed on top of the Bell Tower, and Black Pennsylvania Slate was replaced on the 1908 Stack Wing. A new contemporary pole-mounted sign and modest landscaping was also included in this phase of work. No work was done on the 1954/64 and 1982 additions. Reconstruction of the OFL began in March 2008 and was completed June 2009.

Code	Division Name	%	Sq. Cost	Projected
01	General Requirements	13.06	13.65	161,707
04	Masonry	44.07	46.07	545,888
07	Thermal and Moisture Protection	9.91	10.36	122,773
08	Openings	30.40	31.78	376,560
09	Finishes	0.67	0.70	8,240
10	Specialties	1.89	1.97	23,380
	Total Building Costs	100.00	104.52	1,238,548

COST PER SQUARE FOOT = $104.52

File 46:

The Norfolk County Agricultural High School received a Massachusetts State Grant to modernize a 1960's chemistry classroom. The project goal converts an original 1960's chemistry classroom and “Prep” room into a modernized, accessible teaching facility with new architectural finishes and mechanical systems.

The existing room interior was demolished down to the concrete floor, concrete block walls and steel truss roof framing. The new layout incorporates a separate area for lab work and flexible desk seating for group instruction.

Lab casework includes vented acid and chemical storage, fume hood, emergency eye wash and shower. Each bench includes gas, water, undercounter storage and a networked computer monitor. The fume hood, one lab bench and teaching station are fully accessible.

Desk seating provides viewing to the whiteboard, overhead LCD projector, electronically controlled screen and digital board tablet.

The room is equipped with a separate roof-top mounted heating and cooling system, occupancy lighting sensors, neutralization tanks for waste water, icemaker, lab dishwasher and emergency power, gas and water shut-offs.

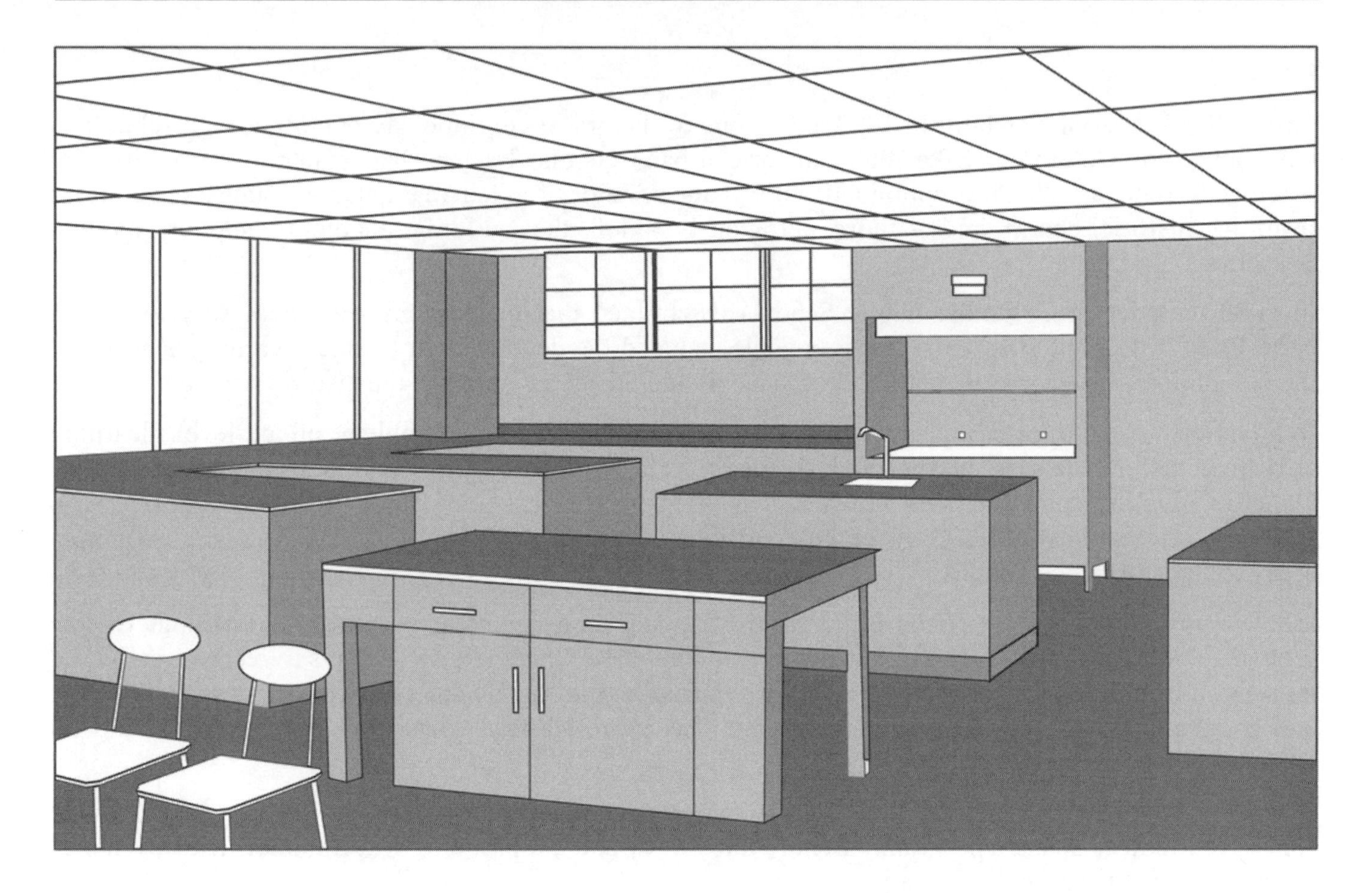

Code	Division Name	%	Sq. Cost	Projected
00	Bidding Requirements	3.56	8.45	10,668
01	General Requirements	3.22	7.64	9,639
03	Concrete	1.90	4.52	5,702
05	Metals	1.36	3.23	4,073
06	Wood & Plastics	23.30	55.29	69,778
07	Thermal & Moisture Protection	1.90	4.52	5,702
08	Doors & Windows	0.36	0.86	1,086
09	Finishes	12.15	28.83	36,382
10	Specialties	2.49	5.92	7,467
15	Mechanical	40.85	96.92	122,315
16	Electrical	8.89	21.08	26,608
	Total Building Costs	100.00	237.26	299,419

COST PER SQUARE FOOT = $237.26

File 47:

Eastern High School was built in 1923 and is one of the oldest continuously operating high schools in the District of Columbia. Like many historic urban schools, Eastern had experienced a series of patchwork renovations that, combined with years of under-funded maintenance budgets, detracted from its historic charm and - more egregiously - left the building unable to support modern educational practices.

In 2008, District of Columbia Public Schools determined that renovations were necessary to restore "The Pride of Capitol Hill." The district's goals included the development of small learning academies, the integration of energy-efficient building systems and the preservation of the historic structure.

Renovations reconfigured classrooms and science labs to resemble college-level learning environments. Academics areas, which formerly featured boarded up windows, are restored to their Collegiate Gothic splendor, with full-height windows and refurbished wood floors. In addition, two former interior light wells are now enclosed atriums. These dramatic spaces serve as student common areas and performance venues.

Many repurposed portions of the building provide new opportunities for hands-on learning. On the ground floor, a Practical/Project Lab includes an ambulance, which allows students to receive real-world training in Health & Medical Science. A robust technology infrastructure supports self-directed learning and programs such as Project Lead the Way. The entire Eastern campus is now wireless, and all classrooms include electronic whiteboards.

"The school did a complete 180 and went from bad to wonderful," said Anaje Boyd, a Senior in the Health & Medical Science program. "I really like it now and am proud to be a Rambler. Kids even stay after school just because it's a nice place to be."

Prior to the renovations, Eastern lacked even basic amenities such as air-conditioning. The design focused on "Warm, Safe, and Dry" improvements, including hazardous materials abatement and roofing and window replacement. All mechanical, electrical and plumbing systems were replaced, and new interior finishes and automated lighting controls were added throughout the building. Other sustainable features include a renovated greenhouse with a supporting rainwater cistern. Eastern earned LEED(R) Gold certification from the U.S. Green Building Council.

While a 21st century learning environment was taking shape, a parallel effort was underway to preserve Eastern's rich history. Preservation efforts included restoration of the following: leaded portico windows at the exterior, woodwork throughout the building, marble in the main stairway, terra cotta flooring in corridors, interior brick walls and interior plaster detailing. The school's auditorium received special attention, with the restoration of all original seats and the reopening of balconies that were walled off during previous renovations. The revitalized space is so state-of-the-art that it has been chosen as the new home of the D.C. Youth Orchestra.

Since reopening its doors in August 2010, the transformed Eastern High School has been greeted by rave reviews. Many faculty and students cried tears of joy as they experienced their new "old" school for the first time.

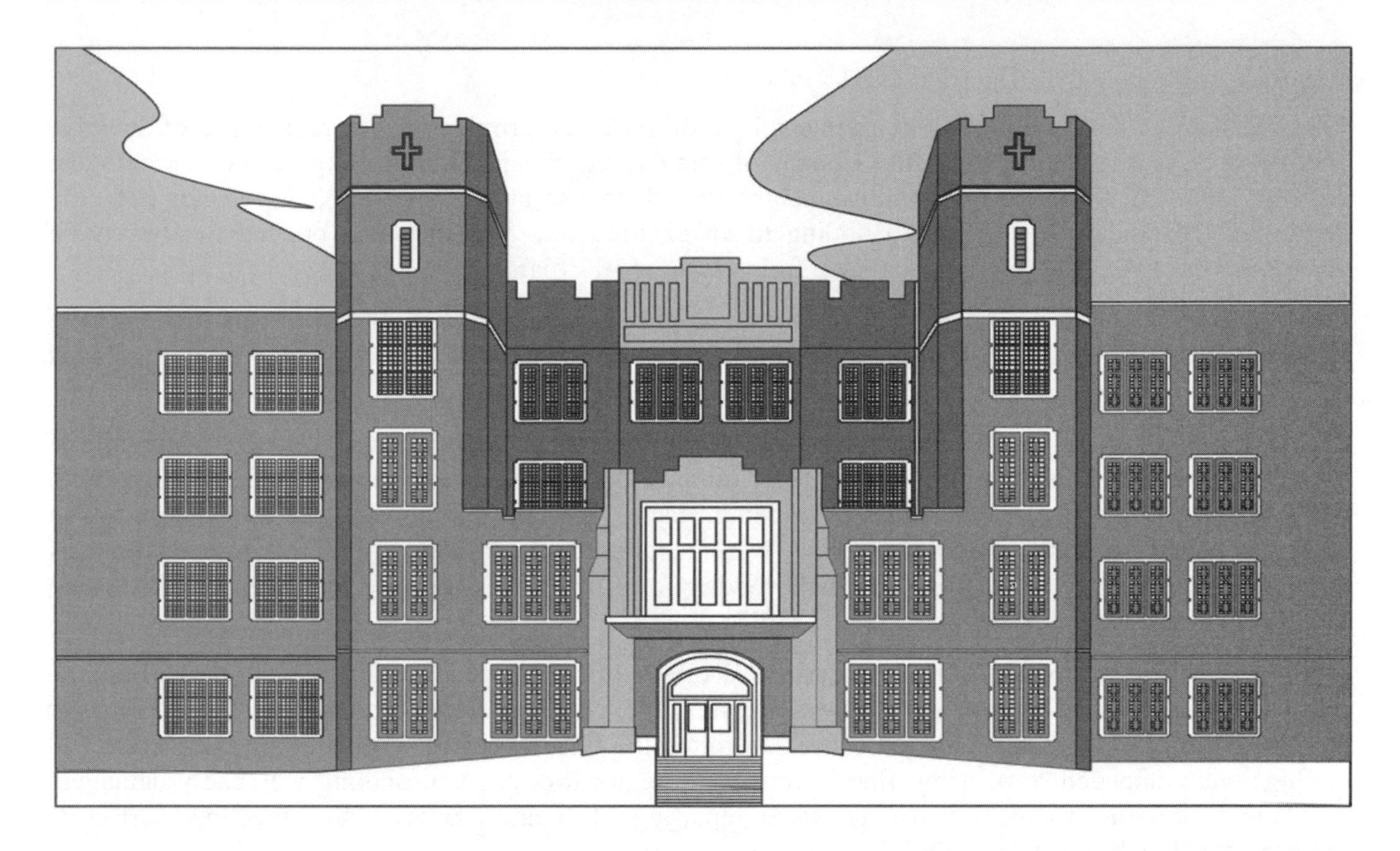

Code	Division Name	%	Sq. Cost	Projected
00	Procurement and Contracting Require	13.61	30.80	8,745,834
01	General Requirements	13.38	30.26	8,594,837
03	Concrete	2.68	6.07	1,723,316
04	Masonry	0.99	2.23	633,846
05	Metals	0.92	2.08	589,764
06	Wood, Plastics, and Composites	3.31	7.50	2,128,803
07	Thermal and Moisture Protection	1.51	3.41	967,278
08	Openings	7.31	16.53	4,695,018
09	Finishes	12.42	28.09	7,978,614
10	Specialties	0.64	1.45	413,014
11	Equipment	0.82	1.84	523,619
12	Furnishings	4.35	9.83	2,791,339
13	Special Construction	0.34	0.77	219,518
14	Conveying Systems	0.44	1.00	284,601
21	Fire Suppression	1.87	4.23	1,201,730
23	HVAC	16.80	38.01	10,794,532
26	Electrical	16.26	36.77	10,442,259
28	Electronic Safety and Security	2.35	5.32	1,510,460
	Total Building Costs	100.00	226.19	64,238,383

COST PER SQUARE FOOT = $226.19

File 48:

The Wofford College Goodall Environmental Studies Center provides a clear example of creative historic preservation and sustainable design, offering a significant learning experience for both the college community and the surrounding neighborhood. In use since July 2009, the Center not only restored the Glendale Mill Office Building to an exciting new use, but also opened the beauty of Lawson's Fork Creek to the public - hidden from view for 100 years.

In 1832, Glendale Mill began operations off Lawson's Fork Creek, just southeast of Spartanburg. The Great Depression brought hard times to the mill and it was sold multiple times and eventually closed in 1961.

In 2007, several local organizations together with Wofford College alumni began a campaign to revitalize Glendale, preserving the history and natural resources of Lawson's Fork Creek. Working with the gift of the old mill office and the surrounding 3 acres, the only remaining structure since a fire in 2004 destroyed the mill, the plaster walls were repaired and refinished, and missing plaster was replaced. All original wainscoting, original woodwork and trim was repaired and refinished. Missing woodwork was replaced to match existing profiles.

A significant transformation was necessary to create a fully restored, sustainable building from the dilapidated structure. The roof parapet was missing and windows were mismatched, boarded up, or painted. The roof had leaked and rainwater had rotted the floors. Plaster surfaces from both walls and ceilings were damaged or missing, floors were sagging, and wooden wainscoting was badly damaged. The most pressing renovation issues were repairing structural damage and meeting LEED(R) requirements in a historical context.

LEED requirements allowed only low VOC materials to be used in the refinishing process. Window repair was not possible due to the extent of deterioration and new windows were designed and constructed to match the original sash configuration. The building's systems were re-designed and replaced to meet sustainability standards, but fitting systems into the existing crawl space proved challenging. Insulation was added to crawl space and attic, but could not be added to exterior masonry walls. Period light fixtures were modified to accommodate fluorescent bulbs and operate on motion sensors. Toilet areas have been designed to use water pumped from the creek instead of potable water. Every space has its own thermostat to enhance occupancy comfort.

In the end, the project achieved LEED Platinum Certification and has found a new home for Wofford College's Environmental Studies Program. Faculty members, students and a variety of visitors have grown to appreciate the peacefulness of the preserved structure in its park-like setting.

Code	Division Name	%	Sq. Cost	Projected
00	Procurement and Contracting Require	17.04	82.85	180,118
01	General Requirements	15.48	75.23	163,560
03	Concrete	1.67	8.09	17,596
04	Masonry	8.25	40.09	87,150
05	Metals	3.30	16.03	34,845
06	Wood, Plastics, and Composites	5.42	26.33	57,251
07	Thermal and Moisture Protection	4.41	21.44	46,614
08	Openings	11.46	55.71	121,114
09	Finishes	7.35	35.75	77,720
10	Specialties	0.66	3.21	6,983
12	Furnishings	0.36	1.73	3,763
22	Plumbing	5.77	28.03	60,945
23	HVAC	11.25	54.70	118,909
26	Electrical	7.59	36.90	80,218
	Total Building Costs	100.00	486.10	1,056,785

COST PER SQUARE FOOT = $486.10

File 49:

The New Holland Recreation Center is an example of taking a tired, old space and converting into a newer and fresher facility. The warehouse that currently contains the New Holland Recreation Center was previously owned by Good's Furniture who was subsequently purchased by Breuner's Furniture. Richard Good, owner of the warehouse offered to sell a portion of the warehouse to the New Holland Recreation Center to which they agreed. Prior to this agreement, a group of building committee members along with representatives from Cornerstone Design-Architects toured the facility in order to evaluate the surrounding site and interior space. Ultimately, it was decided that the space could indeed meet the needs of the program, but also offer a competitive value for the property on which it would be located.

The recreation center contains a wellness area, junior-high regulation size gymnasium, men's, women's, and family room lockers, indoor leisure pool, walking track, aerobics room, child care area, a classroom, game area, and office/administration areas. The design includes a curving, main corridor connecting the main entrance to the gymnasium and pool areas along with the walking track. The walking track is integrated with the public circulation as a concept to reduce program area by integrating the corridors and walking track together. The design of the exterior included adding a base course of a split-face masonry veneer along with adding storefront window openings to allow natural light to penetrate the interior spaces of the facility. The exterior siding was painted with graphics to dress up the front elevations. A large steel canopy was also added to accentuate the main entrance of the facility and guide visitors to the front door.

This project, however, shared its number of challenges within the existing structure. In planning space within the existing pre-engineered building, special care needed to be taken in locating larger spaces such as the gymnasium and indoor leisure pool. The gymnasium was delegated to be located within the largest bay of the facility to accommodate the junior-high regulation size court. Additionally, the indoor leisure pool was interwoven around existing steel columns and one of the columns was engaged into the design of the pool and became a bench feature within the pool itself. Another challenge in working with an existing pre-engineered structure was the inability to locate and support any building element requiring structural support from the pre-engineered structure above. This effected the selected location of mechanical equipment within the shell of the building. To solve this problem, the design team created an equipment platform located between the indoor leisure pool and gymnasium areas. This equipment platform was centrally located to feed ductwork to the main areas of the facility.

The project has also been envisioned for future growth with some of the plans to include an elevated running track and a climbing wall structure.

The project has been considered a success and the recreation center has already surpassed their expectations for membership in the New Holland area of Lancaster County.

Code	Division Name	%	Sq. Cost	Projected
00	Procurement and Contracting Require	15.44	17.06	874,661
03	Concrete	1.75	1.93	99,020
04	Masonry	3.60	3.98	203,937
05	Metals	2.56	2.83	145,013
06	Wood, Plastics, and Composites	2.77	3.06	156,894
07	Thermal and Moisture Protection	1.48	1.64	83,920
08	Openings	3.37	3.72	190,751
09	Finishes	13.87	15.33	785,614
10	Specialties	0.95	1.05	53,895
11	Equipment	0.14	0.16	8,111
13	Special Construction	11.89	13.14	673,552
21	Fire Suppression	2.55	2.82	144,488
22	Plumbing	4.62	5.11	261,689
23	HVAC	20.19	22.31	1,143,464
26	Electrical	14.82	16.37	839,309
	Total Building Costs	100.00	110.51	5,664,318

COST PER SQUARE FOOT = $110.51

File 50:

The Pinnacle Corporate Centre campus is a four-building collection of class A corporate headquarters in Leawood, Kansas (metropolitan Kansas City) providing headquarters for a range of highly professional service firms and financial institutions. Given the nature of their staff and clientele, each space within the campus has been designed to fit the aesthetic and finish level of the campus itself.

The recent Pinnacle III Office Tenant Finish, designed by Hoefer Wysocki Architects, occupies 18,409 square feet on the top floor, connecting to the building's sole balcony on the east facade. The presence of the main entry is striking and immediately visible from the elevator lobby. An abundance of glass partitions allow light to penetrate the entire space through the entry, the main lobby and The Boardroom, the space's primary conference room.

The space is arranged around the central lobby, with open office areas on either side. The open office arrangement, with glass-lined and open executive offices lining each bay, allows light to penetrate easily throughout the space, offering nearly every seat a clear view to the outdoors and ample light.

The essential shape of the main lobby is an elegant ellipse which echoes the ellipse of the first floor lobby. Its shape is outlined in the recessed ceiling details and echoed on the floor through a combination of curved walls, cut terrazzo and carpet. A glass cloud element above the main reception desk echoes the shape again.

The palette of interior materials is warm and modern, utilizing generous amounts of wood, terrazzo, glass, stone and steel baseboard. The central vertical elements of the main lobby are sculpted Armourcoat finishes, mimicking natural stone and giving form to the ellipse from floor to ceiling and offering the highest level of sophistication.

Spread evenly throughout the space are a variety of spaces for teaming and conferencing, from one end of the plan to the other. Three open resource/meeting areas, three glass-enclosed conference rooms and one large, flexible and divisible space for a variety of functions offers a range of spaces for collaboration. The Terrace and The Veranda, flexible spaces on the East end of the plan, serve as all-staff meeting space, presentation space, work areas and the employee kitchen/break area. While the two spaces are primarily used in combination, they can be divided by a fabric partition that recedes into the wall.

Each workstation is connected to the office network, joined by the central IT office and server room. While the Boardroom and Terrace/Veranda spaces are equipped with built-in and stand alone projection and sound systems, an office-wide audio system is controlled from the IT office.

Code	Division Name	%	Sq. Cost	Projected
00	Procurement and Contracting Require	5.98	3.05	56,081
05	Metals	0.10	0.05	948
06	Wood, Plastics, and Composites	5.07	2.59	47,593
08	Openings	6.37	3.25	59,777
09	Finishes	38.60	19.67	362,168
12	Furnishings	0.96	0.49	9,036
21	Fire Suppression	1.22	0.62	11,424
22	Plumbing	1.62	0.82	15,187
23	HVAC	14.12	7.20	132,495
26	Electrical	11.77	6.00	110,456
27	Communications	11.76	5.99	110,326
28	Electronic Safety and Security	2.43	1.24	22,842
	Total Building Costs	100.00	50.97	938,333

COST PER SQUARE FOOT = $50.97

File 51:

Tenth Avenue Holdings (TAH) Corporate Headquarters is a 11,000 square-foot space on the penthouse level of a renovated warehouse building located in the burgeoning Hudson Yards District in New York. TAH turned to MUSHO Architecture and Design, with over 17 years of experience in inspired commercial office design, to create an office that reinforced collaboration between the partners and all of the firm's staff. TAH is a private investment firm that aims to "identify and invest in private and public operating and real estate businesses that demonstrate long term growth and cash flow potential". This firm needed to ensure its offices would represent their unique attitude on business.

Because many of the Partners of TAH began their careers in the hospitality industry, it was very important to consider the entire experience from the building entrance, to their own reception lobby, and throughout their entire space. MUSHO Architecture and Design knew that a feeling of warmth would be achieved by knitting` the existing materials of the original building with new, advanced, complimentary materials. On the lobby level, the brick exterior wall is exposed and a column is clad in a lacy wood veneer. The Penthouse entrance combines the original brick party wall, exposed timber framing, and wood floors from the late 1800's combined with Venetian plasters, Louis Poulsen lighting, and custom made wood furniture.

Once one enters the TAH offices, the visitor and staff alike are greeted by a new brick wall that serves as the divider between public and private. This public conduit runs the length of the space. It begins with a new brick wall, punctuated with curved and straight brick archways. The TAH logo rests perfectly on the brick wall peppered with staggered Artemide wall lights. The new brick wall works in concert with the load bearing brick party wall that holds the important memories of the Partner's original firms.

To further the tenet of the open door policy of every staff member at TAH, floor-to-ceiling glass walls and doors are used at every private office. The executive offices are wrapped in natural light.

Special windows with a Low-E coating, natural light that penetrates internal spaces, and occupancy sensors inside all offices create an element of high performance. Each office is custom designed for each Partner. The common thread is a central iron and etched glass chandelier in each room. MUSHO Architecture and Design also felt it important to provide a variety of areas that would allow purposeful meeting of fellow members of the TAH firm. This was achieved by many conference room types including the large Board room with a custom designed conference table with full video conference capabilities, an Atelier room that functions as their creative breakout room with a small formal meeting area, a lounge area with a TV and full custom counter with refrigerator, and an area with four club chairs to discuss ideas in a less formal environment. There is also a smaller conference room with a Vitra conference room table and seating. The fondly called "Blue Room" enjoys the sunset views over the Hudson.

One issue for many companies is that fellow Owners meet only in quarterly meetings. MUSHO Architecture and Design believes the less formal encounters breed creativity in an office environment. The Architect further accomplished this by the introduction of a café bathed in brick and amber colored glass tile as a modern interpretation of the brick, and using sycamore and black ash woodwork. Everyone feels as if they are eating their lunch together in the comfort of their own home but with an added energy possible only in a well designed space.

Code	Division Name	%	Sq. Cost	Projected
01	General Requirements	1.05	0.76	8,361
04	Masonry	0.24	0.18	1,935
05	Metals	12.25	8.87	97,547
06	Wood, Plastics, and Composites	8.47	6.13	67,444
08	Openings	9.24	6.69	73,572
09	Finishes	18.30	13.25	145,725
11	Equipment	0.94	0.68	7,452
12	Furnishings	17.02	12.32	135,481
13	Special Construction	1.21	0.87	9,600
21	Fire Suppression	2.09	1.51	16,645
22	Plumbing	4.06	2.94	32,334
23	HVAC	5.83	4.22	46,451
26	Electrical	15.12	10.94	120,374
27	Communications	4.17	3.02	33,220
	Total Building Costs	100.00	72.38	796,142

COST PER SQUARE FOOT = $72.38

File 52:

In early 2004, Destination Cleveland County (DCC) began as a public-private partnership to promote economic development through cultural tourism in the Shelby-Cleveland County area. Two major catalyst projects were identified for uptown Shelby to honor the legacy of two Shelby natives: country music singer/songwriter Don Gibson ("I Can't Stop Loving You," "Oh Lonesome Me") and bluegrass banjo pioneer, Earl Scruggs.

Destination Cleveland County (DCC) purchased the former State (Flick) Theatre property to renovate and restore the building into a modern performing arts facility and reception hall. The art deco inspired theatre opened in 1939 and served as a cinema house for over 50 years. In recent years, like many old movie houses, the building was left vacant and fell into disrepair. MBAJ Architecture was charged with transforming the building into a state-of-the-art performing arts venue for regional and national artists.

The original building was modestly appointed in nautical art deco motifs including porthole windowed front doors and a scrolling wave border framing the proscenium opening with sea foam green and pink coral walls throughout. Many of these motifs were restored and updated using contemporary materials. The lobby, reception hall, and other public areas are appointed with colors and patterns reminiscent of art deco, but in a contemporary interpretation paying homage to the original theme of the circa 1939 theatre.

The main auditorium comfortably seats over 400 and is handicap accessible. Twenty-first century technology sound and lighting systems provide the setting for all forms of musical performance, live theater, and audio-visual productions. A new reception hall was constructed on a vacant parking lot adjacent to the original building with a connector to the main lobby providing exhibit space for Don Gibson artifacts and memorabilia.

A new community room is located next to the theatre space and is designed for maximum flexibility. The room features a glass wall that connects to the city streetscape beyond. A bar and serving kitchen provide many options for catered events.

Attention to detail carries through to the restrooms with stage light vanities, accent tile, and glass block partitions.

Details were important - original motifs were uncovered and used to inform the design and color scheme.

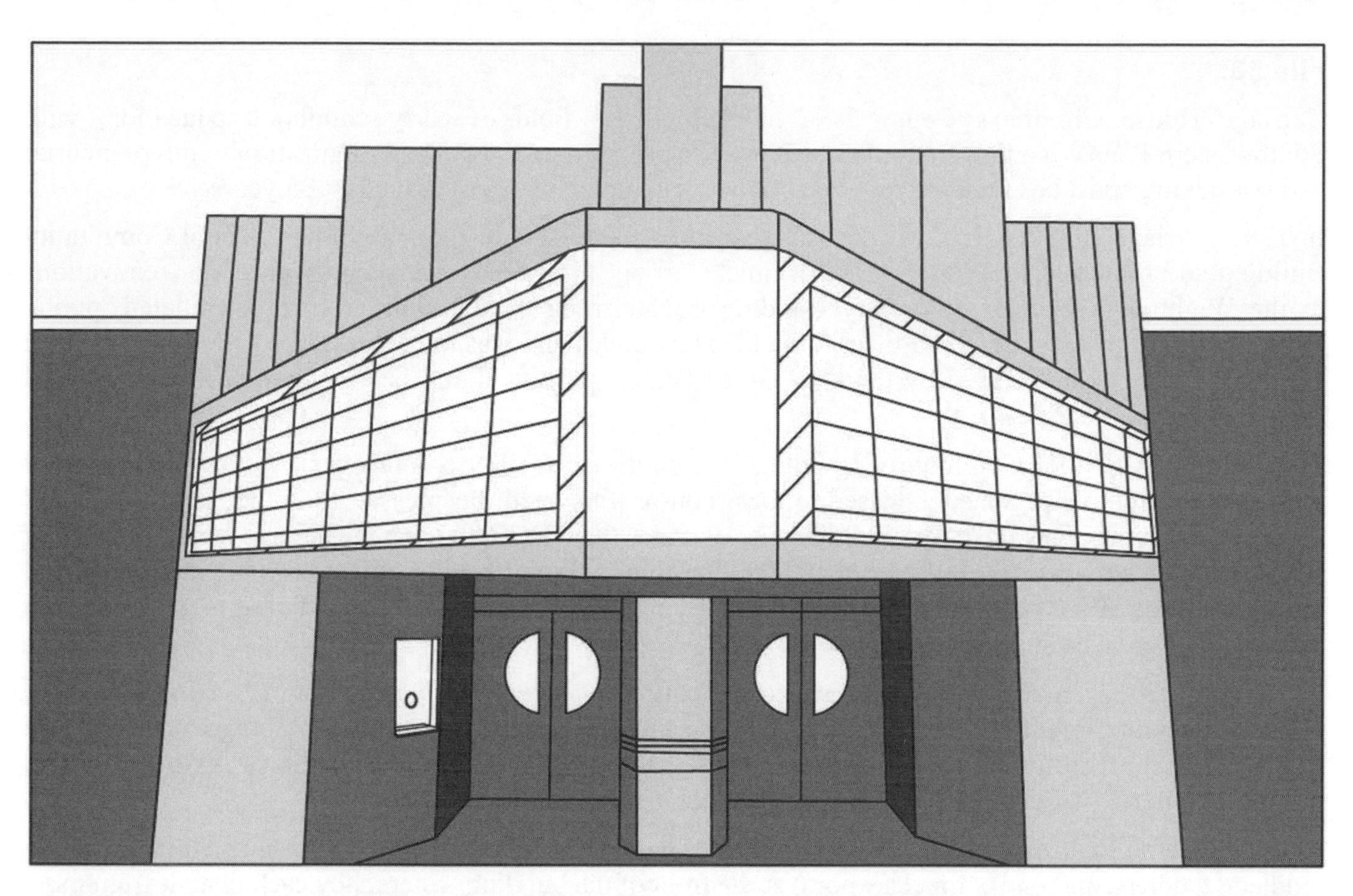

Code	Division Name	%	Sq. Cost	Projected
00	Procurement and Contracting Require	12.66	35.79	479,028
01	General Requirements	0.40	1.14	15,307
03	Concrete	2.59	7.31	97,836
04	Masonry	4.35	12.31	164,771
05	Metals	6.38	18.04	241,491
06	Wood, Plastics, and Composites	3.35	9.47	126,707
07	Thermal and Moisture Protection	6.06	17.14	229,408
08	Openings	5.09	14.40	192,777
09	Finishes	12.15	34.34	459,682
10	Specialties	2.53	7.14	95,636
11	Equipment	14.23	40.24	538,684
12	Furnishings	4.28	12.09	161,843
14	Conveying Systems	0.57	1.60	21,424
21	Fire Suppression	1.95	5.52	73,889
22	Plumbing	3.44	9.73	130,196
23	HVAC	7.34	20.76	277,857
26	Electrical	12.63	35.70	477,914
	Total Building Costs	100.00	282.75	3,784,449

COST PER SQUARE FOOT = $282.75

File 53:

Carriage House Children's Center is a pioneer in the field of early childhood education, with Southwestern Pennsylvania's first infant and toddler program in 1974. The organization's entrepreneurial and risk-taking spirit has resulted in several major accomplishments over the last 35 years.

In 1985 Carriage House purchased the 113-year-old, 40,000-square-foot Wightman School Community Building and relocated in 1986. Since that time, Carriage House has overseen seven major renovations to the Wightman School Community Building transforming the building from a dilapidated, public school building that did not even meet fire and safety codes and was once considered for demolition, to one that is now gold certified by the U.S. Green Building Council and is registered with the National Registry of Historic Places.

The Wightman School Community Building is a multi-use facility where over 17,000 square feet of multipurpose and office space is leased to local non-profits, small businesses and other family-oriented groups. CHCC manages the entire building and operates the CHCC childcare program, which consists of ten classrooms between the lower level and the first floor. Administrative offices, conference rooms, and multiple tenant office spaces are located on the second floor. The third floor is home to a gymnasium and five music/dance studios.

In 2006 and 2007 Carriage House renovated the entire lower level of the building (9,720 square feet), which houses the infant and toddler programs, the kitchen, the boiler, and other storage and multi-use rooms. Carriage House also retrofitted many of the building's lighting and plumbing fixtures to meet LEED(R) criteria. Air conditioning was added to the first floor.

Extensive demolition of non-load bearing and bearing walls located all four classrooms (infants, young toddlers, toddlers, and one extra classroom) at the front of the building, where they each benefit from more natural light. Spaces not used by children, such as the kitchen and the laundry room, have taken their place where the windows struggle to receive light. The center of the lower level has been opened up to create a large indoor play area that is subdivided for two groups to use at the same time. Access to daylighting and views have been opened to increase the amount of natural light in the center of the lower level. Two classrooms have unique entrances to this central space- two enclosed porches for the young toddlers and older toddlers. Preschool sized bathrooms have been located in two of the classrooms for children who are making this transition.

The new "green" kitchen has reach-in coolers, food storage areas, and the commercial dishwasher adjacent to the elevator for good delivery access, and for ease of sending prepared food up to the other classrooms. The kitchen is designed to comply with Energy Star ratings at 60 or above. The entire building is now rated as Energy Star 81.

All plumbing faucets and toilets are low-flow fixtures. With the exception of one teacher sink per classroom, all children's faucets are hands-free to promote healthy handwashing methods.

The new, lower-level classrooms have a suspended ceiling for acoustical control, as high as the bottom of the original beams, and not blocking the windows. Heated and cooled air is delivered from the individual heat pumps via exposed round ducts below the ceiling. All classrooms are equipped with individual thermostats. On the first and lower-level indirect lighting illuminates the ceiling, giving off an impression of openness and more light output with less energy. T-8, daylighting systems have been installed throughout the lower-level. The lights are dimmable in all classrooms and are programmed to coordinate with the children's napping schedules.

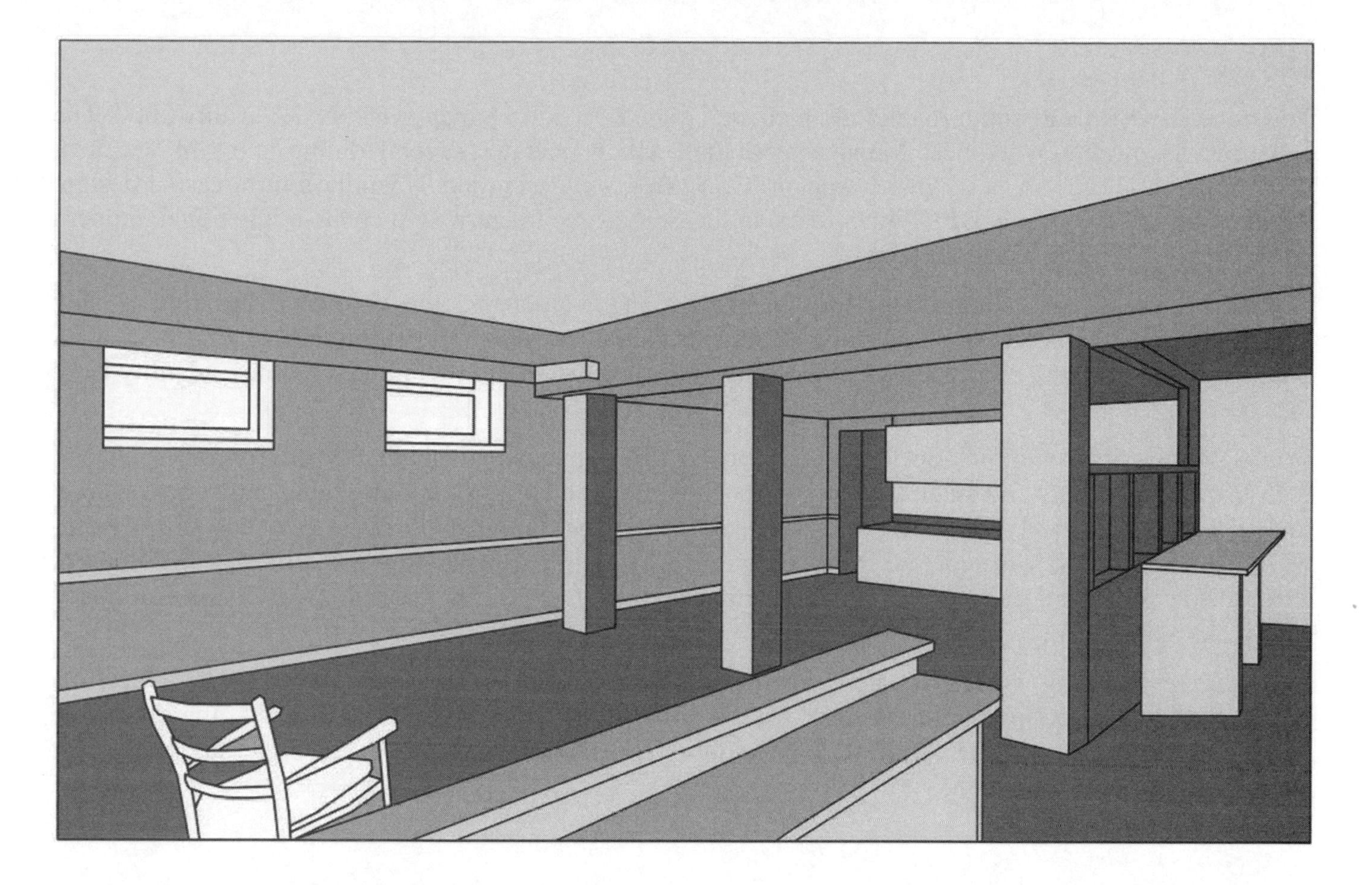

Code	Division Name	%	Sq. Cost	Projected
00	Procurement and Contracting Require	2.88	3.03	60,549
01	General Requirements	15.92	16.72	334,412
03	Concrete	2.82	2.96	59,213
04	Masonry	2.05	2.15	43,016
05	Metals	2.04	2.14	42,878
06	Wood, Plastics, and Composites	7.33	7.70	154,030
07	Thermal and Moisture Protection	3.33	3.49	69,896
08	Openings	3.68	3.86	77,186
09	Finishes	10.17	10.68	213,612
10	Specialties	0.32	0.34	6,746
11	Equipment	3.07	3.22	64,468
12	Furnishings	0.09	0.09	1,798
22	Plumbing	8.03	8.44	168,720
23	HVAC	27.68	29.06	581,236
26	Electrical	10.31	10.82	216,493
28	Electronic Safety and Security	0.27	0.29	5,766
	Total Building Costs	100.00	105.00	2,100,019

COST PER SQUARE FOOT = $105.00

File 54:

Townline BBQ, an authentic, roadhouse, barbeque joint, opened in Sagaponack, N.Y., in July 2007. The restaurant is owned by Honest Management, Inc., which operates several dining spots in the area, including Nick and Tony's in East Hampton. CCS Architecture crafted Townline's ultra-casual design, which relates to the classic BBQ joints found in the South. The intent was to create a functional, modern "dive" for on-site dining and take-out.

Occupying the old Allison's at the Beach location in Sagaponack, the renovated building is now enclosed with reclaimed barn wood siding and a corrugated, galvanized metal roof. A new fireplace with a tall chimney and large steel letters reading BBQ anchor the structure and create a new identity from the road.

Inside, patrons order and pick-up food at the counter. Built-in seating is made from shop-grade plywood with exposed fasteners and steel. Custom tables, including the large community table and benches, are a mix of galvanized metal, linoleum, and wood. A sink in the dining room gives easy access for hand-washing. The small bar is separate from the dining area, with its own tables and a fireplace. Exposed, bare Edison lamps and galvanized fixtures illuminate the restaurant. The bar and order counter are faced with black slate.

The primary cooking vessel, a large wood-fired meat smoker from Texas called "The Oiler," is positioned in the open kitchen to be seen. A deck with picnic tables for summer use is at the south side of the site with views of the farmland to the south. With 2,000 square feet, Townline has seating for about 75.

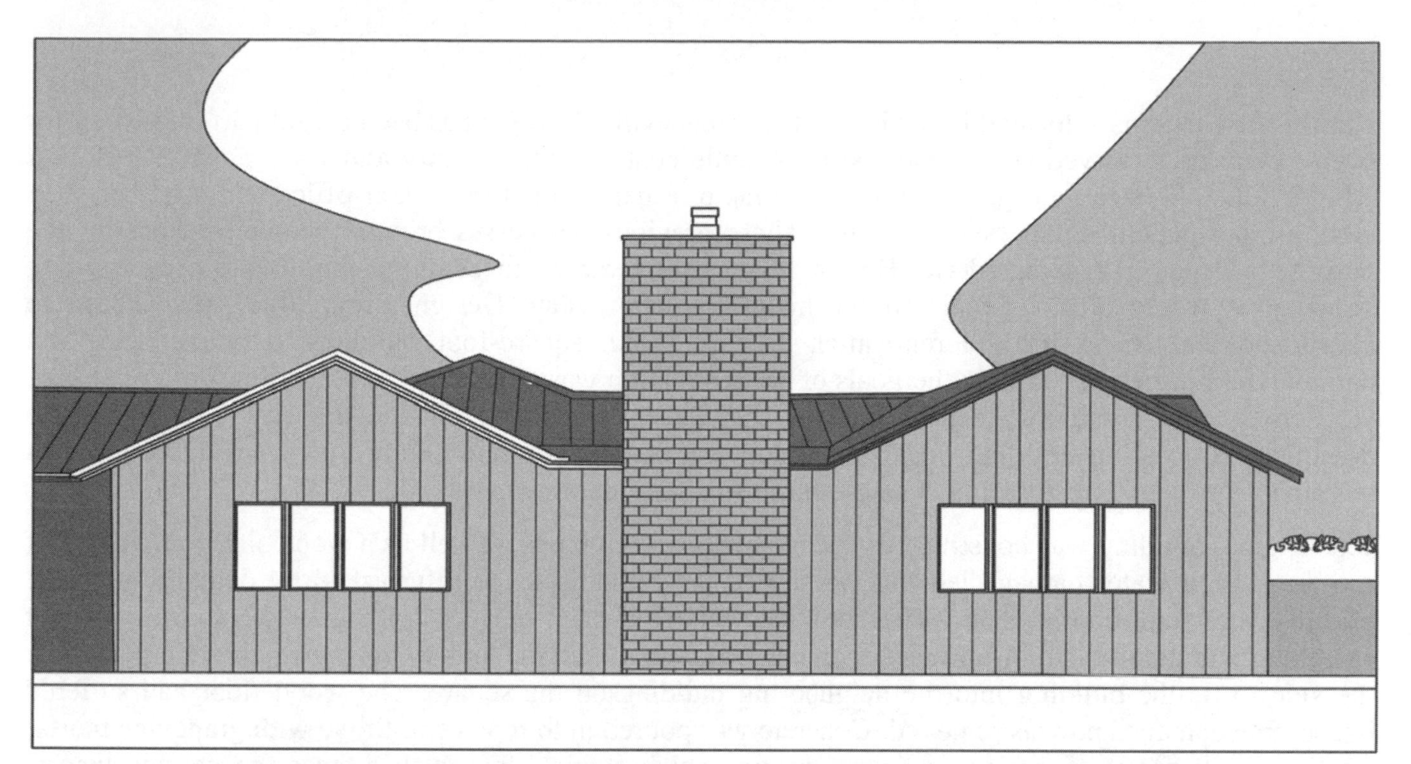

Code	Division Name	%	Sq. Cost	Projected
00	Procurement and Contracting Require	0.05	0.18	706
03	Concrete	2.25	7.25	29,019
04	Masonry	0.17	0.55	2,190
05	Metals	0.30	0.96	3,833
06	Wood, Plastics, and Composites	15.06	48.46	193,824
07	Thermal and Moisture Protection	7.96	25.62	102,464
08	Openings	4.01	12.89	51,577
09	Finishes	9.93	31.95	127,792
10	Specialties	9.53	30.66	122,646
11	Equipment	22.81	73.42	293,692
12	Furnishings	4.06	13.06	52,234
13	Special Construction	2.04	6.57	26,281
14	Conveying Systems	0.18	0.57	2,300
22	Plumbing	7.57	24.36	97,459
23	HVAC	3.57	11.50	45,992
25	Integrated Automation	0.70	2.26	9,045
26	Electrical	6.70	21.57	86,290
27	Communications	0.94	3.01	12,046
28	Electronic Safety and Security	1.28	4.11	16,426
40	Process Integration	0.32	1.04	4,161
44	Pollution Control Equipment	0.57	1.83	7,337
	Total Building Costs	100.00	321.83	1,287,313

COST PER SQUARE FOOT = $321.83

File 55:

This historic landmark located in the heart of Lawrenceville, Georgia has been a vital part of the city for over a century. It served as a horse and mule trade center for the county and was known as "Honest Alley". Later, it became a garage, a car dealership, a hardware store, a taxi office and a barber shop among other general retail establishments. These previous businesses brought people together for the purpose of trade and camaraderie. Honest Alley, LLC wanted to continue this tradition by creating spaces that would attract people to the historic square. Pate Design Group, Inc. was chosen to coordinate the design for the renovation of this 16,000-square-foot building to house retail and commercial businesses. Among the goals of the renovation was to protect the structure, further enhance the activity and commerce-themed projects that have served to revitalize the city. Rather than to demolish the existing building, local investment partners Randy and Cindy Sutt were interested in a sustainable project to restore and enhance the site's traditional uses.

The original building was constructed of stone and wood timbers, as well as a wood slat floor. Years of roof leaks and water damage led this portion of the building to be refurbished by demolition of the existing roof and floor system. The roof was removed and replaced with new wood trusses, roof sheathing and a combination of metal standing seam roof material and shingles, which were placed on the side to tie the building into the neighboring building on the square. The wood floor had suffered irreparable damage and was removed. Concrete was poured in to replace it. Stone with grapevine mortar joints were kept intact, which made up the original building's facade that faces the nearby historic courthouse and was divided into two separate tenant spaces.

A two story CMU second addition to the building was added in the 1950's. This portion was open throughout and had a concrete floor and wood trusses with a shingled roof. The intent of the project was to shore up the existing structure with steel reinforcement and create a poured concrete floor that separated the later addition into two floors. This would allow for retail space above and future restaurant space below. The concrete floor was cut to allow for new foundation footers to be poured. Steel columns were erected on these new footers to support a steel beam in the center. Bar joists that support the decking for the second floor is supported by this beam and mechanically attached steel angles through the existing CMU walls. A balcony and poured ramp were added to provide access to the second floor retail and commercial portion of the building.

An elaborate garden in the courtyard of the building is the centerpiece of the site. This garden was designed to use indigenous plants that would naturally attract butterflies to create a place where patrons and visitors to the town square could relax and enjoy the scenery. The garden serves as an invitation to visit Honest Alley and experience life as it has been for the past century.

Code	Division Name	%	Sq. Cost	Projected
01	General Requirements	13.76	14.80	236,163
03	Concrete	6.42	6.91	110,227
04	Masonry	12.93	13.90	221,919
05	Metals	17.28	18.58	296,552
06	Wood, Plastics, and Composites	4.74	5.09	81,321
07	Thermal and Moisture Protection	9.65	10.37	165,583
08	Openings	5.63	6.05	96,616
09	Finishes	7.84	8.43	134,510
10	Specialties	0.20	0.21	3,390
21	Fire Suppression	3.04	3.27	52,222
22	Plumbing	2.61	2.80	44,762
23	HVAC	6.35	6.83	108,950
26	Electrical	9.57	10.29	164,245
	Total Building Costs	100.00	107.54	1,716,459

COST PER SQUARE FOOT = $107.54

File 56:

Rees Associates' solution to a space that was originally designed to be part of a parking garage resulted in a wide open facility with technology and futuristic equipment on display. On the leading edge of equipment, the entire facility is designed for utilization of Shared Area Technology (SAN).

The WJLA space is approximately 80,000 square feet and accommodates two stations, WJLA (an ABC affiliate) and NewsChannel 8 (a 24-hour cable news channel), three multi-media conference rooms and over 200 workstations for reporters, anchors and administration. The facility is located in a retail mall of small shops, restaurants, business services, and medical clinics.

Rees offered knowledge of thc broadcast industry and technology plus a 14-year relationship with Allbritton Communications in accommodating the news stations to this unusual space. Rees created a functional and technically efficient plan while offering a brilliant design that is comfortable and inviting to all who enter.

The facility is located in an area that spans the base of two 34-story office towers, which partially overlooks the Potomac River. WJLA's studio, control room and audio control are located one level above the main facility while, the NewsChannel 8 studio and operation are fully embedded with activity of the main floor level.

Code	Division Name	%	Sq. Cost	Projected
00	Bidding Requirements	0.00	0.00	338
01	General Requirements	5.70	10.28	822,222
03	Concrete	0.51	0.92	73,382
04	Masonry	0.17	0.30	23,823
05	Metals	0.57	1.02	81,798
06	Wood & Plastics	11.10	20.01	1,600,562
08	Doors & Windows	5.01	9.02	721,677
09	Finishes	20.92	37.70	3,015,862
10	Specialties	0.82	1.48	118,255
11	Equipment	0.41	0.74	59,137
12	Furnishings	0.16	0.29	23,437
15	Mechanical	30.40	54.78	4,382,756
16	Electrical	24.23	43.66	3,492,723
	Total Building Costs	100.00	180.20	14,415,972

COST PER SQUARE FOOT = $180.20

File 57:

In order to provide optimal person-centered care for their residents, Homestead Village chose to renovate approximately 28,149 square feet of traditional departmental nursing care into the "household" model of patient care at their existing facility located in Lancaster, Penn. Transitioning from traditional nursing care eliminates the institutional stereotype often associated with Nursing care facilities, which is often conjured by the large central nursing station, medication and linen carts littered throughout corridors, residents in wheelchairs surrounding the central nursing station, and limited dining times. This project is considered phase one of a two phase plan, and creates two resident households from the existing nursing facility. Phase two will complete the renovation, involve two small additions, and turn a 60-bed nursing facility into three households, including a memory support household, with a maximum population of 58 residents. Phase two also includes the renovation of the existing assisted living memory support household.

In lieu of the aforementioned institutional items, a goal of the "household" model of person-centered care is to create smaller, more personal households for the residents to reside within. Each household contains living room space, a dining room, laundry facilities dedicated personal resident items, nursing team spaces rather than large central desks, spa and salon space, and a country kitchen evoking a homelike environment for serving residents as well as providing the opportunity for cooking activities. Each household is supported by an increased number of caregivers, allowing greater responsiveness to resident needs.

Common spaces shared between households include a central production kitchen that serves each country kitchen, physical therapy space, a small parlor, and a medical records room. The central production kitchen will be available to serve residents meals during extended times, providing greater flexibility and satisfaction. The central production kitchen also has the capability to be opened for residents to see food preparation and the smells associated with home cooking, but can also be cordoned off during a fire event with automatic rolling shutters.

Each resident room is equipped with its own European style roll-in shower, providing greater privacy for bathing, or residents may elect to visit the spa and utilize the accessible spa tubs for bathing. Furniture was replaced in each room, providing a new wardrobe, dresser, nightstand, over bed table, and chair. All finishes were updated within the rooms to provide a clean, homelike environment.

The greatest challenge of this project was completing renovations within a fully functional, occupied nursing facility. As the General Contractor, Paul Risk Associates rose to the occasion, using their experience to provide phasing direction and minimal disturbance to the residents. Overall, the project has been deemed a success by Homestead Village and most importantly, provides the quality of life that their residents deserve.

Code	Division Name	%	Sq. Cost	Projected
00	Procurement and Contracting Require	7.31	6.46	181,869
01	General Requirements	15.17	13.41	377,522
03	Concrete	2.12	1.88	52,825
04	Masonry	0.06	0.05	1,396
05	Metals	0.60	0.53	15,025
06	Wood, Plastics, and Composites	9.45	8.36	235,235
07	Thermal and Moisture Protection	1.11	0.98	27,504
08	Openings	3.58	3.16	89,000
09	Finishes	17.21	15.21	428,153
10	Specialties	1.76	1.56	43,785
11	Equipment	2.95	2.60	73,315
12	Furnishings	0.06	0.05	1,375
21	Fire Suppression	2.15	1.90	53,429
22	Plumbing	8.67	7.66	215,721
23	HVAC	11.21	9.91	279,037
26	Electrical	16.59	14.67	412,890
	Total Building Costs	100.00	88.39	2,488,080

COST PER SQUARE FOOT = $88.39

File 58:

Home & Hospice Care of Rhode Island is the state's largest and most comprehensive provider of hospice and palliative care, and is the third oldest hospice in the country. In 2006, Home & Hospice purchased 1085 North Main Street in Providence, with plans to consolidate their hospice facility, administrative offices, and education and bereavement center into one building. On May 31, 2009, a crowd of nearly 500 people celebrated the grand opening of Home & Hospice's new headquarters.

The renovation of the four-story building is currently pursuing LEED(R) Gold certification and is expected to be the first fully operational LEED certified health care facility in Rhode Island. Sustainable design aligns with Home & Hospice's philosophy on the cycles of life and the cycles of nature. During design, Home & Hospice consulted with a cultural anthropologist on critical design issues.

The first, major sustainable design commitment Home & Hospice made was to convert an abandoned building, instead of building new. "Not only does reusing an existing facility significantly divert demolition and construction waste from landfills," states David Sluter, CEO of New England Construction, contractor for the renovation, "it enhances the neighborhood by converting a vacant building into a thriving healthcare facility that is open to community use." Throughout construction, 92.6% of all construction waste was recycled. In addition, 95% of the existing wall, floor, and roof construction was reused. "When walking through the new Home & Hospice," says Diana Franchitto, President and CEO of Home & Hospice Care of Rhode Island, "you would never believe that 95% of what you see existed here before. Everything looks brand new."

Other sustainable design features include a reflective roof to prevent heat absorption; low-flow water fixtures with motion sensors; high-performing and energy-efficient building mechanical and electrical systems; and low or no VOC-emitting carpets, paints, adhesives, and wood products. Home & Hospice has also committed to obtaining at least 35% of their electricity from renewable sources, and using only green cleaning methods and products to reduce chemicals in the environment.

Besides the project's sustainable design features, the goal of the project was to provide a facility in which Home & Hospice Care could fulfill their mission to provide compassionate, professional, state of the art physical, emotional and spiritual care for all people facing life-threatening illness. "Vision 3 Architects wrapped the entire design of the facility around this mission," affirms Keith Davignon, Principal of Vision 3 Architects. "We listened closely to Home & Hospice's staff, and provided them with a comfortable and dignified environment for patients and their families."

"Our new home reflects thoughtful planning geared toward the needs of our patients, families and staff. Our goals included creating a sustainable hospice environment that offers patients and family members comfort, peace and plenty of space for reflection and quiet time," states Franchitto. "With the creativity and guidance of Vision 3 and New England Construction, we've achieved these goals and look forward to continuing our important role in the state's health care scheme."

Code	Division Name	%	Sq. Cost	Projected
01	General Requirements	16.25	24.88	1,187,780
03	Concrete	1.17	1.78	85,192
04	Masonry	0.65	1.00	47,786
05	Metals	6.07	9.30	443,703
06	Wood, Plastics, and Composites	8.03	12.29	586,791
07	Thermal and Moisture Protection	2.49	3.80	181,620
08	Openings	6.40	9.81	468,051
09	Finishes	11.60	17.76	847,781
10	Specialties	0.81	1.24	59,200
11	Equipment	0.07	0.10	4,956
14	Conveying Systems	2.51	3.84	183,182
21	Fire Suppression	2.60	3.98	189,837
22	Plumbing	6.85	10.49	500,770
23	HVAC	24.31	37.22	1,776,440
26	Electrical	10.20	15.62	745,409
	Total Building Costs	100.00	153.11	7,308,496

COST PER SQUARE FOOT = $153.11

File 59:

Enterprise Integration started in 1997 with 5 people that has grown to 245 people, and is known in the IT industry as one of the top 20 largest Managed Service Providers in the world. After reviewing preliminary plans for a new building and struggling to find a site appropriate for their needs and future expansion, EI made the decision to purchase and renovate an existing warehouse/office building consisting of approximately 32,000 square feet of office space and 25,000 square feet of warehouse space. The intent was to renovate the warehouse space into office space to house their IT network operations center.

Blue LED lights illuminate hallways and conference rooms, starry night fiber optic lighting cover the wide open NOC area, smart glass is used in conference rooms that frost over for privacy at the push of a button, and silver metallic automatic slider pocket doors are as "trekkie" as it gets. Elaborate break rooms, gyms, and even massage rooms are all typical perks in the building(s).

The existing building that was purchased for renovation was originally constructed with concrete tilt-up panel walls. The warehouse roof system was constructed as a pre-engineered metal building consisting of an assembly of bar joists, vinyl-coated insulation, and metal standing-seam roof panels. The roof assembly over the office area consists of bar joists, conventional structural metal decking, insulation board, decking material, and standing-seam metal roofing to match the rest of the warehouse area roof.

The original intent in the design was to reconfigure the roof assembly of the existing warehouse area to an assembly more suited to office space design much like what currently existed on the office area portion of the building. The design originally called for removing the metal roofing and the vinyl-faced insulation over the warehouse portion, thereby exposing the interior of the warehouse area, in order to place structural metal decking, insulation, and a new roof assembly. Needless to say, exposing the interior of an existing building to the elements would have meant a tremendous amount of rework in existing areas-to-remain as there would be no way to protect finished work areas from the elements. Auld & White posed an idea to the designers. If the existing metal standing-seam roof panels were of adequate gauge to be considered the structural metal decking layer proposed for the roof assembly, then why remove them? A structural engineer was engaged to verify that the roof panels are 25 gauge metal, adequate to act as the structural deck system thus allowing them to be used as the substrate for new roofing material. This eliminated the additional steps of demolishing the existing roof system and protecting existing finishes to remain in the building. Additionally, the Owner would realize cost savings.

Removing the metal roof panels to add the structural metal decking alone would have added $75,000 to the costs of the project. This option does not take into account the additional work and/or rework for protecting finishes already in place. The option of shot-pinning the existing roof panels added roughly $6,000 in costs, however, the overall savings in the construction activities alone equated to nearly $70,000, not withstanding the potentially high amount of rework in the existing areas that were to remain in place.

Although this was not a "green" (LEED®) project, sustainable practices were certainly included. For example, since the metal roof panels were kept intact, the existing building envelope, along with existing finishes, interior doors, cabinets, etc., were reused and diverted from landfills.

Code	Division Name	%	Sq. Cost	Projected
00	Procurement and Contracting Require	13.44	6.76	390,182
01	General Requirements	1.55	0.78	45,045
03	Concrete	1.80	0.90	52,165
04	Masonry	1.54	0.77	44,634
05	Metals	10.78	5.42	313,126
06	Wood, Plastics, and Composites	2.49	1.25	72,428
07	Thermal and Moisture Protection	19.31	9.71	560,669
08	Openings	7.47	3.76	216,874
09	Finishes	15.62	7.86	453,601
10	Specialties	0.50	0.25	14,650
11	Equipment	0.09	0.05	2,601
21	Fire Suppression	0.97	0.49	28,205
22	Plumbing	0.98	0.49	28,478
23	HVAC	5.73	2.88	166,489
26	Electrical	17.71	8.91	514,254
	Total Building Costs	100.00	50.30	2,903,402

COST PER SQUARE FOOT = $50.30

File 60:

In the summer of 2010, Davis & Davis Interior Design had the pleasure of meeting Mr. Zack Taylor, owner of Lee Steel Corporation. Mr. Taylor had recently purchased a building in Novi, Michigan for the new site of his corporate office and was working with interior furnishing associates, Facility Matrix Group.

Through meeting and discussing his ideas for the space, it became clear Mr. Taylor was looking for a state-of-the-art office environment that not only supported his staff, but also infused a modern, futuristic atmosphere for clients. He had a unique challenge for the design team: NO exposed wood products. The Taylor family has owned and operated Lee Steel Corporation for over 60 years and has established itself as a leader in cutting-edge technology and a reliable source for quality steel products. The new office needed to reflect the company's success and innovation in their industry.

During the design process, Davis & Davis introduced a number of unique and modern elements such as back-lit LED wall panels, stainless steel mesh curtain walls, thirty-foot long skylights, large format textured glass tiles and floating acrylic panel ceilings. After the initial programming, space planning and preliminary design phases, the team presented the design concept with a number of 3-D photo-realistic renderings that showed Mr. Taylor what it would be like to stand in the finished space. With his enthusiastic approval, Davis & Davis spent about four months creating and developing a 100+ sheet set of fully engineered construction drawings to clearly define each detail and material going in the space.

That following fall the owner and project team met with D.J. Maltese, the construction manager, who has worked with Lee Steel on various projects over the past three decades. D.J. Maltese reviewed the scope of the project and developed an estimate for the complex build-out. Since this was such a custom project, there were several specialized details and field conditions that needed attention from sub-contractors prior to construction. Once the final budget was determined, an eight-month schedule was set in place and D. J. Maltese began construction in November of 2010.

Throughout the construction phase, Davis & Davis continued to work with Facility Matrix Group to specify high-end, ultramodern furnishings for the space. Furnishings include a back-painted glass conference table, futuristic lounge chairs, sleek executive desks and, of course, steel elements such as end tables and workstation panels.

The end result is a modern, innovative and cutting-edge office environment, particularly unique to the region. It successfully reflects Lee Steel's company culture, as well as their future success. Mr. Taylor and his staff are very pleased with the outcome and have received numerous accolades from clients.

Code	Division Name	%	Sq. Cost	Projected
00	Procurement and Contracting Require	0.47	0.67	10,530
01	General Requirements	2.29	3.24	51,193
03	Concrete	0.44	0.62	9,860
05	Metals	4.01	5.67	89,547
06	Wood, Plastics, and Composites	24.82	35.13	554,309
07	Thermal and Moisture Protection	0.60	0.85	13,492
08	Openings	5.90	8.35	131,750
09	Finishes	28.63	40.52	639,370
21	Fire Suppression	1.13	1.60	25,299
22	Plumbing	4.09	5.79	91,420
23	HVAC	5.21	7.37	116,327
26	Electrical	15.12	21.40	337,695
27	Communications	3.09	4.38	69,067
28	Electronic Safety and Security	3.14	4.44	70,035
48	Electrical power Generation	1.06	1.50	23,602
	Total Building Costs	100.00	141.53	2,233,496

COST PER SQUARE FOOT = $141.53

File 61:

Cooke Douglass Farr Lemons Architects and Engineers, PA was awarded a large renovation in late 2007 by the Mississippi Bureau of Building, Grounds and Real Property Management that presented the firm with many opportunities to employ environmentally sustainable techniques and materials. The CDFL team was charged with maximizing the indoor environmental quality of two buildings with failed exterior surfaces and ineffective mechanical systems. The Mississippi Department of Environmental Quality currently occupies both buildings.

The first structure that was renovated was a 6-story, 110,000 square-foot facility located at 515 East Amite Street which previously housed the LDDS WorldCom headquarters. Exterior renovations included removal of the ineffective Exterior Insulated Fenestration System (EIFS) building envelope, or “skin,” that was replaced with a 2-inch insulated metal panel system with integrated windows providing a water-tight facade. All of the windows were replaced with insulated “Low-E” glass to keep out harmful ultra-violet light rays and solar heat gain further enhancing the new HVAC system and occupant comfort. The primary sub-contractor, F. L. Crane and Sons, recycled all existing aluminum window frames removed during the renovation.

Interior upgrades involved removing 8,500 yards of old carpet that was recycled through Mohawk Group's Recover Program. This was the largest quantity of carpet ever recycled not only in Mississippi but also in the surrounding states. CDFL's Interior Architecture department chose one of Mohawk's newest modular carpets for the renovation. Mohawk's products are created from recycled materials, such as plastic soda and water bottles, and specifically designed to meet the United States Green Building Council's (USGBC) stringent low-chemical emissivity standards to improve indoor air quality. Furthermore, all interior walls received low-VOC paints to minimize odor and the harmful Volatile Organic Compounds found in most paints. Evan Johnson & Sons Construction served as the general contractor for the project that was budgeted at $6,000,000.

The second phase of the project will focus on the 5-story, 62,670-square-foot building at 700 State Street where similar interior and mechanical renovations are necessary.

Code	Division Name	%	Sq. Cost	Projected
00	Procurement and Contracting Require	5.05	4.06	491,726
01	General Requirements	4.48	3.60	436,340
03	Concrete	1.07	0.86	104,273
04	Masonry	0.33	0.26	31,905
05	Metals	1.55	1.25	150,916
06	Wood, Plastics, and Composites	3.36	2.70	327,563
07	Thermal and Moisture Protection	42.98	34.53	4,184,187
08	Openings	10.38	8.34	1,010,426
09	Finishes	20.44	16.42	1,989,443
10	Specialties	1.25	1.01	121,953
11	Equipment	1.15	0.93	112,418
14	Conveying Systems	0.63	0.50	61,147
21	Fire Suppression	0.71	0.57	68,640
22	Plumbing	0.09	0.07	8,479
23	HVAC	2.75	2.21	267,418
26	Electrical	3.79	3.04	368,592
	Total Building Costs	100.00	80.35	9,735,426

COST PER SQUARE FOOT = $80.35

File 62:

Spalding Tougias Architects, Inc. was selected to design a neighborhood office in Boston's Jamaica Plain section. Located on the second floor of a former industrial building converted into office use, the site is convenient to public transportation including bus and rail. The project consists of 5,100 square feet of area incorporating reception, conference and board room, main work space, private offices, kitchen, lounge and support space. The uniqueness of the space and challenge to STA was that the ma

in work space is defined by deep steel trusses and receives natural day lighting from three new skylights and existing high windows on the exterior side. In addition the roof framing slopes from a low point at the interior corridor demising wall to a high point at the exterior wall.

Because of the height gained closer to the exterior wall, STA captured additional program space by inserting a mezzanine level. Understanding that natural daylight from the mezzanine level serves the main work space; the architect enclosed the director's office with transparent glass walls while leaving an adjacent informal conference area open to below. Included on this level is the office kitchen and coffee bar with an exterior view.

The new mezzanine level frames into one of the steel truss lines which serves as the edge of the circulation path leading to the stair. The exposed brick and steel characteristics of the existing space are enhanced by new work utilizing an industrial vocabulary. The mezzanine stair is supported by an exposed painted steel stringer with steel and wire mesh railing system. Ductwork and fire protection systems are left exposed and light fixtures are suspended from steel cable.

The large conference room can facilitate public gatherings and board meetings or can be subdivided into two smaller spaces including the modular conference room table.

The overall openness of the space coupled with selective architectural components, new materials and lighting fosters an environment that allows communication and collaboration.

Code	Division Name	%	Sq. Cost	Projected
00	Procurement and Contracting Require	20.94	16.43	83,799
05	Metals	5.00	3.92	19,997
06	Wood, Plastics, and Composites	13.46	10.56	53,859
07	Thermal and Moisture Protection	3.73	2.93	14,923
08	Openings	7.34	5.76	29,373
09	Finishes	23.85	18.72	95,457
10	Specialties	0.99	0.78	3,979
12	Furnishings	1.09	0.86	4,377
21	Fire Suppression	2.71	2.13	10,844
22	Plumbing	1.04	0.82	4,178
23	HVAC	6.46	5.07	25,866
26	Electrical	13.39	10.51	53,603
	Total Building Costs	100.00	78.48	400,255

COST PER SQUARE FOOT = $78.48

File 63:

Vision 3 Architects provided architectural and interior design services for Thundermist Community Health Center's newest location at 186 Providence Street in West Warwick. This project is an adaptive reuse of a 120-year-old historic granite mill building that is known in the community as The Cotton Shed at Royal Mills. Working with State Historic Preservation and Heritage Commission, Vision 3 prepared a design concept that preserves and features many historic elements of the building including the existing clerestory windows, heavy timber construction and exposed interior stone and brick walls. The new 18,000-square-foot health center greatly expands Thundermist's ability to serve their patients, and includes 28 exam rooms, a 75-100 person multi-purpose conference room, clinical, staff, and administrative spaccs all on one level. Continuing to make an enormous impact on the lives of over 6,000 patients who have used the West Warwick center on Main Street in the six years it has been open, this new facility will enable Thundermist to expand its medical services to meet the increasing needs of West Warwick and surrounding areas.

Prior to Thundermist Health Center purchasing the property, a developer had begun renovating the building and site for a spec/retail use. Rough grading and paving, and site retaining walls were in place. A new roof had been installed, and most of the exterior windows and doors had already been replaced. Project scope included completion of site work, new bridges at entries, and miscellaneous exterior renovations. The basement was converted to the building's mechanical room, the lower level was left as shell space for future tenants, and the upper level completely built-out for the new health center.

The challenge was how to create a quality healthcare facility in a 120-year-old mill building, while preserving as many historic features as possible. Vision 3 Architects took on this design challenge, and carefully evaluated the Center's needs in order to design a health center that not only complimented the historical features of the 2-story mill building, but also created an environment that supported the Patient-Centered Medical Home approach. This included creating spaces that were flexible in size and layout to foster collaboration between the clinical teams, and that focus on ways to improve patient education.

Vision 3 Architects created a warm, hotel style lobby environment that welcomes patients and families while challenging the concepts of traditional medical waiting and check in procedures. The urgent care exam room, right off the lobby space, serves patients efficiently and with extended hours that can greatly reduce the number of unnecessary emergency room visits. The large Community Room, with a full teaching kitchen, an attached exam room, and teleconferencing capabilities, can serve as a community classroom, a staff fitness area, or when subdivided into smaller rooms, can serve multiple functions at once.

For over 24 years, Vision 3 Architects has provided design services to over 50 healthcare clients including Providence Community Health Centers, Home & Hospice Care of Rhode Island, and WellOne Community Health Center, to name a few. They are committed to working closely with healthcare clients to develop design strategies focused on patient care, staff needs, and maximum efficiency.

Code	Division Name	%	Sq. Cost	Projected
01	General Requirements	10.15	16.87	307,320
03	Concrete	0.59	0.97	17,758
04	Masonry	1.76	2.93	53,365
05	Metals	1.51	2.50	45,613
06	Wood, Plastics, and Composites	4.66	7.75	141,119
07	Thermal and Moisture Protection	2.12	3.53	64,254
08	Openings	2.98	4.96	90,333
09	Finishes	13.57	22.56	410,986
10	Specialties	1.41	2.34	42,579
14	Conveying Systems	1.53	2.54	46,198
21	Fire Suppression	2.29	3.81	69,320
22	Plumbing	5.22	8.68	158,202
23	HVAC	24.99	41.54	756,754
26	Electrical	27.23	45.27	824,632
	Total Building Costs	100.00	166.24	3,028,433

COST PER SQUARE FOOT = $166.24

File 64:

The Wellness Center at Meadows Regional Hospital was borne of a shared vision to provide Toombs and Montgomery counties with more than rehabilitation and fitness services. Meadows Regional Medical Center and Toombs Therapy and Sports Medicine joined together to create a unique destination for wellness, prevention and health education.

Meadows Regional Medical Center (MRMC) established a set of objectives to guide the creation of the wellness facility. First, they wanted to do more than absorb a successful independent business into the hospital. Second, the location needed to be easily accessible for community members. Third, the rehabilitation business, although part of the hospital, should retain its own identity. And last, they wanted to separate therapy into two segments, with inpatient therapy occurring at the hospital and outpatient at the new site.

Bringing the vision to life required a lot of square footage. Luckily a large warehouse was found that could be rehabbed for much less than the cost of building a brand new facility.

The Educational Mall was the organizing concept for the design of the Center. With large amounts of anticipated users, a single entry point for security, control and health education was needed. Each user must pass through the educational mall, complete with museum quality display cases, providing MRMC with the opportunity to offer continuous medical educational.

The Physical Therapy area was designed to be open to the fitness areas, yet securable in the evening and maintain a separate identity. The floor in Physical Therapy is "fuzzy vinyl" product. This was selected to soften the acoustical energy of a fitness center and provide a warm, low maintenance yet fun, environment for the medically necessary therapies.

An indoor walking track was included in the plan. The positioning of the 1/10th mile oval around the existing column grid was a major influence on the arraignment of the other spaces.

A 25-meter lap pool for lap swimming, water aerobics and therapeutic rehabilitation was dug from the existing slab. The partitions that separate the pools are the only partitions that reach to the roof structure. This was to contain the humidity and odor, while designing a designated, self-contained HVAC system.

Low-maintenance, no-touch design features in the locker rooms and toilets included automatic flush valves, hand-washing faucets, and paper towel dispenser help reduce the spread of germs.

The Doc's Cafe serves as a place to hang-out, get a drink and light meal.

Additional classrooms for training hospital employees were added - including a 100-seat meeting room - with all available to the public. Meeting rooms include state-of-the-art audio-visual equipment, motorized screens, overhead projection, and surround sound.

The ultimate vision for the Wellness Center was to create more than a combined rehabilitation and fitness center, and to create a center of wellness, prevention and health education for the health of the employees and the community. Building on this goal of also providing health services, an orthopedic surgeon's practice joined the facility and Phase II construction will add an imaging center and additional physician practices.

The Wellness Center is a giant step toward a new model of healthcare that nurtures the mind as well as the body. The architect and owner's hope is to bring healthy lifestyles to the residents of Toombs and Montgomery counties, and their lives will become richer in the process.

Code	Division Name	%	Sq. Cost	Projected
01	General Requirements	15.17	16.58	761,529
03	Concrete	0.98	1.07	49,318
04	Masonry	0.18	0.19	8,835
05	Metals	1.25	1.36	62,602
06	Wood, Plastics, and Composites	6.28	6.87	315,256
07	Thermal and Moisture Protection	20.08	21.96	1,008,256
08	Openings	17.60	19.25	883,678
09	Finishes	10.27	11.23	515,664
10	Specialties	0.69	0.76	34,699
11	Equipment	0.26	0.29	13,120
12	Furnishings	0.15	0.16	7,489
13	Special Construction	4.52	4.94	226,797
21	Fire Suppression	2.03	2.22	101,992
22	Plumbing	3.61	3.95	181,286
23	HVAC	6.67	7.29	334,850
26	Electrical	10.28	11.24	516,147
	Total Building Costs	100.00	109.36	5,021,518

COST PER SQUARE FOOT = $109.36

File 65:

Currently, Sumter Regional Hospital is a 143-bed acute care facility with more than 50 active medical staff members representing more than 25 specialties. SRH has served the Middle Flint region since 1953. A big-box retail property became available adjacent to an existing medical complex. The property created an opportunity to expand specialty out-patient services in a new, high touch - high tech environment. Stegenga + PARTNERS helped the leadership at SRH master plan the renovation and modification of the 65,000 square feet existing building into a community-based outpatient services called the "HealthPlex".

The first phase of the HealthPlex at Sumter Regional includes Imaging & Diagnostic Services along with Women's Health Services. This is the achievement of a dream that SRH Foundation and SRH had... a dream to provide state-of-the-art preventive care services and facility to the citizens of Southwest Georgia.

The first phase of the HealthPlex includes an Imaging & Diagnostic facility anchored by the latest state-of-the art MRI Scanner. It also features Women's Mammography and Health Services.

Customers who have traditionally gone to the hospital for diagnostic services such as routine X-rays, mammograms, laboratory services, blood tests, and bone density scanning now have access to these same services in a faster and more comfortable environment. The site, a former retail furniture store, has more than 5 acres of parking. Patients and customers can park near the front door and walk right in.

The current master site plan, and future phases of the Project, includes softening the hardscape with plantings, tree canopies, and an out door walking track.

Using the skeleton of the previous furniture store presented several challenges. The demands of new technologies, from electrical and mechanical to patient accessibility, required that most of the existing system had to be removed. New electrical services, roof-top HVAC units, and a new fire suppression system had to be integrated into the skeleton.

Structurally, the building shell could accommodate the new use. A new TPO roof was installed over the entire facility. The concrete slab frequently had to be cut to accommodate the new utility requirements. The slab in the MRI area had to be removed and replace to accommodate the new utilities and floor leveling requirements.

While the magnitude of replacement was extensive, the location and availability of the big-box was financially viable. In a small rural community like Americus there are limited re-use options for these big-box retail locations. The purchase price and adjacency to the main hospital was favorable to the success and growth of the health care system.

Creative interior medical planning organized the programmed services to help segregate the male / female population to preserve patient confidentiality and limit the possibility of gender crossover traffic. These programmed functions were organized to comfort and respect the patient. Services that are shared by gender were designed in the center of the plan.

Warm and friendly colors and materials accent the space. Soaring gypsum board ceiling and indirect lighting articulate the sub-wait areas outside the mammography and ultrasound suites creating a soothing and private area for the patient. The warm colors are calming and spa-like. Private video education rooms are provided in each waiting area. The emphasis on education reinforces the patient hospital partnership.

Phase II of the building project is set to take place within the next few years as the SRH Foundation continues their philanthropic efforts to fund this project.

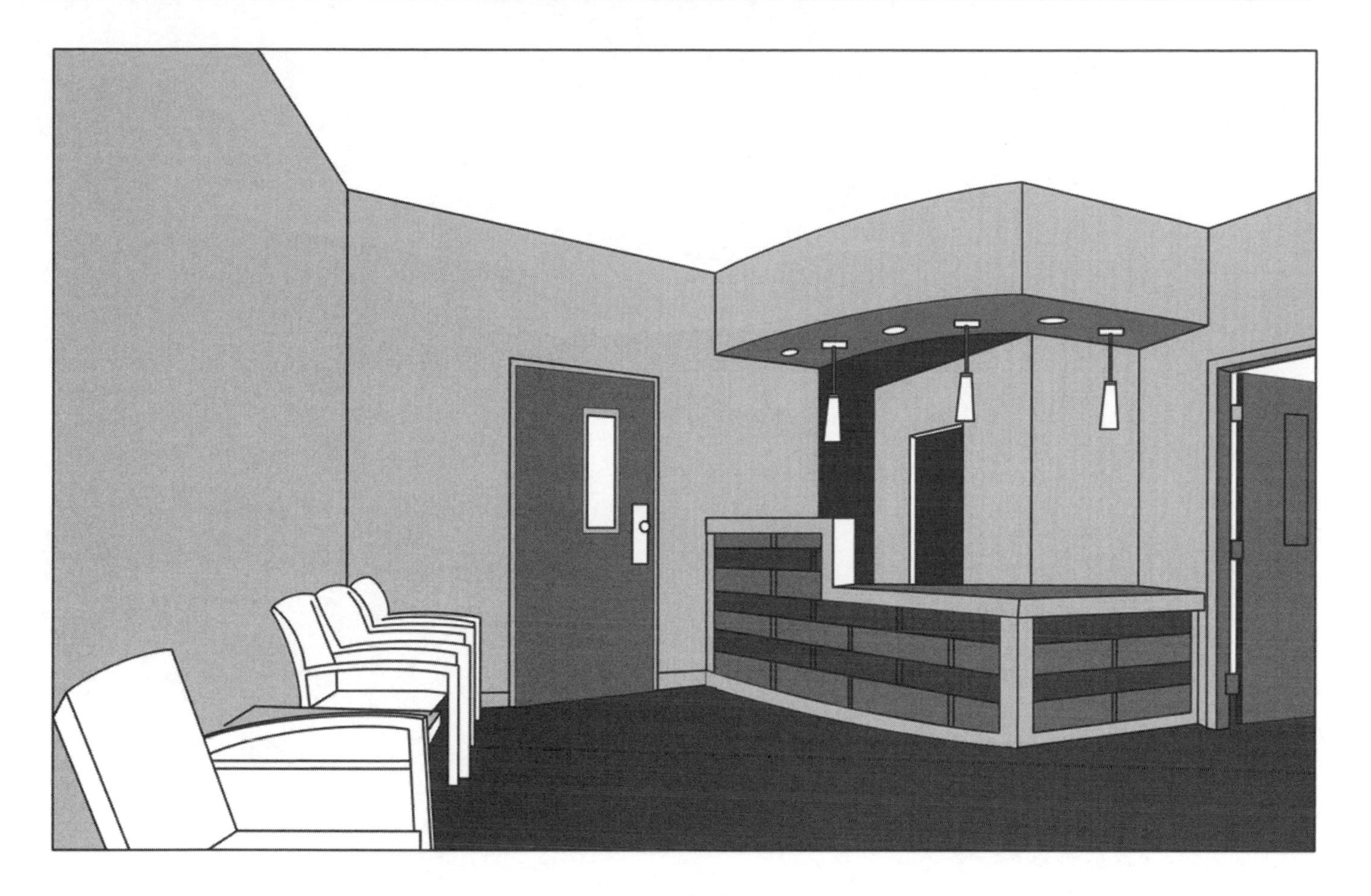

Code	Division Name	%	Sq. Cost	Projected
00	Bidding Requirements	12.40	35.94	256,265
01	General Requirements	6.95	20.15	143,635
03	Concrete	1.22	3.55	25,295
04	Masonry	0.19	0.55	3,943
05	Metals	11.24	32.58	232,278
06	Wood & Plastics	5.54	16.06	114,506
07	Thermal & Moisture Protection	4.38	12.71	90,595
08	Doors & Windows	2.49	7.20	51,363
09	Finishes	16.99	49.24	351,085
10	Specialties	0.94	2.73	19,474
13	Special Construction	3.13	9.08	64,769
15	Mechanical	22.44	65.04	463,729
16	Electrical	12.08	35.02	249,726
	Total Building Costs	100.00	289.85	2,066,660

COST PER SQUARE FOOT = $289.85

Part Two

Unit-In-Place Costs

DIVISION	1	GENERAL CONDITIONS
DIVISION	2	SITEWORK
DIVISION	3	CONCRETE
DIVISION	4	MASONRY
DIVISION	5	METALS
DIVISION	6	WOOD & PLASTICS
DIVISION	7	THERMAL & MOISTURE PROTECTION
DIVISION	8	DOORS & WINDOWS
DIVISION	9	FINISHES
DIVISION	10	SPECIALTIES
DIVISION	11	EQUIPMENT
DIVISION	12	FURNISHINGS
DIVISION	13	SPECIAL CONSTRUCTION
DIVISION	14	CONVEYING
DIVISION	15	MECHANICAL
DIVISION	16	ELECTRICAL

01020.10 ALLOWANCES

Item	Unit	Total
Overhead		
$20,000 project		
Minimum	PCT.	15.00
Average	PCT.	20.00
Maximum	PCT.	40.00
$100,000 project		
Minimum	PCT.	12.00
Average	PCT.	15.00
Maximum	PCT.	25.00
$500,000 project		
Minimum	PCT.	10.00
Average	PCT.	12.00
Maximum	PCT.	20.00
Profit		
$20,000 project		
Minimum	PCT.	10.00
Average	PCT.	15.00
Maximum	PCT.	25.00
$100,000 project		
Minimum	PCT.	10.00
Average	PCT.	12.00
Maximum	PCT.	20.00
$500,000 project		
Minimum	PCT.	5.00
Average	PCT.	10.00
Maximum	PCT.	15.00
Professional fees, Architectural		
$100,000 project		
Minimum	PCT.	5.00
Average	PCT.	10.00
Maximum	PCT.	20.00
$500,000 project		
Minimum	PCT.	5.00
Average	PCT.	8.00
Maximum	PCT.	12.00
Structural engineering		
Minimum	PCT.	2.00
Average	PCT.	3.00
Maximum	PCT.	5.00
Mechanical engineering		
Minimum	PCT.	4.00
Average	PCT.	5.00
Maximum	PCT.	15.00
Taxes, Sales tax		
Minimum	PCT.	4.00
Average	PCT.	5.00
Maximum	PCT.	10.00
Unemployment		
Minimum	PCT.	3.00
Average	PCT.	6.50
Maximum	PCT.	8.00
Social security (FICA)	PCT.	7.85

01050.10 FIELD STAFF

Item	Unit	Total
Superintendent		
Minimum	YEAR	87,500
Average	YEAR	109,500
Maximum	YEAR	131,500
Foreman		
Minimum	YEAR	58,200
Average	YEAR	93,100
Maximum	YEAR	109,000
Bookkeeper/timekeeper		
Minimum	YEAR	33,700
Average	YEAR	44,000
Maximum	YEAR	56,900
Watchman		
Minimum	YEAR	25,100
Average	YEAR	33,600
Maximum	YEAR	42,400

01330.10 SURVEYING

Item	Unit	Total
Surveying		
Small crew	DAY	880
Average crew	DAY	1,350
Large crew	DAY	1,750
Lot lines and boundaries		
Minimum	ACRE	630
Average	ACRE	1,350
Maximum	ACRE	2,200

01380.10 JOB REQUIREMENTS

Item	Unit	Total
Job photographs, small jobs		
Minimum	EA.	120
Average	EA.	180
Maximum	EA.	420
Large projects		
Minimum	EA.	610
Average	EA.	910
Maximum	EA.	3,050

01410.10 TESTING

Item	Unit	Total
Testing concrete, per test		
Minimum	EA.	21.00
Average	EA.	35.00
Maximum	EA.	70.00

01500.10 TEMPORARY FACILITIES

Item	Unit	Total
Barricades, temporary		
Highway		
Concrete	L.F.	17.00
Wood	L.F.	6.03
Steel	L.F.	5.84
Pedestrian barricades		
Plywood	S.F.	5.27
Chain link fence	S.F.	4.69
Trailers, general office type, per month		
Minimum	EA.	210
Average	EA.	340
Maximum	EA.	690
Crew change trailers, per month		
Minimum	EA.	120
Average	EA.	140
Maximum	EA.	210

01505.10 MOBILIZATION

Item	Unit	Total
Equipment mobilization		
Bulldozer		
Minimum	EA.	200
Average	EA.	410
Maximum	EA.	680
Backhoe/front-end loader		
Minimum	EA.	120
Average	EA.	200
Maximum	EA.	450
Truck crane		
Minimum	EA.	490
Average	EA.	760
Maximum	EA.	1,300

01525.10 CONSTRUCTION AIDS

Item	Unit	Total
Scaffolding/staging, rent per month		
Measured by lineal feet of base		
10' high	L.F.	12.50
20' high	L.F.	22.50
30' high	L.F.	31.50
Measured by square foot of surface		
Minimum	S.F.	.55
Average	S.F.	.95
Maximum	S.F.	1.69
Tarpaulins, fabric, per job		
Minimum	S.F.	.25
Average	S.F.	.43
Maximum	S.F.	1.11

	Unit	Total
01570.10 SIGNS		
Construction signs, temporary		
Signs, 2' x 4'		
Minimum	EA.	36.50
Average	EA.	87.75
Maximum	EA.	310
Signs, 4' x 8'		
Minimum	EA.	76.75
Average	EA.	200
Maximum	EA.	860
Signs, 8' x 8'		
Minimum	EA.	98.75
Average	EA.	310
Maximum	EA.	3,100
01600.10 EQUIPMENT		
Air compressor		
60 cfm		
By day	EA.	96.00
By week	EA.	290
By month	EA.	870
300 cfm		
By day	EA.	200
By week	EA.	630
By month	EA.	1,900
Air tools, per compressor, per day		
Minimum	EA.	39.50
Average	EA.	49.50
Maximum	EA.	69.25
Generators, 5 kw		
By day	EA.	98.75
By week	EA.	290
By month	EA.	910
Heaters, salamander type, per week		
Minimum	EA.	120
Average	EA.	170
Maximum	EA.	360
Pumps, submersible		
50 gpm		
By day	EA.	79.00
By week	EA.	240
By month	EA.	710
Pickup truck		
By day	EA.	150
By week	EA.	430
By month	EA.	1,350
Dump truck		
6 cy truck		
By day	EA.	400
By week	EA.	1,200
By month	EA.	3,550
10 cy truck		
By day	EA.	490
By week	EA.	1,500
By month	EA.	4,450
16 cy truck		
By day	EA.	790
By week	EA.	2,350
By month	EA.	7,100

	Unit	Total
01600.10 EQUIPMENT (Cont.)		
Backhoe, track mounted		
1/2 cy capacity		
By day	EA.	810
By week	EA.	2,450
By month	EA.	7,300
Backhoe/loader, rubber tired		
1/2 cy capacity		
By day	EA.	490
By week	EA.	1,500
By month	EA.	4,450
3/4 cy capacity		
By day	EA.	590
By week	EA.	1,800
By month	EA.	5,350
Bulldozer		
75 hp		
By day	EA.	690
By week	EA.	2,050
By month	EA.	6,200
Cranes, crawler type		
15 ton capacity		
By day	EA.	890
By week	EA.	2,650
By month	EA.	8,000
Truck mounted, hydraulic		
15 ton capacity		
By day	EA.	840
By week	EA.	2,500
By month	EA.	7,250
Loader, rubber tired		
1 cy capacity		
By day	EA.	590
By week	EA.	1,800
By month	EA.	5,350

	Unit	Total

02115.66 SEPTIC TANK REMOVAL

	Unit	Total
Remove septic tank		
1000 gals	EA.	200
2000 gals	EA.	240

02210.10 SOIL BORING

	Unit	Total
Borings, uncased, stable earth		
2-1/2" dia.	L.F.	30.00
4" dia.	L.F.	34.25
Cased, including samples		
2-1/2" dia.	L.F.	40.00
4" dia.	L.F.	68.75
Drilling in rock, No sampling	L.F.	63.25
With casing and sampling	L.F.	80.00
Test pits		
Light soil	EA.	400
Heavy soil	EA.	600

02220.10 COMPLETE BUILDING DEMOLITION

	Unit	Total
Building, complete w/ disposal, Wood frame	C.F.	.35

02220.15 SELECTIVE BUILDING DEMOLITION

	Unit	Total
Partition removal		
Concrete block partitions, 8" thick	S.F.	2.92
Brick masonry partitions		
4" thick	S.F.	2.19
8" thick	S.F.	2.74
Stud partitions		
Metal or wood, w/ drywall both sides	S.F.	2.19
Door and frame removal, Wood in framed wall		
2'6"x6'8"	EA.	31.25
3'x6'8"	EA.	36.50
Ceiling removal		
Acoustical tile ceiling		
Adhesive fastened	S.F.	.44
Furred and glued	S.F.	.37
Suspended grid	S.F.	.27
Drywall ceiling		
Furred and nailed	S.F.	.49
Nailed to framing	S.F.	.44
Window removal		
Metal windows, trim included		
2'x3'	EA.	43.75
3'x4'	EA.	54.75
4'x8'	EA.	110
Wood windows, trim included		
2'x3'	EA.	24.25
3'x4'	EA.	29.25
6'x8'	EA.	43.75
Concrete block walls, not including toothing		
4" thick	S.F.	2.44
6" thick	S.F.	2.58
8" thick	S.F.	2.74
Rubbish handling, Load in dumpster or truck		
Minimum	C.F.	.97
Maximum	C.F.	1.46
Rubbish hauling		
Hand loaded on trucks, 2 mile trip	C.Y.	37.00
Machine loaded on trucks, 2 mile trip	C.Y.	24.00

02225.13 CORE DRILLING

	Unit	Total
Concrete		
6" thick, 3" dia.	EA.	41.00
8" thick, 3" dia.	EA.	57.25

02225.15 CURB & GUTTER DEMOLITION

	Unit	Total
Removal, plain concrete curb	L.F.	6.01
Plain concrete curb and 2' gutter	L.F.	8.29

02225.20 FENCE DEMOLITION

	Unit	Total
Remove fencing		
Chain link, 8' high		
For disposal	L.F.	2.19
For reuse	L.F.	5.48
Wood, 4' high	S.F.	1.46
Masonry, 8" thick		
4' high	S.F.	4.38
6' high	S.F.	5.48

02225.25 GUARDRAIL DEMOLITION

	Unit	Total
Remove standard guardrail		
Steel	L.F.	8.01
Wood	L.F.	6.16

02225.30 HYDRANT DEMOLITION

	Unit	Total
Remove and reset fire hydrant	EA.	1,200

02225.40 PAVEMENT/SIDEWALK DEMOLITION

	Unit	Total
Concrete pavement, 6" thick		
No reinforcement	S.Y.	16.00
With wire mesh	S.Y.	24.00
With rebars	S.Y.	30.00
Sidewalk, 4" thick, with disposal	S.Y.	8.01

02225.42 DRAINAGE PIPING DEMOLITION

	Unit	Total
Remove drainage pipe, not including excavation		
12" dia.	L.F.	10.00
18" dia.	L.F.	12.75

02225.43 GAS PIPING DEMOLITION

	Unit	Total
Remove welded steel pipe, not including excavation		
4" dia.	L.F.	15.00
5" dia.	L.F.	24.00

02225.45 SANITARY PIPING DEMOLITION

	Unit	Total
Remove sewer pipe, not including excavation		
4" dia.	L.F.	9.61

02225.48 WATER PIPING DEMOLITION

	Unit	Total
Remove water pipe, not including excavation		
4" dia.	L.F.	11.00

02225.50 SAW CUTTING PAVEMENT

	Unit	Total
Pavement, bituminous		
2" thick	L.F.	1.85
3" thick	L.F.	2.31
Concrete pavement, with wire mesh		
4" thick	L.F.	3.56
5" thick	L.F.	3.85
Plain concrete, unreinforced		
4" thick	L.F.	3.08
5" thick	L.F.	3.56

02230.10 CLEAR WOODED AREAS

	Unit	Total
Clear wooded area		
Light density	ACRE	6,000
Medium density	ACRE	8,000
Heavy density	ACRE	9,600

02230.50 TREE CUTTING & CLEARING

	Unit	Total
Cut trees and clear out stumps		
9" to 12" dia.	EA.	480
To 24" dia.	EA.	600
24" dia. and up	EA.	800
Loading and trucking		
For machine load, per load, round trip		
1 mile	EA.	96.00
3 mile	EA.	110
5 mile	EA.	120
10 mile	EA.	160
20 mile	EA.	240
Hand loaded, round trip		
1 mile	EA.	230
3 mile	EA.	260
5 mile	EA.	310
10 mile	EA.	370
20 mile	EA.	460

02315.10 BASE COURSE

	Unit	Total
Base course, crushed stone		
3" thick	S.Y.	4.33
4" thick	S.Y.	5.60
6" thick	S.Y.	8.09
Base course, bank run gravel		
4" deep	S.Y.	3.71
6" deep	S.Y.	5.37
Prepare and roll sub base		
Minimum	S.Y.	.65
Average	S.Y.	.82
Maximum	S.Y.	1.09

02315.20 BORROW

Description	Unit	Total
Borrow fill, F.O.B. at pit, Sand, haul to site, round trip		
10 mile	C.Y.	33.50
20 mile	C.Y.	42.25
30 mile	C.Y.	53.25
Place borrow fill and compact		
Less than 1 in 4 slope	C.Y.	27.00
Greater than 1 in 4 slope	C.Y.	29.25

02315.30 BULK EXCAVATION

Description	Unit	Total
Excavation, by small dozer		
Large areas	C.Y.	1.85
Small areas	C.Y.	3.08
Trim banks	C.Y.	4.62
Hydraulic excavator		
1 cy capacity, Light material	C.Y.	4.01
Medium material	C.Y.	4.81
Wet material	C.Y.	6.01
Blasted rock	C.Y.	6.87
1-1/2 cy capacity, Light material	C.Y.	1.64
Medium material	C.Y.	2.18
Wet material	C.Y.	2.62
Wheel mounted front-end loader		
7/8 cy capacity, Light material	C.Y.	3.27
Medium material	C.Y.	3.74
Wet material	C.Y.	4.36
Blasted rock	C.Y.	5.24
1-1/2 cy capacity, Light material	C.Y.	1.87
Medium material	C.Y.	2.01
Wet material	C.Y.	2.18
Blasted rock	C.Y.	2.38
2-1/2 cy capacity, Light material	C.Y.	1.54
Medium material	C.Y.	1.64
Wet material	C.Y.	1.75
Blasted rock	C.Y.	1.87
Track mounted front-end loader		
1-1/2 cy capacity, Light material	C.Y.	2.18
Medium material	C.Y.	2.38
Wet material	C.Y.	2.62
Blasted rock	C.Y.	2.91
2-3/4 cy capacity, Light material	C.Y.	1.31
Medium material	C.Y.	1.45
Wet material	C.Y.	1.64
Blasted rock	C.Y.	1.87

02315.40 BUILDING EXCAVATION

Description	Unit	Total
Structural excavation, unclassified earth		
3/8 cy backhoe	C.Y.	17.50
3/4 cy backhoe	C.Y.	13.00
1 cy backhoe	C.Y.	11.00
Foundation backfill/compaction by machine	C.Y.	26.25

02315.45 HAND EXCAVATION

Description	Unit	Total
Excavation		
To 2' deep		
Normal soil	C.Y.	48.75
Sand and gravel	C.Y.	43.75
Medium clay	C.Y.	54.75
Heavy clay	C.Y.	62.75
Loose rock	C.Y.	73.00
To 6' deep		
Normal soil	C.Y.	62.75
Sand and gravel	C.Y.	54.75
Medium clay	C.Y.	73.00
Heavy clay	C.Y.	87.75
Loose rock	C.Y.	110
Backfilling foundation without compaction		
6" lifts	C.Y.	27.50
Compaction of backfill around structures or in trench		
By hand with air tamper	C.Y.	31.25
By hand with vibrating plate tamper	C.Y.	29.25
1 ton roller	C.Y.	46.25
Miscellaneous hand labor		
Trim slopes, sides of excavation	S.F.	.07
Trim bottom of excavation	S.F.	.09
Excavation around obstructions/services	C.Y.	150

02315.50 ROADWAY EXCAVATION

Description	Unit	Total
Roadway excavation		
1/4 mile haul	C.Y.	2.62
2 mile haul	C.Y.	4.36
5 mile haul	C.Y.	6.55
Spread base course	C.Y.	3.27
Roll and compact	C.Y.	4.36

02315.60 TRENCHING

Description	Unit	Total
Trenching and continuous footing excavation		
By gradall, 1 cy capacity		
Light soil	C.Y.	3.74
Medium soil	C.Y.	4.03
Heavy/wet soil	C.Y.	4.36
Loose rock	C.Y.	4.76
Blasted rock	C.Y.	5.04
By hydraulic excavator		
1/2 cy capacity		
Light soil	C.Y.	4.36
Medium soil	C.Y.	4.76
Heavy/wet soil	C.Y.	5.24
Loose rock	C.Y.	5.82
Blasted rock	C.Y.	6.55
1 cy capacity		
Light soil	C.Y.	3.08
Medium soil	C.Y.	3.27
Heavy/wet soil	C.Y.	3.49
Loose rock	C.Y.	3.74
Blasted rock	C.Y.	4.03
1-1/2 cy capacity		
Light soil	C.Y.	2.76
Medium soil	C.Y.	2.91
Heavy/wet soil	C.Y.	3.08
Loose rock	C.Y.	3.27
Blasted rock	C.Y.	3.49
2 cy capacity		
Light soil	C.Y.	2.62
Medium soil	C.Y.	2.76
Heavy/wet soil	C.Y.	2.91
Loose rock	C.Y.	3.08
Blasted rock	C.Y.	3.27
Hand excavation		
Bulk, wheeled 100'		
Normal soil	C.Y.	48.75
Sand or gravel	C.Y.	43.75
Medium clay	C.Y.	62.75
Heavy clay	C.Y.	87.75
Loose rock	C.Y.	110
Trenches, up to 2' deep		
Normal soil	C.Y.	54.75
Sand or gravel	C.Y.	48.75
Medium clay	C.Y.	73.00
Heavy clay	C.Y.	110
Loose rock	C.Y.	150
Trenches, to 6' deep		
Normal soil	C.Y.	62.75
Sand or gravel	C.Y.	54.75
Medium clay	C.Y.	87.75
Heavy clay	C.Y.	150
Loose rock	C.Y.	220
Backfill trenches, with compaction		
By hand	C.Y.	36.50
By 60 hp tracked dozer	C.Y.	2.31

02315.70 UTILITY EXCAVATION

Description	Unit	Total
Trencher, sandy clay, 8" wide trench		
18" deep	L.F.	2.05
24" deep	L.F.	2.31
36" deep	L.F.	2.64
Trench backfill, 95% compaction		
Tamp by hand	C.Y.	27.50
Vibratory compaction	C.Y.	22.00
Trench backfilling, with borrow sand		
Place & compact	C.Y.	42.50

02315.75 GRAVEL AND STONE

Item	Unit	Total
F.O.B. PLANT, No. 21 crusher run stone	C.Y.	44.00
No. 26 crusher run stone	C.Y.	44.00
No. 57 stone	C.Y.	44.00
No. 67 gravel	C.Y.	33.00
No. 68 stone	C.Y.	44.00
No. 78 stone	C.Y.	44.00
No. 78 gravel, (pea gravel)	C.Y.	33.00
No. 357 or B-3 stone	C.Y.	44.00
Structural & foundation backfill		
No. 21 crusher run stone	TON	35.25
No. 26 crusher run stone	TON	35.25
No. 57 stone	TON	35.25
No. 67 gravel	TON	26.50
No. 68 stone	TON	35.25
No. 78 stone	TON	35.25
No. 78 gravel, (pea gravel)	TON	26.50
No. 357 or B-3 stone	TON	35.25

02315.80 HAULING MATERIAL

Item	Unit	Total
Haul material by 10 cy dump truck, round trip distance		
1 mile	C.Y.	5.14
2 mile	C.Y.	6.16
5 mile	C.Y.	8.40
10 mile	C.Y.	9.24
20 mile	C.Y.	10.25
30 mile	C.Y.	12.25
Grading, cut/fill, sandy clay, 200' haul, 75 hp dozer	C.Y.	3.70
Spread topsoil by equipment on site	C.Y.	4.11
Site grading (cut and fill to 6") less than 1 acre		
75 hp dozer	C.Y.	6.16
1.5 cy backhoe/loader	C.Y.	9.24

02340.05 SOIL STABILIZATION

Item	Unit	Total
Straw bale secured with rebar	L.F.	9.01
Filter barrier, 18" high filter fabric	L.F.	6.21
Sediment fence, 36" fabric with 6" mesh	L.F.	9.80
Soil stabilization w/ tar paper, burlap, straw/stakes	S.F.	.42

02360.20 SOIL TREATMENT

Item	Unit	Total
Soil treatment, termite control pretreatment		
Under slabs	S.F.	.62
By walls	S.F.	.67

02370.40 RIPRAP

Item	Unit	Total
Riprap		
Crushed stone blanket, max size 2-1/2"	TON	100
Stone, quarry run, 300 lb. stones	TON	110
400 lb. stones	TON	110
500 lb. stones	TON	100
750 lb. stones	TON	100
Dry concrete in bags 3" thick, 80 lb. per bag	BAG	9.42

02455.60 STEEL PILES

Item	Unit	Total
H-section piles, 8x8, 36 lb/ft		
30' long	L.F.	29.75
40' long	L.F.	27.25
Tapered friction piles, fluted casing, up to 50'		
With 4000 psi concrete no reinforcing		
12" dia.	L.F.	25.25
14" dia.	L.F.	28.00

02455.65 STEEL PIPE PILES

Item	Unit	Total
Concrete filled, 3000# concrete, up to 40'		
8" dia.	L.F.	34.50
10" dia.	L.F.	41.75
12" dia.	L.F.	47.00
Pipe piles, non-filled, 8" dia.	L.F.	30.75
10" dia.	L.F.	37.00
12" dia.	L.F.	43.50
Splice, 8" dia.	EA.	190
10" dia.	EA.	200
12" dia.	EA.	230
Standard point, 8" dia.	EA.	230
10" dia.	EA.	270
12" dia.	EA.	300
Heavy duty point, 8" dia.	EA.	350
10" dia.	EA.	450
12" dia.	EA.	510

02455.80 WOOD AND TIMBER PILES

Item	Unit	Total
Treated wood piles, 12" butt, 8" tip		
25' long	L.F.	26.25
30' long	L.F.	24.75
35' long	L.F.	23.00
40' long	L.F.	21.75

02465.50 PRESTRESSED PILING

Item	Unit	Total
Prestressed concrete piling, less than 60' long		
10" sq.	L.F.	24.00
12" sq.	L.F.	31.50
Straight cylinder, less than 60' long		
12" dia.	L.F.	30.00
14" dia.	L.F.	38.50

02510.10 WELLS

Item	Unit	Total
Domestic water, drilled and cased		
4" dia.	L.F.	99.25
6" dia.	L.F.	110

02510.40 DUCTILE IRON PIPE

Item	Unit	Total
Ductile iron pipe, cement lined, slip-on joints		
4"	L.F.	22.25
6"	L.F.	25.75
8"	L.F.	32.00
Mechanical joint pipe		
4"	L.F.	26.75
6"	L.F.	30.75
8"	L.F.	38.50
Fittings, mechanical joint, 90 degree elbow		
4"	EA.	230
6"	EA.	300
8"	EA.	420
45 degree elbow		
4"	EA.	210
6"	EA.	270
8"	EA.	380

02510.60 PLASTIC PIPE

Item	Unit	Total
PVC, class 150 pipe		
4" dia.	L.F.	10.50
6" dia.	L.F.	15.25
8" dia.	L.F.	20.50
Schedule 40 pipe		
1-1/2" dia.	L.F.	3.74
2" dia.	L.F.	4.45
2-1/2" dia.	L.F.	5.53
3" dia.	L.F.	6.67
4" dia.	L.F.	8.66
6" dia.	L.F.	13.75
90 degree elbows		
1"	EA.	8.33
1-1/2"	EA.	9.25
2"	EA.	11.00
2-1/2"	EA.	18.00
3"	EA.	20.75
4"	EA.	28.75
6"	EA.	71.00
45 degree elbows		
1"	EA.	8.88
1-1/2"	EA.	10.00
2"	EA.	11.50
2-1/2"	EA.	18.00
3"	EA.	24.25
4"	EA.	34.25
6"	EA.	72.00
Tees		
1"	EA.	10.25
1-1/2"	EA.	11.25
2"	EA.	13.50
2-1/2"	EA.	23.50
3"	EA.	28.75
4"	EA.	41.00
6"	EA.	110
Couplings		
1"	EA.	8.14
1-1/2"	EA.	8.49
2"	EA.	9.79
2-1/2"	EA.	12.75
3"	EA.	16.00
4"	EA.	19.25
6"	EA.	40.50

02510.60 PLASTIC PIPE (Cont.)

	Unit	Total
Drainage pipe		
PVC schedule 80		
1" dia.	L.F.	4.84
1-1/2" dia.	L.F.	5.31
ABS, 2" dia.	L.F.	6.24
2-1/2" dia.	L.F.	7.90
3" dia.	L.F.	8.99
4" dia.	L.F.	11.50
6" dia.	L.F.	17.75
8" dia.	L.F.	24.00
10" dia.	L.F.	31.25
12" dia.	L.F.	46.50
90 degree elbows		
1"	EA.	11.00
1-1/2"	EA.	12.00
2"	EA.	13.75
2-1/2"	EA.	22.25
3"	EA.	23.75
4"	EA.	35.75
6"	EA.	68.50
45 degree elbows		
1"	EA.	13.50
1-1/2"	EA.	15.00
2"	EA.	17.50
2-1/2"	EA.	26.75
3"	EA.	29.00
4"	EA.	47.50
6"	EA.	99.00

02530.20 VITRIFIED CLAY PIPE

	Unit	Total
Vitrified clay pipe, extra strength		
6" dia.	L.F.	16.25
8" dia.	L.F.	17.75
10" dia.	L.F.	21.50

02530.30 MANHOLES

	Unit	Total
Precast sections, 48" dia.		
Base section	EA.	530
1'0" riser	EA.	250
1'4" riser	EA.	280
2'8" riser	EA.	360
4'0" riser	EA.	510
2'8" cone top	EA.	440
Precast manholes, 48" dia.		
4' deep	EA.	1,100
6' deep	EA.	1,550
7' deep	EA.	1,800
8' deep	EA.	2,050
10' deep	EA.	2,350
Cast-in-place, 48" dia., with frame and cover		
5' deep	EA.	1,800
6' deep	EA.	2,150
8' deep	EA.	2,750
10' deep	EA.	3,250
Brick manholes, 48" dia. with cover, 8" thick		
4' deep	EA.	1,150
6' deep	EA.	1,400
8' deep	EA.	1,650
10' deep	EA.	2,000
Frames and covers, 24" diameter		
300 lb	EA.	410
400 lb	EA.	440
Steps for manholes		
7" x 9"	EA.	21.25
8" x 9"	EA.	25.75

02530.40 SANITARY SEWERS

	Unit	Total
Clay, 6" pipe	L.F.	15.00
PVC		
4" pipe	L.F.	9.48
6" pipe	L.F.	13.25

02540.10 DRAINAGE FIELDS

	Unit	Total
Perforated PVC pipe, for drain field		
4" pipe	L.F.	7.40
6" pipe	L.F.	9.57

02540.50 SEPTIC TANKS

	Unit	Total
Septic tank, precast concrete		
1000 gals	EA.	1,150
2000 gals	EA.	3,000

02540.50 SEPTIC TANKS (Cont.)

	Unit	Total
Leaching pit, precast concrete, 72" diameter		
3' deep	EA.	990
6' deep	EA.	1,550
8' deep	EA.	1,950

02630.70 UNDERDRAIN

	Unit	Total
Drain tile, clay		
6" pipe	L.F.	9.87
8" pipe	L.F.	12.75
Porous concrete, standard strength		
6" pipe	L.F.	9.41
8" pipe	L.F.	9.99
Corrugated metal pipe, perforated type		
6" pipe	L.F.	11.75
8" pipe	L.F.	13.00
Perforated clay pipe		
6" pipe	L.F.	12.25
8" pipe	L.F.	14.25
Drain tile, concrete		
6" pipe	L.F.	8.57
8" pipe	L.F.	10.50
Perforated rigid PVC underdrain pipe		
4" pipe	L.F.	5.92
6" pipe	L.F.	8.48
8" pipe	L.F.	11.00
Underslab drainage, crushed stone		
3" thick	S.F.	1.05
4" thick	S.F.	1.26
6" thick	S.F.	1.52
Plastic filter fabric for drain lines	S.F.	.59

02740.20 ASPHALT SURFACES

	Unit	Total
Asphalt wearing surface, flexible pavement		
1" thick	S.Y.	6.69
1-1/2" thick	S.Y.	9.35
Binder course		
1-1/2" thick	S.Y.	8.80
2" thick	S.Y.	11.50
Bituminous sidewalk, no base		
2" thick	S.Y.	12.25
3" thick	S.Y.	17.00

02750.10 CONCRETE PAVING

	Unit	Total
Concrete paving, reinforced, 5000 psi concrete		
6" thick	S.Y.	46.00
7" thick	S.Y.	51.50
8" thick	S.Y.	57.25

02810.40 LAWN IRRIGATION

	Unit	Total
Residential system, complete		
Minimum	ACRE	15,900
Maximum	ACRE	30,300

02820.10 CHAIN LINK FENCE

	Unit	Total
Chain link fence, 9 ga., galvanized, with posts 10' o.c.		
4' high	L.F.	9.84
5' high	L.F.	13.00
6' high	L.F.	15.75
Corner or gate post, 3" post		
4' high	EA.	92.75
5' high	EA.	100
6' high	EA.	120
Gate with gate posts, galvanized, 3' wide		
4' high	EA.	200
5' high	EA.	260
6' high	EA.	280
Fabric, galvanized chain link, 2" mesh, 9 ga.		
4' high	L.F.	5.12
5' high	L.F.	6.21
6' high	L.F.	8.44
Line post, no rail fitting, galvanized, 2-1/2" dia.		
4' high	EA.	38.00
5' high	EA.	41.50
6' high	EA.	44.75
Vinyl coated, 9 ga., with posts 10' o.c.		
4' high	L.F.	10.50
5' high	L.F.	12.75
6' high	L.F.	15.75

	Unit	Total
02820.10 CHAIN LINK FENCE (Cont.)		
Gate, with posts, 3' wide		
4' high	EA.	220
5' high	EA.	270
6' high	EA.	290
Fabric, vinyl, chain link, 2" mesh, 9 ga.		
4' high	L.F.	5.12
5' high	L.F.	6.21
6' high	L.F.	8.44
Swing gates, galvanized, 4' high		
Single gate		
3' wide	EA.	310
4' wide	EA.	330
6' high, Single gate		
3' wide	EA.	410
4' wide	EA.	430
02880.70 RECREATIONAL COURTS		
Walls, galvanized steel		
8' high	L.F.	23.25
10' high	L.F.	27.00
12' high	L.F.	31.25
Vinyl coated		
8' high	L.F.	22.50
10' high	L.F.	26.75
12' high	L.F.	30.25
Gates, galvanized steel, Single, 3' transom		
3'x7'	EA.	560
4'x7'	EA.	610
5'x7'	EA.	780
6'x7'	EA.	880
Vinyl coated		
Single, 3' transom		
3'x7'	EA.	880
4'x7'	EA.	970
5'x7'	EA.	1,000
6'x7'	EA.	1,100
02910.10 TOPSOIL		
Spread topsoil, with equipment		
Minimum	C.Y.	13.00
Maximum	C.Y.	16.25
By hand		
Minimum	C.Y.	43.75
Maximum	C.Y.	54.75
Area prep. seeding (grade, rake and clean)		
Square yard	S.Y.	.35
By acre	ACRE	1,750
Remove topsoil and stockpile on site		
4" deep	C.Y.	11.00
6" deep	C.Y.	10.00
Spreading topsoil from stock pile		
By loader	C.Y.	12.00
By hand	C.Y.	130
Top dress by hand	S.Y.	1.31
Place imported top soil		
By loader		
4" deep	S.Y.	1.31
6" deep	S.Y.	1.45
By hand		
4" deep	S.Y.	4.87
6" deep	S.Y.	5.48
Plant bed preparation, 18" deep		
With backhoe/loader	S.Y.	3.27
By hand	S.Y.	7.31
02920.10 FERTILIZING		
Fertilizing (23#/1000 sf)		
By square yard	S.Y.	.17
By acre	ACRE	880
Liming (70#/1000 sf)		
By square yard	S.Y.	.22
By acre	ACRE	1,100
02920.30 SEEDING		
Mechanical seeding, 175 lb/acre		
By square yard	S.Y.	.31
By acre	ACRE	1,350
450 lb/acre		
By square yard	S.Y.	.64
By acre	ACRE	2,600

	Unit	Total
02920.30 SEEDING (Cont.)		
Seeding by hand, 10 lb per 100 s.y.		
By square yard	S.Y.	.70
By acre	ACRE	2,900
Reseed disturbed areas	S.F.	.28
02930.60 TREES		
Cornus Florida, 5'-6' (White Dogwood)	EA.	130
Caroliniana, 6'-8' (Carolina Cherry Laurel)	EA.	160
Cercis Canadensis, 6'-8' (Eastern Redbud)	EA.	130
Koelreuteria Paniculata, 8'-10' (Goldenrain)	EA.	200
Acer Platanoides, 1-3/4"-2" (11'-13')	EA.	260
Rubrum, 1-3/4"-2" (11'-13') (Red Maple)	EA.	210
Saccharum, 1-3/4"-2" (Sugar Maple)	EA.	320
Fraxinus Pennsylvanica, 1-3/4"-2"	EA.	190
Celtis Occidentalis, 1-3/4"-2"	EA.	250
Glenditsia Triacantos Inermis, 2"	EA.	240
Prunus Cerasifera 'Thundercloud', 6'-8'	EA.	140
Yeodensis, 6'-8' (Yoshino Cherry)	EA.	140
Lagerstroemia Indica, 8'-10' (Crapemyrtle)	EA.	220
Crataegus Phaenopyrum, 8'-10'	EA.	310
Quercus Borealis, 1-2" (Northern Red Oak)	EA.	220
Quercus Acutissima, 1-3/4"-2" (8'-10')	EA.	210
Saliz Babylonica, 1-3/4"-2" (Weeping Willow)	EA.	140
Tilia Cordata Greenspire, 1-3/4"-2" (10'-12')	EA.	380
Malus, 2"-2-1/2" (8'-10') (Flowering Crabapple)	EA.	220
Platanus Occidentalis, (12'-14')	EA.	320
Pyrus Calleryana Bradford, 2"-2-1/2"	EA.	250
Quercus Palustris, 2"-2-1/2" (12'-14') (Pin Oak)	EA.	270
Phellos, 2-1/2"-3" (Willow Oak)	EA.	310
Nigra, 2"-2-1/2" (Water Oak)	EA.	260
Magnolia Soulangeana, 4'-5' (Magnolia)	EA.	150
Grandiflora, 6'-8' (Southern Magnolia)	EA.	190
Cedrus Deodara, 10'-12' (Deodare Cedar)	EA.	320
Gingko Biloba, 10'-12' (2"-2-1/2")	EA.	300
Pinus Thunbergi, 5'-6' (Japanese Black Pine)	EA.	130
Strobus, 6'-8' (White Pine)	EA.	140
Taeda, 6'-8' (Loblolly Pine)	EA.	130
Quercus Virginiana, 2"-2-1/2" (Live Oak)	EA.	310
02935.10 SHRUB & TREE MAINTENANCE		
Moving shrubs on site		
3' high	EA.	43.75
4' high	EA.	48.75
Moving trees on site		
6' high	EA.	53.50
8' high	EA.	60.00
10' high	EA.	80.00
Palm trees		
10' high	EA.	80.00
40' high	EA.	480
02935.30 WEED CONTROL		
Bromicil, 15 lb./acre, wettable powder	ACRE	510
Vegetation control, by application of plant killer	S.Y.	.20
Weed killer, lawns and fields	S.Y.	.33
02945.20 LANDSCAPE ACCESSORIES		
Steel edging, 3/16" x 4"	L.F.	1.20
Landscaping stepping stones, 15"x15", white	EA.	8.02
Wood chip mulch	C.Y.	70.00
2" thick	S.Y.	3.38
4" thick	S.Y.	5.96
6" thick	S.Y.	8.63
Gravel mulch, 3/4" stone	C.Y.	76.00
White marble chips, 1" deep	S.F.	1.08
Peat moss		
2" thick	S.Y.	4.43
4" thick	S.Y.	8.13
6" thick	S.Y.	12.00
Landscaping timbers, treated lumber		
4" x 4"	L.F.	2.81
6" x 6"	L.F.	4.27
8" x 8"	L.F.	6.23

03110.05 BEAM FORMWORK

	Unit	Total
Beam forms, job built		
Beam bottoms		
1 use	S.F.	13.50
4 uses	S.F.	9.76
5 uses	S.F.	9.39
Beam sides		
1 use	S.F.	9.15
5 uses	S.F.	6.33

03110.15 COLUMN FORMWORK

	Unit	Total
Column, square forms, job built		
8" x 8" columns		
1 use	S.F.	14.75
5 uses	S.F.	11.00
12" x 12" columns		
1 use	S.F.	13.50
5 uses	S.F.	9.91
Round fiber forms, 1 use		
10" dia.	L.F.	15.75
12" dia.	L.F.	17.00

03110.18 CURB FORMWORK

	Unit	Total
Curb forms		
Straight, 6" high		
1 use	L.F.	7.67
5 uses	L.F.	5.42
Curved, 6" high		
1 use	L.F.	9.24
5 uses	L.F.	6.62

03110.25 EQUIPMENT PAD FORMWORK

	Unit	Total
Equipment pad, job built		
1 use	S.F.	10.50
3 uses	S.F.	7.96
5 uses	S.F.	6.68

03110.35 FOOTING FORMWORK

	Unit	Total
Wall footings, job built, continuous		
1 use	S.F.	7.30
3 uses	S.F.	6.08
5 uses	S.F.	5.42

03110.50 GRADE BEAM FORMWORK

	Unit	Total
Grade beams, job built		
1 use	S.F.	8.28
3 uses	S.F.	6.27
5 uses	S.F.	5.47

03110.53 PILE CAP FORMWORK

	Unit	Total
Pile cap forms, job built, Square		
1 use	S.F.	10.00
5 uses	S.F.	6.62

03110.55 SLAB / MAT FORMWORK

	Unit	Total
Mat foundations, job built		
1 use	S.F.	9.66
3 uses	S.F.	7.35
5 uses	S.F.	6.37
Edge forms		
6" high		
1 use	L.F.	7.76
3 uses	L.F.	5.79
5 uses	L.F.	5.07

03110.65 WALL FORMWORK

	Unit	Total
Wall forms, exterior, job built		
Up to 8' high wall		
1 use	S.F.	8.38
3 uses	S.F.	6.44
5 uses	S.F.	5.68
Retaining wall forms		
1 use	S.F.	8.80
3 uses	S.F.	6.79
5 uses	S.F.	5.97
Column pier and pilaster		
1 use	S.F.	14.25
5 uses	S.F.	9.37

03110.90 MISCELLANEOUS FORMWORK

	Unit	Total
Keyway forms (5 uses)		
2 x 4	L.F.	3.04
2 x 6	L.F.	3.46
Bulkheads		
Walls, with keyways, 3 piece	L.F.	10.75
Ground slab, with keyway		
2 piece	L.F.	8.73
3 piece	L.F.	10.00
Chamfer strips		
Wood		
1/2" wide	L.F.	1.47
3/4" wide	L.F.	1.54
1" wide	L.F.	1.64
PVC		
1/2" wide	L.F.	2.25
3/4" wide	L.F.	2.34
1" wide	L.F.	2.84

03210.05 BEAM REINFORCING

	Unit	Total
Beam-girders		
#3 - #4	TON	2,800
#5 - #6	TON	2,300

03210.15 COLUMN REINFORCING

	Unit	Total
Columns		
#3 - #4	TON	3,000
#5 - #6	TON	2,400

03210.20 ELEVATED SLAB REINFORCING

	Unit	Total
Elevated slab		
#3 - #4	TON	2,050
#5 - #6	TON	1,800

03210.25 EQUIP. PAD REINFORCING

	Unit	Total
Equipment pad		
#3 - #4	TON	2,500
#5 - #6	TON	2,200

03210.35 FOOTING REINFORCING

	Unit	Total
Footings		
#3 - #4	TON	2,300
#5 - #6	TON	1,950
#7 - #8	TON	1,800
Straight dowels, 24" long		
3/4" dia. (#6)	EA.	9.45
5/8" dia. (#5)	EA.	7.99
1/2" dia. (#4)	EA.	6.52

03210.45 FOUNDATION REINFORCING

	Unit	Total
Foundations		
#3 - #4	TON	2,300
#5 - #6	TON	1,950
#7 - #8	TON	1,800

03210.50 GRADE BEAM REINFORCING

	Unit	Total
Grade beams		
#3 - #4	TON	2,250
#5 - #6	TON	1,900
#7 - #8	TON	1,750

03210.53 PILE CAP REINFORCING

	Unit	Total
Pile caps		
#3 - #4	TON	2,800
#5 - #6	TON	2,400
#7 - #8	TON	2,250

03210.55 SLAB / MAT REINFORCING

	Unit	Total
Bars, slabs		
#3 - #4	TON	2,300
#5 - #6	TON	1,950
Wire mesh, slabs		
Galvanized		
4x4		
W1.4xW1.4	S.F.	.71
W2.0xW2.0	S.F.	.84
W2.9xW2.9	S.F.	1.04
W4.0xW4.0	S.F.	1.37

03210.55 SLAB / MAT REINFORCING (Cont.)

Item	Unit	Total
6x6		
W1.4xW1.4	S.F.	.60
W2.0xW2.0	S.F.	.75
W2.9xW2.9	S.F.	.92
W4.0xW4.0	S.F.	1.01

03210.65 WALL REINFORCING

Item	Unit	Total
Walls		
#3 - #4	TON	2,150
#5 - #6	TON	1,850
Masonry wall (horizontal)		
#3 - #4	TON	3,650
#5 - #6	TON	3,050
Galvanized		
#3 - #4	TON	4,550
#5 - #6	TON	4,050
Masonry wall (vertical)		
#3 - #4	TON	4,200
#5 - #6	TON	3,450
Galvanized		
#3 - #4	TON	5,100
#5 - #6	TON	4,450

03250.40 CONCRETE ACCESSORIES

Item	Unit	Total
Expansion joint, poured		
Asphalt		
1/2" x 1"	L.F.	1.63
1" x 2"	L.F.	3.28
Expansion joint, premolded, in slabs		
Asphalt		
1/2" x 6"	L.F.	2.02
1" x 12"	L.F.	3.00
Cork		
1/2" x 6"	L.F.	2.94
1" x 12"	L.F.	8.41
Neoprene sponge		
1/2" x 6"	L.F.	3.80
1" x 12"	L.F.	11.25
Polyethylene foam		
1/2" x 6"	L.F.	2.14
1" x 12"	L.F.	6.26
Polyurethane foam		
1/2" x 6"	L.F.	2.48
1" x 12"	L.F.	4.48
Polyvinyl chloride foam		
1/2" x 6"	L.F.	4.04
1" x 12"	L.F.	7.80
Rubber, gray sponge		
1/2" x 6"	L.F.	5.68
1" x 12"	L.F.	21.25
Asphalt felt control joints or bond breaker, screed joints		
4" slab	L.F.	2.12
6" slab	L.F.	2.52
8" slab	L.F.	3.12
Waterstops		
Polyvinyl chloride		
Ribbed		
3/16" thick x		
4" wide	L.F.	3.66
6" wide	L.F.	4.67
1/2" thick x		
9" wide	L.F.	8.67
Ribbed with center bulb		
3/16" thick x 9" wide	L.F.	7.72
3/8" thick x 9" wide	L.F.	8.59
Dumbbell type, 3/8" thick x 6" wide	L.F.	8.37
Plain, 3/8" thick x 9" wide	L.F.	10.50
Center bulb, 3/8" thick x 9" wide	L.F.	12.25
Rubber, Vapor barrier		
4 mil polyethylene	S.F.	.21
6 mil polyethylene	S.F.	.23

03250.40 CONCRETE ACCESSORIES (Cont.)

Item	Unit	Total
Gravel porous fill, under floor slabs, 3/4" stone	C.Y.	93.50
Reinforcing accessories		
Beam bolsters		
1-1/2" high, plain	L.F.	1.12
Galvanized	L.F.	1.77
3" high		
Plain	L.F.	1.50
Galvanized	L.F.	2.64
Slab bolsters		
1" high		
Plain	L.F.	.87
Galvanized	L.F.	1.47
2" high		
Plain	L.F.	.97
Galvanized	L.F.	1.70
Chairs, high chairs		
3" high		
Plain	EA.	3.00
Galvanized	EA.	3.16
8" high		
Plain	EA.	4.28
Galvanized	EA.	6.13
Continuous, high chair		
3" high		
Plain	L.F.	2.56
Galvanized	L.F.	3.08

03300.10 CONCRETE ADMIXTURES

Item	Unit	Total
Concrete admixtures		
Water reducing admixture	GAL	10.75
Set retarder	GAL	23.00
Air entraining agent	GAL	10.00

03350.10 CONCRETE FINISHES

Item	Unit	Total
Floor finishes		
Broom	S.F.	.63
Screed	S.F.	.55
Darby	S.F.	.55
Steel float	S.F.	.73
Wall finishes		
Burlap rub, with cement paste	S.F.	.84

03360.10 PNEUMATIC CONCRETE

Item	Unit	Total
Pneumatic applied concrete (gunite)		
2" thick	S.F.	8.47
3" thick	S.F.	10.75
4" thick	S.F.	13.00
Finish surface		
Minimum	S.F.	2.80
Maximum	S.F.	5.60

03370.10 CURING CONCRETE

Item	Unit	Total
Sprayed membrane		
Slabs	S.F.	.15
Walls	S.F.	.19
Curing paper		
Slabs	S.F.	.20
Walls	S.F.	.21
Burlap		
7.5 oz.	S.F.	.22
12 oz.	S.F.	.25

03380.05 BEAM CONCRETE

Item	Unit	Total
Beams and girders		
2500# or 3000# concrete		
By crane	C.Y.	200
By pump	C.Y.	190
By hand buggy	C.Y.	150
3500# or 4000# concrete		
By crane	C.Y.	210
By pump	C.Y.	200
By hand buggy	C.Y.	160

03380.15 COLUMN CONCRETE

	Unit	Total
Columns		
2500# or 3000# concrete		
By crane	C.Y.	190
By pump	C.Y.	180
3500# or 4000# concrete		
By crane	C.Y.	200
By pump	C.Y.	190

03380.20 ELEVATED SLAB CONCRETE

	Unit	Total
Elevated slab		
2500# or 3000# concrete		
By crane	C.Y.	150
By pump	C.Y.	140
By hand buggy	C.Y.	150

03380.25 EQUIPMENT PAD CONCRETE

	Unit	Total
Equipment pad		
2500# or 3000# concrete		
By chute	C.Y.	120
By pump	C.Y.	170
By crane	C.Y.	180
3500# or 4000# concrete		
By chute	C.Y.	120
By pump	C.Y.	170

03380.35 FOOTING CONCRETE

	Unit	Total
Continuous footing		
2500# or 3000# concrete		
By chute	C.Y.	120
By pump	C.Y.	170
By crane	C.Y.	170
Spread footing		
2500# or 3000# concrete		
By chute	C.Y.	120
By pump	C.Y.	170
By crane	C.Y.	180

03380.50 GRADE BEAM CONCRETE

	Unit	Total
Grade beam		
2500# or 3000# concrete		
By chute	C.Y.	120
By crane	C.Y.	170
By pump	C.Y.	170
By hand buggy	C.Y.	150
3500# or 4000# concrete		
By chute	C.Y.	130
By crane	C.Y.	180
By pump	C.Y.	180
By hand buggy	C.Y.	160

03380.53 PILE CAP CONCRETE

	Unit	Total
Pile cap		
2500# or 3000 concrete		
By chute	C.Y.	120
By crane	C.Y.	180
By pump	C.Y.	170
By hand buggy	C.Y.	150

03380.55 SLAB / MAT CONCRETE

	Unit	Total
Slab on grade		
2500# or 3000# concrete		
By chute	C.Y.	120
By crane	C.Y.	150
By pump	C.Y.	140
By hand buggy	C.Y.	140

03380.58 SIDEWALKS

	Unit	Total
Walks, cast in place with wire mesh, base not incl.		
4" thick	S.F.	3.06
5" thick	S.F.	3.91
6" thick	S.F.	4.84

03380.65 WALL CONCRETE

	Unit	Total
Walls		
2500# or 3000# concrete		
To 4'		
By chute	C.Y.	120
By crane	C.Y.	180
By pump	C.Y.	180
To 8'		
By crane	C.Y.	190
By pump	C.Y.	180
Filled block (CMU)		
3000# concrete, by pump		
4" wide	S.F.	3.56
6" wide	S.F.	4.61
8" wide	S.F.	5.88

03400.90 PRECAST SPECIALTIES

	Unit	Total
Precast concrete, coping, 4' to 8' long		
12" wide	L.F.	14.75
10" wide	L.F.	14.75
Splash block, 30"x12"x4"	EA.	53.50
Stair unit, per riser	EA.	130
Sun screen and trellis, 8' long, 12" high		
4" thick blades	EA.	120

03600.10 GROUTING

	Unit	Total
Grouting for bases		
Non-metallic grout		
1" deep	S.F.	17.00
2" deep	S.F.	23.25
Portland cement grout (1 cement to 3 sand)		
1/2" joint thickness		
6" wide joints	L.F.	2.10
8" wide joints	L.F.	2.50
1" joint thickness		
4" wide joints	L.F.	2.00
6" wide joints	L.F.	2.32

	Unit	Total
04100.10 MASONRY GROUT		
Grout, non shrink, non-metallic, trowelable	C.F.	6.95
Grout door frame, hollow metal		
Single	EA.	73.50
Double	EA.	82.00
Grout-filled concrete block (CMU)		
4" wide	S.F.	2.36
6" wide	S.F.	3.12
8" wide	S.F.	3.78
12" wide	S.F.	4.79
Grout-filled individual CMU cells		
4" wide	L.F.	1.50
6" wide	L.F.	1.60
8" wide	L.F.	1.74
10" wide	L.F.	2.04
12" wide	L.F.	2.18
Bond beams or lintels, 8" deep		
6" thick	L.F.	2.80
8" thick	L.F.	3.26
10" thick	L.F.	3.77
12" thick	L.F.	4.35
Cavity walls		
2" thick	S.F.	3.81
3" thick	S.F.	4.26
4" thick	S.F.	4.91
6" thick	S.F.	6.33
04150.10 MASONRY ACCESSORIES		
Foundation vents	EA.	53.50
Bar reinforcing		
Horizontal		
#3 - #4	Lb.	2.78
#5 - #6	Lb.	2.42
Vertical		
#3 - #4	Lb.	3.31
#5 - #6	Lb.	2.78
Horizontal joint reinforcing		
Truss type		
4" wide, 6" wall	L.F.	.42
6" wide, 8" wall	L.F.	.43
8" wide, 10" wall	L.F.	.48
10" wide, 12" wall	L.F.	.49
12" wide, 14" wall	L.F.	.56
Ladder type		
4" wide, 6" wall	L.F.	.36
6" wide, 8" wall	L.F.	.39
8" wide, 10" wall	L.F.	.41
10" wide, 12" wall	L.F.	.45
Rectangular wall ties		
3/16" dia., galvanized		
2" x 6"	EA.	1.28
2" x 8"	EA.	1.30
2" x 10"	EA.	1.36
2" x 12"	EA.	1.42
4" x 6"	EA.	1.51
4" x 8"	EA.	1.57
4" x 10"	EA.	1.71
4" x 12"	EA.	1.81
1/4" dia., galvanized		
2" x 6"	EA.	1.61
2" x 8"	EA.	1.69
2" x 10"	EA.	1.80
2" x 12"	EA.	1.93
4" x 6"	EA.	1.89
4" x 8"	EA.	1.98
4" x 10"	EA.	2.11
4" x 12"	EA.	2.16
"Z" type wall ties, galvanized		
6" long		
1/8" dia.	EA.	1.23
3/16" dia.	EA.	1.25
1/4" dia.	EA.	1.28

	Unit	Total
04150.10 MASONRY ACCESSORIES (Cont.)		
"Z" type wall ties, galvanized		
8" long		
1/8" dia.	EA.	1.25
3/16" dia.	EA.	1.28
1/4" dia.	EA.	1.30
10" long		
1/8" dia.	EA.	1.28
3/16" dia.	EA.	1.33
1/4" dia.	EA.	1.39
Dovetail anchor slots, Galvanized steel, filled		
24 ga.	L.F.	2.22
20 ga.	L.F.	3.19
16 oz. copper, foam filled	L.F.	3.52
Dovetail anchors		
16 ga.		
3-1/2" long	EA.	1.16
5-1/2" long	EA.	1.22
12 ga.		
3-1/2" long	EA.	1.24
5-1/2" long	EA.	1.48
Dovetail, triangular galvanized ties, 12 ga.		
3" x 3"	EA.	1.49
5" x 5"	EA.	1.54
7" x 7"	EA.	1.62
7" x 9"	EA.	1.67
Brick anchors		
Corrugated, 3-1/2" long		
16 ga.	EA.	1.14
12 ga.	EA.	1.33
Non-corrugated, 3-1/2" long		
16 ga.	EA.	1.25
12 ga.	EA.	1.53
Cavity wall anchors, corrugated, galvanized		
5" long		
16 ga.	EA.	1.68
12 ga.	EA.	2.06
7" long		
28 ga.	EA.	1.75
24 ga.	EA.	1.98
22 ga.	EA.	2.01
16 ga.	EA.	2.15
Mesh ties, 16 ga., 3" wide		
8" long	EA.	1.94
12" long	EA.	2.06
20" long	EA.	2.50
24" long	EA.	2.67
04150.20 MASONRY CONTROL JOINTS		
Control joint, cross shaped PVC	L.F.	3.52
Closed cell joint filler		
1/2"	L.F.	1.72
3/4"	L.F.	2.11
Rubber, for		
4" wall	L.F.	3.85
PVC, for		
4" wall	L.F.	2.65
04150.50 MASONRY FLASHING		
Through-wall flashing		
5 oz. coated copper	S.F.	8.14
0.030" elastomeric	S.F.	4.77
04210.10 BRICK MASONRY		
Standard size brick, running bond		
Face brick, red (6.4/sf)		
Veneer	S.F.	14.25
Cavity wall	S.F.	13.00
9" solid wall	S.F.	26.00
Common brick (6.4/sf)		
Select common for veneers	S.F.	12.50
Back-up		
4" thick	S.F.	9.85
8" thick	S.F.	17.00

04210.10 BRICK MASONRY (Cont.)

	Unit	Total
Glazed brick (7.4/sf)		
Veneer	S.F.	24.50
Buff or gray face brick (6.4/sf)		
Veneer	S.F.	15.25
Cavity wall	S.F.	14.00
Jumbo or oversize brick (3/sf)		
4" veneer	S.F.	9.46
4" back-up	S.F.	8.57
8" back-up	S.F.	12.50
Norman brick, red face, (4.5/sf)		
4" veneer	S.F.	12.50
Cavity wall	S.F.	11.75
Chimney, standard brick, including flue		
16" x 16"	L.F.	84.00
16" x 20"	L.F.	110
16" x 24"	L.F.	110
20" x 20"	L.F.	110
20" x 24"	L.F.	130
20" x 32"	L.F.	140
Window sill, face brick on edge	L.F.	16.25

04210.60 PAVERS, MASONRY

	Unit	Total
Brick walk laid on sand, sand joints		
Laid flat, (4.5 per sf)	S.F.	9.71
Laid on edge, (7.2 per sf)	S.F.	15.00
Precast concrete patio blocks		
2" thick		
Natural	S.F.	4.46
Colors	S.F.	5.52
Exposed aggregates, local aggregate		
Natural	S.F.	9.87
Colors	S.F.	9.87
Granite or limestone aggregate	S.F.	10.25
White tumblestone aggregate	S.F.	7.83
Stone pavers, set in mortar		
Bluestone		
1" thick		
Irregular	S.F.	19.50
Snapped rectangular	S.F.	20.00
1-1/2" thick, random rectangular	S.F.	24.00
2" thick, random rectangular	S.F.	28.00
Slate		
Natural cleft		
Irregular, 3/4" thick	S.F.	23.00
Random rectangular		
1-1/4" thick	S.F.	30.00
1-1/2" thick	S.F.	33.50
Granite blocks		
3" thick, 3" to 6" wide		
4" to 12" long	S.F.	28.75
6" to 15" long	S.F.	22.50

04220.10 CONCRETE MASONRY UNITS

	Unit	Total
Hollow, load bearing		
4"	S.F.	5.51
6"	S.F.	6.38
8"	S.F.	7.06
10"	S.F.	8.45
12"	S.F.	9.48
Solid, load bearing		
4"	S.F.	6.39
6"	S.F.	6.84
8"	S.F.	8.18
10"	S.F.	8.82
12"	S.F.	11.25
Back-up block, 8" x 16"		
2"	S.F.	4.68
4"	S.F.	4.84
6"	S.F.	5.83
8"	S.F.	6.41
10"	S.F.	7.75
12"	S.F.	8.63

04220.10 CONCRETE MASONRY UNITS (Cont.)

	Unit	Total
Foundation wall, 8" x 16"		
6"	S.F.	6.29
8"	S.F.	6.96
10"	S.F.	8.39
12"	S.F.	9.38
Solid		
6"	S.F.	7.11
8"	S.F.	8.54
10"	S.F.	9.21
12"	S.F.	11.75
Exterior, styrofoam inserts, std weight, 8" x 16"		
6"	S.F.	8.47
8"	S.F.	9.16
10"	S.F.	11.00
12"	S.F.	13.75
Lightweight		
6"	S.F.	8.96
8"	S.F.	9.91
10"	S.F.	10.75
12"	S.F.	13.00
Acoustical slotted block		
4"	S.F.	9.91
6"	S.F.	10.25
8"	S.F.	12.00
Filled cavities		
4"	S.F.	11.25
6"	S.F.	12.50
8"	S.F.	14.75
Hollow, split face		
4"	S.F.	7.42
6"	S.F.	8.12
8"	S.F.	8.66
10"	S.F.	9.57
12"	S.F.	10.25
Split rib profile		
4"	S.F.	9.06
6"	S.F.	9.74
8"	S.F.	10.75
10"	S.F.	11.25
12"	S.F.	11.75
Solar screen concrete block		
4" thick		
6" x 6"	S.F.	15.75
8" x 8"	S.F.	15.50
12" x 12"	S.F.	13.00
8" thick		
8" x 16"	S.F.	12.50
Vertical reinforcing		
4' o.c., add 5% to labor		
2'8" o.c., add 15% to labor		
Interior partitions, add 10% to labor		

04220.90 BOND BEAMS & LINTELS

	Unit	Total
Bond beam, no grout or reinforcement		
8" x 16" x		
4" thick	L.F.	5.80
6" thick	L.F.	6.85
8" thick	L.F.	7.40
10" thick	L.F.	8.29
12" thick	L.F.	9.00
Beam lintel, no grout or reinforcement		
8" x 16" x		
10" thick	L.F.	12.00
12" thick	L.F.	14.50

04220.90 BOND BEAMS & LINTELS (Cont.)

Item	Unit	Total
Precast masonry lintel		
6 lf, 8" high x		
4" thick	L.F.	15.00
6" thick	L.F.	16.75
8" thick	L.F.	18.75
10" thick	L.F.	20.50
10 lf, 8" high x		
4" thick	L.F.	13.00
6" thick	L.F.	15.00
8" thick	L.F.	16.75
10" thick	L.F.	20.50
Steel angles and plates		
Minimum	Lb.	1.86
Maximum	Lb.	2.96
Various size angle lintels		
1/4" stock		
3" x 3"	L.F.	9.00
3" x 3-1/2"	L.F.	9.58
3/8" stock		
3" x 4"	L.F.	13.25
3-1/2" x 4"	L.F.	13.50
4" x 4"	L.F.	14.50
5" x 3-1/2"	L.F.	15.25
6" x 3-1/2"	L.F.	16.75
1/2" stock		
6" x 4"	L.F.	18.25

04270.10 GLASS BLOCK

Item	Unit	Total
Glass block, 4" thick		
6" x 6"	S.F.	48.00
8" x 8"	S.F.	32.25
12" x 12"	S.F.	35.00

04295.10 PARGING / MASONRY PLASTER

Item	Unit	Total
Parging		
1/2" thick	S.F.	3.86
3/4" thick	S.F.	4.82
1" thick	S.F.	5.85

04400.10 STONE

Item	Unit	Total
Rubble stone		
Walls set in mortar		
8" thick	S.F.	28.25
12" thick	S.F.	39.50
18" thick	S.F.	50.75
24" thick	S.F.	65.75
Dry set wall		
8" thick	S.F.	26.00
12" thick	S.F.	32.25
18" thick	S.F.	44.25
24" thick	S.F.	53.50
Thresholds, 7/8" thick, 3' long, 4" to 6" wide		
Plain	EA.	71.50
Beveled	EA.	74.50
Window sill		
6" wide, 2" thick	L.F.	36.50
Stools		
5" wide, 7/8" thick	L.F.	43.50
Granite veneer facing panels, polished		
7/8" thick		
Black	S.F.	72.00
Gray	S.F.	61.25
Slate, panels		
1" thick	S.F.	46.25
Sills or stools		
1" thick		
6" wide	L.F.	33.00
10" wide	L.F.	42.25

04520.10 RESTORATION AND CLEANING

Item	Unit	Total
Masonry cleaning		
Washing brick		
Smooth surface	S.F.	1.10
Rough surface	S.F.	1.49
Steam clean masonry		
Smooth face		
Minimum	S.F.	.72
Maximum	S.F.	1.04
Rough face		
Minimum	S.F.	.96
Maximum	S.F.	1.43

04550.10 REFRACTORIES

Item	Unit	Total
Flue liners		
Rectangular		
8" x 12"	L.F.	17.25
12" x 12"	L.F.	20.00
12" x 18"	L.F.	29.00
16" x 16"	L.F.	31.50
18" x 18"	L.F.	37.25
20" x 20"	L.F.	54.00
24" x 24"	L.F.	64.00
Round		
18" dia.	L.F.	50.25
24" dia.	L.F.	89.50

05050.10 STRUCTURAL WELDING

Item	Unit	Total
Welding		
Single pass		
1/8"	L.F.	3.42
3/16"	L.F.	4.67
1/4"	L.F.	5.92

05050.90 METAL ANCHORS

Item	Unit	Total
Anchor bolts		
3/8" x		
8" long	EA.	1.01
12" long	EA.	1.20
1/2" x		
8" long	EA.	1.51
12" long	EA.	1.76
5/8" x		
8" long	EA.	1.40
12" long	EA.	1.65
3/4" x		
8" long	EA.	2.01
12" long	EA.	2.25
Non-drilling anchor		
1/4"	EA.	.65
3/8"	EA.	.80
1/2"	EA.	1.23
Self-drilling anchor		
1/4"	EA.	1.63
3/8"	EA.	2.44
1/2"	EA.	3.26

05050.95 METAL LINTELS

Item	Unit	Total
Lintels, steel		
Plain	Lb.	2.88
Galvanized	Lb.	3.55

05120.10 STRUCTURAL STEEL

Item	Unit	Total
Beams and girders, A-36		
Welded	TON	3,550
Bolted	TON	3,450
Columns		
Pipe		
6" dia.	Lb.	2.34
Structural tube		
6" square		
Light sections	TON	5,200

05410.10 METAL FRAMING

Item	Unit	Total
Furring channel, galvanized		
Beams and columns, 3/4"		
12" o.c.	S.F.	6.62
16" o.c.	S.F.	5.96
Walls, 3/4"		
12" o.c.	S.F.	3.53
16" o.c.	S.F.	2.92
24" o.c.	S.F.	2.30
1-1/2"		
12" o.c.	S.F.	3.82
16" o.c.	S.F.	3.12
24" o.c.	S.F.	2.44

05410.10 METAL FRAMING (Cont.)

Item	Unit	Total
Stud, load bearing, 16" o.c.		
16 ga.		
2-1/2"	S.F.	4.08
3-5/8"	S.F.	4.32
4"	S.F.	4.38
6"	S.F.	5.15
18 ga.		
2-1/2"	S.F.	3.84
3-5/8"	S.F.	4.08
4"	S.F.	4.14
6"	S.F.	4.84
8"	S.F.	5.21
20 ga.		
2-1/2"	S.F.	3.35
3-5/8"	S.F.	3.48
4"	S.F.	3.54
6"	S.F.	4.06
8"	S.F.	4.24
24" o.c.		
16 ga.		
2-1/2"	S.F.	3.29
3-5/8"	S.F.	3.47
4"	S.F.	3.53
6"	S.F.	3.97
8"	S.F.	4.33
18 ga.		
2-1/2"	S.F.	3.11
3-5/8"	S.F.	3.23
4"	S.F.	3.29
6"	S.F.	3.73
8"	S.F.	3.97
20 ga.		
2-1/2"	S.F.	2.82
3-5/8"	S.F.	2.88
4"	S.F.	2.93
6"	S.F.	3.30
8"	S.F.	3.46

05520.10 RAILINGS

Item	Unit	Total
Railing, pipe, 1-1/4" diameter, welded steel		
2-rail		
Primed	L.F.	44.00
Galvanized	L.F.	53.00
3-rail		
Primed	L.F.	56.25
Galvanized	L.F.	68.25
Wall mounted, single rail, welded steel		
Primed	L.F.	30.75
Galvanized	L.F.	37.00
Wall mounted, single rail, welded steel		
Primed	L.F.	31.50
Galvanized	L.F.	38.00
Wall mounted, single rail, welded steel		
Primed	L.F.	34.00
Galvanized	L.F.	41.00

05700.10 ORNAMENTAL METAL

Item	Unit	Total
Railings, square bars, 6" o.c., shaped top rails		
Steel	L.F.	120
Aluminum	L.F.	140
Bronze	L.F.	230
Stainless steel	L.F.	230
Laminated metal or wood handrails		
2-1/2" round or oval shape	L.F.	310
Aluminum louvers, Residential use, fixed type, with screen		
8" x 8"	EA.	48.75
12" x 12"	EA.	50.50
12" x 18"	EA.	54.50
14" x 24"	EA.	64.75
18" x 24"	EA.	68.75
30" x 24"	EA.	85.75

06050.10 ACCESSORIES

	Unit	Total
Column/post base, cast aluminum		
4" x 4"	EA.	29.75
6" x 6"	EA.	35.75
Bridging, metal, per pair		
12" o.c.	EA.	7.73
16" o.c.	EA.	7.06
Anchors		
Bolts, threaded two ends, with nuts and washers		
1/2" dia.		
4" long	EA.	5.99
7-1/2" long	EA.	6.39
3/4" dia.		
7-1/2" long	EA.	8.99
15" long	EA.	11.75
Framing anchors, 10 gauge	EA.	5.64
Bolts, carriage		
1/4 x 4	EA.	6.25
5/16 x 6	EA.	7.35
3/8 x 6	EA.	8.85
1/2 x 6	EA.	10.00
Joist and beam hangers		
18 ga.		
2 x 4	EA.	6.77
2 x 6	EA.	7.00
2 x 8	EA.	7.23
2 x 10	EA.	7.97
2 x 12	EA.	9.27
16 ga.		
3 x 6	EA.	10.25
3 x 8	EA.	11.25
3 x 10	EA.	12.25
3 x 12	EA.	13.75
3 x 14	EA.	14.75
4 x 6	EA.	13.25
4 x 8	EA.	14.25
4 x 10	EA.	16.00
4 x 12	EA.	19.50
4 x 14	EA.	20.50
Rafter anchors, 18 ga., 1-1/2" wide		
5-1/4" long	EA.	5.54
10-3/4" long	EA.	5.96
Shear plates		
2-5/8" dia.	EA.	7.41
4" dia.	EA.	11.25
Sill anchors		
Embedded in concrete	EA.	7.89
Split rings		
2-1/2" dia.	EA.	8.10
4" dia.	EA.	10.50
Strap ties, 14 ga., 1-3/8" wide		
12" long	EA.	7.01
18" long	EA.	7.62
24" long	EA.	9.36
36" long	EA.	11.50
Toothed rings		
2-5/8" dia.	EA.	11.50
4" dia.	EA.	13.75

06110.10 BLOCKING

	Unit	Total
Steel construction		
Walls		
2x4	L.F.	4.21
2x6	L.F.	5.04
2x8	L.F.	5.63
2x10	L.F.	6.38
2x12	L.F.	7.26
Ceilings		
2x4	L.F.	4.78
2x6	L.F.	5.83
2x8	L.F.	6.57
2x10	L.F.	7.51
2x12	L.F.	8.66
Wood construction		
Walls		
2x4	L.F.	3.59
2x6	L.F.	4.24
2x8	L.F.	4.70
2x10	L.F.	5.29
2x12	L.F.	5.96

06110.10 BLOCKING (Cont.)

	Unit	Total
Ceilings		
2x4	L.F.	3.98
2x6	L.F.	4.74
2x8	L.F.	5.27
2x10	L.F.	5.95
2x12	L.F.	6.75

06110.20 CEILING FRAMING

	Unit	Total
Ceiling joists		
12" o.c.		
2x4	S.F.	2.05
2x6	S.F.	2.43
2x8	S.F.	2.99
2x10	S.F.	3.28
2x12	S.F.	4.83
16" o.c.		
2x4	S.F.	1.66
2x6	S.F.	1.99
2x8	S.F.	2.40
2x10	S.F.	2.61
2x12	S.F.	3.87
24" o.c.		
2x4	S.F.	1.31
2x6	S.F.	1.62
2x8	S.F.	2.01
2x10	S.F.	2.27
2x12	S.F.	4.21
Headers and nailers		
2x4	L.F.	2.29
2x6	L.F.	2.61
2x8	L.F.	2.97
2x10	L.F.	3.44
2x12	L.F.	3.91
Sister joists for ceilings		
2x4	L.F.	4.48
2x6	L.F.	5.40
2x8	L.F.	6.57
2x10	L.F.	8.29
2x12	L.F.	11.00

06110.30 FLOOR FRAMING

	Unit	Total
Floor joists		
12" o.c.		
2x6	S.F.	2.00
2x8	S.F.	2.44
2x10	S.F.	2.96
2x12	S.F.	3.85
2x14	S.F.	5.17
3x6	S.F.	4.16
3x8	S.F.	5.09
3x10	S.F.	6.11
3x12	S.F.	7.14
3x14	S.F.	8.03
4x6	S.F.	5.04
4x8	S.F.	6.19
4x10	S.F.	7.63
4x12	S.F.	9.06
4x14	S.F.	10.50
16" o.c.		
2x6	S.F.	1.69
2x8	S.F.	2.02
2x10	S.F.	2.26
2x12	S.F.	2.62
2x14	S.F.	4.64
3x6	S.F.	3.45
3x8	S.F.	4.18
3x10	S.F.	5.04
3x12	S.F.	5.92
3x14	S.F.	6.85
4x6	S.F.	4.14
4x8	S.F.	5.36
4x10	S.F.	6.43
4x12	S.F.	7.44
4x14	S.F.	8.72

06110.30 FLOOR FRAMING (Cont.)	Unit	Total
Sister joists for floors		
2x4	L.F.	3.98
2x6	L.F.	4.74
2x8	L.F.	5.63
2x10	L.F.	6.89
2x12	L.F.	8.66
3x6	L.F.	8.02
3x8	L.F.	9.19
3x10	L.F.	11.00
3x12	L.F.	12.75
4x6	L.F.	8.71
4x8	L.F.	10.25
4x10	L.F.	12.50
4x12	L.F.	14.00
06110.40 FURRING		
Furring, wood strips		
Walls		
On masonry or concrete walls		
1x2 furring		
12" o.c.	S.F.	2.13
16" o.c.	S.F.	1.93
24" o.c.	S.F.	1.79
1x3 furring		
12" o.c.	S.F.	2.23
16" o.c.	S.F.	2.04
24" o.c.	S.F.	1.81
On wood walls		
1x2 furring		
12" o.c.	S.F.	1.62
16" o.c.	S.F.	1.45
24" o.c.	S.F.	1.33
1x3 furring		
12" o.c.	S.F.	1.74
16" o.c.	S.F.	1.54
24" o.c.	S.F.	1.36
Ceilings		
On masonry or concrete ceilings		
1x2 furring		
12" o.c.	S.F.	3.49
16" o.c.	S.F.	3.13
24" o.c.	S.F.	2.85
1x3 furring		
12" o.c.	S.F.	3.59
16" o.c.	S.F.	3.22
24" o.c.	S.F.	2.88
On wood ceilings		
1x2 furring		
12" o.c.	S.F.	2.45
16" o.c.	S.F.	2.20
24" o.c.	S.F.	2.01
1x3		
12" o.c.	S.F.	2.55
16" o.c.	S.F.	2.29
24" o.c.	S.F.	2.04
06110.50 ROOF FRAMING		
Roof framing		
Rafters, gable end		
0-2 pitch (flat to 2-in-12)		
12" o.c.		
2x4	S.F.	1.86
2x6	S.F.	2.19
2x8	S.F.	2.66
2x10	S.F.	3.06
2x12	S.F.	4.58
16" o.c.		
2x6	S.F.	1.87
2x8	S.F.	2.26
2x10	S.F.	2.47
2x12	S.F.	3.67
24" o.c.		
2x6	S.F.	1.33
2x8	S.F.	1.88
2x10	S.F.	2.08
2x12	S.F.	3.00

06110.50 ROOF FRAMING (Cont.)	Unit	Total
4-6 pitch (4-in-12 to 6-in-12)		
12" o.c.		
2x4	S.F.	1.91
2x6	S.F.	2.30
2x8	S.F.	2.91
2x10	S.F.	3.19
2x12	S.F.	4.23
16" o.c.		
2x6	S.F.	1.91
2x8	S.F.	2.47
2x10	S.F.	2.70
2x12	S.F.	3.52
24" o.c.		
2x6	S.F.	1.56
2x8	S.F.	2.08
2x10	S.F.	2.20
2x12	S.F.	3.02
8-12 pitch (8-in-12 to 12-in-12)		
12" o.c.		
2x4	S.F.	2.03
2x6	S.F.	2.51
2x8	S.F.	3.06
2x10	S.F.	3.41
2x12	S.F.	4.52
16" o.c.		
2x6	S.F.	2.05
2x8	S.F.	2.67
2x10	S.F.	2.90
2x12	S.F.	3.71
24" o.c.		
2x6	S.F.	1.66
2x8	S.F.	2.16
2x10	S.F.	2.35
2x12	S.F.	3.21
Ridge boards		
2x6	L.F.	3.54
2x8	L.F.	4.08
2x10	L.F.	4.79
2x12	L.F.	5.66
Hip rafters		
2x6	L.F.	2.74
2x8	L.F.	3.04
2x10	L.F.	3.44
2x12	L.F.	3.90
Jack rafters		
4-6 pitch (4-in-12 to 6-in-12)		
16" o.c.		
2x6	S.F.	2.55
2x8	S.F.	3.09
2x10	S.F.	3.39
2x12	S.F.	4.22
24" o.c.		
2x6	S.F.	1.96
2x8	S.F.	2.48
2x10	S.F.	2.75
2x12	S.F.	3.40
8-12 pitch (8-in-12 to 12-in-12)		
16" o.c.		
2x6	S.F.	3.14
2x8	S.F.	3.54
2x10	S.F.	4.36
2x12	S.F.	5.38
24" o.c.		
2x6	S.F.	2.43
2x8	S.F.	2.75
2x10	S.F.	3.61
2x12	S.F.	4.61
Sister rafters		
2x4	L.F.	4.48
2x6	L.F.	5.40
2x8	L.F.	6.57
2x10	L.F.	8.29
2x12	L.F.	11.00

06110.50 ROOF FRAMING (Cont.)

Item	Unit	Total
Fascia boards		
2x4	L.F.	3.28
2x6	L.F.	3.54
2x8	L.F.	4.08
2x10	L.F.	4.40
2x12	L.F.	5.16
Cant strips		
Fiber		
3x3	L.F.	1.98
4x4	L.F.	2.24
Wood		
3x3	L.F.	3.70

06110.60 SLEEPERS

Item	Unit	Total
Sleepers, over concrete		
12" o.c.		
1x2	S.F.	1.53
1x3	S.F.	1.73
2x4	S.F.	2.41
2x6	S.F.	2.90
16" o.c.		
1x2	S.F.	1.36
1x3	S.F.	1.46
2x4	S.F.	2.05
2x6	S.F.	2.46

06110.65 SOFFITS

Item	Unit	Total
Soffit framing		
2x3	L.F.	4.37
2x4	L.F.	4.76
2x6	L.F.	5.34
2x8	L.F.	6.05

06110.70 WALL FRAMING

Item	Unit	Total
Framing wall, studs		
12" o.c.		
2x3	S.F.	1.52
2x4	S.F.	1.72
2x6	S.F.	2.11
2x8	S.F.	2.49
16" o.c.		
2x3	S.F.	1.27
2x4	S.F.	1.42
2x6	S.F.	1.72
2x8	S.F.	2.20
24" o.c.		
2x3	S.F.	1.07
2x4	S.F.	1.18
2x6	S.F.	1.46
2x8	S.F.	1.68
Plates, top or bottom		
2x3	L.F.	2.02
2x4	L.F.	2.21
2x6	L.F.	2.55
2x8	L.F.	2.96
Headers, door or window		
2x6		
Single		
3' long	EA.	30.25
6' long	EA.	39.50
Double		
3' long	EA.	35.50
6' long	EA.	49.00
2x8		
Single		
4' long	EA.	39.00
8' long	EA.	51.25
Double		
4' long	EA.	48.25
8' long	EA.	67.00
2x10		
Single		
5' long	EA.	49.25
10' long	EA.	68.25
Double		
5' long	EA.	59.00
10' long	EA.	80.75

06110.70 WALL FRAMING (Cont.)

Item	Unit	Total
Headers, door or window		
2x12		
Single		
6' long	EA.	52.00
12' long	EA.	73.50
Double		
6' long	EA.	68.25
12' long	EA.	97.25

06115.10 FLOOR SHEATHING

Item	Unit	Total
Sub-flooring, plywood, CDX		
1/2" thick	S.F.	1.23
5/8" thick	S.F.	1.56
3/4" thick	S.F.	2.33
Structural plywood		
1/2" thick	S.F.	1.54
5/8" thick	S.F.	2.13
3/4" thick	S.F.	2.26
Board type subflooring		
1x6		
Minimum	S.F.	2.50
Maximum	S.F.	3.01
1x8		
Minimum	S.F.	2.58
Maximum	S.F.	2.96
1x10		
Minimum	S.F.	3.08
Maximum	S.F.	3.34
Underlayment, Hardboard, 1/4" tempered	S.F.	1.48
Plywood, CDX		
3/8" thick	S.F.	1.51
1/2" thick	S.F.	1.72
5/8" thick	S.F.	1.92
3/4" thick	S.F.	2.26

06115.20 ROOF SHEATHING

Item	Unit	Total
Sheathing		
Plywood, CDX		
3/8" thick	S.F.	1.53
1/2" thick	S.F.	1.72
5/8" thick	S.F.	1.92
3/4" thick	S.F.	2.26
Structural plywood		
3/8" thick	S.F.	1.24
1/2" thick	S.F.	1.42
5/8" thick	S.F.	1.61
3/4" thick	S.F.	1.84

06115.30 WALL SHEATHING

Item	Unit	Total
Sheathing		
Plywood, CDX		
3/8" thick	S.F.	1.64
1/2" thick	S.F.	1.83
5/8" thick	S.F.	2.05
3/4" thick	S.F.	2.42
Waferboard		
3/8" thick	S.F.	1.35
1/2" thick	S.F.	1.53
5/8" thick	S.F.	1.74
3/4" thick	S.F.	1.91
Structural plywood		
3/8" thick	S.F.	1.64
1/2" thick	S.F.	1.83
5/8" thick	S.F.	2.05
3/4" thick	S.F.	1.99
Gypsum, 1/2" thick	S.F.	1.38
Asphalt impregnated fiberboard, 1/2" thick	S.F.	1.75

06125.10 WOOD DECKING

Item	Unit	Total
Decking, T&G solid		
Cedar		
3" thick	S.F.	11.00
4" thick	S.F.	13.50
Fir		
3" thick	S.F.	5.61
4" thick	S.F.	6.61
Southern yellow pine		
3" thick	S.F.	5.81
4" thick	S.F.	6.18
White pine		
3" thick	S.F.	6.52
4" thick	S.F.	8.41

06130.10 HEAVY TIMBER

	Unit	Total
Mill framed structures		
Beams to 20' long		
Douglas fir		
6x8	L.F.	14.00
6x10	L.F.	15.50
6x12	L.F.	17.50
6x14	L.F.	19.75
6x16	L.F.	21.00
8x10	L.F.	18.00
8x12	L.F.	20.25
8x14	L.F.	22.75
8x16	L.F.	25.00
Southern yellow pine		
6x8	L.F.	12.50
6x10	L.F.	14.00
6x12	L.F.	16.25
6x14	L.F.	18.00
6x16	L.F.	19.25
8x10	L.F.	16.25
8x12	L.F.	18.75
8x14	L.F.	20.75
8x16	L.F.	22.75
Columns to 12' high		
Douglas fir		
6x6	L.F.	15.75
8x8	L.F.	19.25
10x10	L.F.	26.75
12x12	L.F.	30.25
Southern yellow pine		
6x6	L.F.	15.25
8x8	L.F.	18.00
10x10	L.F.	23.00
12x12	L.F.	27.25
Posts, treated		
4x4	L.F.	3.90
6x6	L.F.	7.62

06190.20 WOOD TRUSSES

	Unit	Total
Truss, fink, 2x4 members		
3-in-12 slope		
24' span	EA.	160
26' span	EA.	160
28' span	EA.	180
30' span	EA.	190
34' span	EA.	190
38' span	EA.	190
5-in-12 slope		
24' span	EA.	160
28' span	EA.	180
30' span	EA.	190
32' span	EA.	200
40' span	EA.	240
Gable, 2x4 members		
5-in-12 slope		
24' span	EA.	180
26' span	EA.	190
28' span	EA.	220
30' span	EA.	220
32' span	EA.	230
36' span	EA.	240
40' span	EA.	250
King post type, 2x4 members		
4-in-12 slope		
16' span	EA.	130
18' span	EA.	140
24' span	EA.	150
26' span	EA.	160
30' span	EA.	190
34' span	EA.	190
38' span	EA.	220
42' span	EA.	250

06200.10 FINISH CARPENTRY

	Unit	Total
Mouldings and trim		
Apron, flat		
9/16 x 2	L.F.	4.34
9/16 x 3-1/2	L.F.	6.50

06200.10 FINISH CARPENTRY (Cont.)

	Unit	Total
Base		
Colonial		
7/16 x 2-1/4	L.F.	4.64
7/16 x 3	L.F.	5.18
7/16 x 3-1/4	L.F.	5.23
9/16 x 3	L.F.	5.33
9/16 x 3-1/4	L.F.	5.44
11/16 x 2-1/4	L.F.	5.72
Ranch		
7/16 x 2-1/4	L.F.	4.81
7/16 x 3-1/4	L.F.	5.18
9/16 x 2-1/4	L.F.	5.14
9/16 x 3	L.F.	5.33
9/16 x 3-1/4	L.F.	5.38
Casing		
11/16 x 2-1/2	L.F.	4.43
11/16 x 3-1/2	L.F.	4.79
Chair rail		
9/16 x 2-1/2	L.F.	4.81
9/16 x 3-1/2	L.F.	5.58
Closet pole		
1-1/8" dia.	L.F.	5.09
1-5/8" dia.	L.F.	5.74
Cove		
9/16 x 1-3/4	L.F.	4.34
11/16 x 2-3/4	L.F.	5.18
Crown		
9/16 x 1-5/8	L.F.	5.74
9/16 x 2-5/8	L.F.	6.49
11/16 x 3-5/8	L.F.	7.04
11/16 x 4-1/4	L.F.	8.64
11/16 x 5-1/4	L.F.	9.57
Drip cap		
1-1/16 x 1-5/8	L.F.	4.93
Glass bead		
3/8 x 3/8	L.F.	4.27
1/2 x 9/16	L.F.	4.45
5/8 x 5/8	L.F.	4.51
3/4 x 3/4	L.F.	4.69
Half round		
1/2	L.F.	3.13
5/8	L.F.	3.43
3/4	L.F.	3.85
Lattice		
1/4 x 7/8	L.F.	2.96
1/4 x 1-1/8	L.F.	3.01
1/4 x 1-3/8	L.F.	3.06
1/4 x 1-3/4	L.F.	3.16
1/4 x 2	L.F.	3.31
Ogee molding		
5/8 x 3/4	L.F.	4.22
11/16 x 1-1/8	L.F.	6.12
11/16 x 1-3/8	L.F.	5.41
Parting bead		
3/8 x 7/8	L.F.	4.69
Quarter round		
1/4 x 1/4	L.F.	2.66
3/8 x 3/8	L.F.	2.83
1/2 x 1/2	L.F.	3.01
11/16 x 11/16	L.F.	3.20
3/4 x 3/4	L.F.	3.85
1-1/16 x 1-1/16	L.F.	3.66
Railings, balusters		
1-1/8 x 1-1/8	L.F.	9.40
1-1/2 x 1-1/2	L.F.	9.53
Screen moldings		
1/4 x 3/4	L.F.	5.61
5/8 x 5/16	L.F.	5.85
Shoe		
7/16 x 11/16	L.F.	3.43
Sash beads		
1/2 x 3/4	L.F.	6.02
1/2 x 7/8	L.F.	6.20
1/2 x 1-1/8	L.F.	6.75
5/8 x 7/8	L.F.	6.75
Stop		
5/8 x 1-5/8		
Colonial	L.F.	4.32
Ranch	L.F.	4.32

06200.10 FINISH CARPENTRY (Cont.)

	Unit	Total
Stools		
11/16 x 2-1/4	L.F.	9.84
11/16 x 2-1/2	L.F.	10.00
11/16 x 5-1/4	L.F.	11.00
Exterior trim, casing, select pine, 1x3	L.F.	5.41
Douglas fir		
1x3	L.F.	4.04
1x4	L.F.	4.34
1x6	L.F.	5.12
1x8	L.F.	6.28
Cornices, white pine, #2 or better		
1x2	L.F.	3.57
1x4	L.F.	3.75
1x6	L.F.	4.65
1x8	L.F.	5.18
1x10	L.F.	5.93
1x12	L.F.	6.75
Shelving, pine		
1x8	L.F.	5.66
1x10	L.F.	6.26
1x12	L.F.	6.92
Plywood shelf, 3/4", with edge band, 12" wide	L.F.	8.03
Adjustable shelf, and rod, 12" wide		
3' to 4' long	EA.	33.50
5' to 8' long	EA.	55.00
Prefinished wood shelves with brackets and supports		
8" wide		
3' long	EA.	71.00
4' long	EA.	79.25
6' long	EA.	110
10" wide		
3' long	EA.	77.00
4' long	EA.	110
6' long	EA.	110

06220.10 MILLWORK

	Unit	Total
Countertop, laminated plastic		
25" x 7/8" thick		
Minimum	L.F.	29.25
Average	L.F.	47.50
Maximum	L.F.	64.75
25" x 1-1/4" thick		
Minimum	L.F.	37.25
Average	L.F.	59.25
Maximum	L.F.	83.25
Add for cutouts	EA.	35.00
Backsplash, 4" high, 7/8" thick	L.F.	31.50
Plywood, sanded, A-C		
1/4" thick	S.F.	3.18
3/8" thick	S.F.	3.42
1/2" thick	S.F.	3.76
A-D		
1/4" thick	S.F.	3.11
3/8" thick	S.F.	3.42
1/2" thick	S.F.	3.69
Base cab., 34-1/2" high, 24" deep, hardwood		
Minimum	L.F.	220
Average	L.F.	260
Maximum	L.F.	290
Wall cabinets		
Minimum	L.F.	79.25
Average	L.F.	100
Maximum	L.F.	130

06300.10 WOOD TREATMENT

	Unit	Total
Creosote preservative treatment		
8 lb/cf	B.F.	.62
10 lb/cf	B.F.	.74
Salt preservative treatment		
Oil borne		
Minimum	B.F.	.56
Maximum	B.F.	.79
Water borne		
Minimum	B.F.	.40
Maximum	B.F.	.62
Fire retardant treatment		
Minimum	B.F.	.79
Maximum	B.F.	.96
Kiln dried, softwood, add to framing costs		
1" thick	B.F.	.29
2" thick	B.F.	.40
3" thick	B.F.	.51
4" thick	B.F.	.62

06420.10 PANEL WORK

	Unit	Total
Hardboard, tempered, 1/4" thick		
Natural faced	S.F.	2.35
Plastic faced	S.F.	3.02
Pegboard, natural	S.F.	2.59
Plastic faced	S.F.	3.02
Untempered, 1/4" thick		
Natural faced	S.F.	2.29
Plastic faced	S.F.	3.14
Pegboard, natural	S.F.	2.35
Plastic faced	S.F.	2.96
Plywood unfinished, 1/4" thick		
Birch		
Natural	S.F.	2.88
Select	S.F.	3.35
Knotty pine	S.F.	3.83
Cedar (closet lining)		
Standard boards T&G	S.F.	4.30
Particle board	S.F.	3.35
Plywood, prefinished, 1/4" thick, premium grade		
Birch veneer	S.F.	5.79
Cherry veneer	S.F.	6.39
Chestnut veneer	S.F.	10.25
Lauan veneer	S.F.	3.78
Mahogany veneer	S.F.	6.33
Oak veneer (red)	S.F.	6.33
Pecan veneer	S.F.	7.40
Rosewood veneer	S.F.	10.25
Teak veneer	S.F.	7.52
Walnut veneer	S.F.	6.81

06430.10 STAIRWORK

	Unit	Total
Risers, 1x8, 42" wide		
White oak	EA.	70.75
Pine	EA.	66.00
Treads, 1-1/16" x 9-1/2" x 42"		
White oak	EA.	86.00

06440.10 COLUMNS

	Unit	Total
Column, hollow, round wood		
12" diameter		
10' high	EA.	830
12' high	EA.	1,000
14' high	EA.	1,200
16' high	EA.	1,450
24" diameter		
16' high	EA.	3,200
18' high	EA.	3,700
20' high	EA.	4,500
22' high	EA.	4,750
24' high	EA.	5,150

07100.10 WATERPROOFING

Item	Unit	Total
Membrane waterproofing, elastomeric		
Butyl		
1/32" thick	S.F.	2.96
1/16" thick	S.F.	3.41
Neoprene		
1/32" thick	S.F.	3.82
1/16" thick	S.F.	4.80
Plastic vapor barrier (polyethylene)		
4 mil	S.F.	.23
6 mil	S.F.	.26
10 mil	S.F.	.34
Bituminous membrane, asphalt felt, 15 lb.		
One ply	S.F.	1.86
Two ply	S.F.	2.22
Three ply	S.F.	2.67
Bentonite waterproofing, panels		
3/16" thick	S.F.	2.71
1/4" thick	S.F.	2.93

07150.10 DAMPPROOFING

Item	Unit	Total
Silicone dampproofing, sprayed on		
Concrete surface		
1 coat	S.F.	.89
2 coats	S.F.	1.41
Concrete block		
1 coat	S.F.	.94
2 coats	S.F.	1.47
Brick		
1 coat	S.F.	1.09
2 coats	S.F.	1.60

07160.10 BITUMINOUS DAMPPROOFING

Item	Unit	Total
Building paper, asphalt felt		
15 lb	S.F.	1.95
30 lb	S.F.	2.20
Asphalt, troweled, cold, primer plus		
1 coat	S.F.	2.14
2 coats	S.F.	3.62
3 coats	S.F.	4.79
Fibrous asphalt, hot troweled, primer plus		
1 coat	S.F.	2.43
2 coats	S.F.	3.87
3 coats	S.F.	5.18
Asphaltic paint dampproofing, per coat		
Brush on	S.F.	.98
Spray on	S.F.	.99

07190.10 VAPOR BARRIERS

Item	Unit	Total
Vapor barrier, polyethylene		
2 mil	S.F.	.23
6 mil	S.F.	.29
8 mil	S.F.	.32
10 mil	S.F.	.33

07210.10 BATT INSULATION

Item	Unit	Total
Ceiling, fiberglass, unfaced		
3-1/2" thick, R11	S.F.	.90
6" thick, R19	S.F.	1.09
9" thick, R30	S.F.	1.67
Suspended ceiling, unfaced		
3-1/2" thick, R11	S.F.	.87
6" thick, R19	S.F.	1.06
9" thick, R30	S.F.	1.63
Crawl space, unfaced		
3-1/2" thick, R11	S.F.	1.05
6" thick, R19	S.F.	1.24
9" thick, R30	S.F.	1.80
Wall, fiberglass, Paper backed		
2" thick, R7	S.F.	.71
3" thick, R8	S.F.	.77
4" thick, R11	S.F.	.97
6" thick, R19	S.F.	1.22
Foil backed, 1 side		
2" thick, R7	S.F.	1.04
3" thick, R11	S.F.	1.11
4" thick, R14	S.F.	1.17
6" thick, R21	S.F.	1.40
Foil backed, 2 sides		
2" thick, R7	S.F.	1.18
3" thick, R11	S.F.	1.39
4" thick, R14	S.F.	1.57
6" thick, R21	S.F.	1.70

07210.10 BATT INSULATION (Cont.)

Item	Unit	Total
Unfaced, 2" thick, R7	S.F.	.83
3" thick, R9	S.F.	.91
4" thick, R11	S.F.	.97
6" thick, R19	S.F.	1.13
Mineral wool batts, Paper backed		
2" thick, R6	S.F.	.70
4" thick, R12	S.F.	1.02
6" thick, R19	S.F.	1.22
Fasteners, self adhering, attached to ceiling deck		
2-1/2" long	EA.	.93
4-1/2" long	EA.	1.02
Capped, self-locking washers	EA.	.64

07210.20 BOARD INSULATION

Item	Unit	Total
Perlite board, roof		
1.00" thick, R2.78	S.F.	.95
1.50" thick, R4.17	S.F.	1.28
Rigid urethane		
1" thick, R6.67	S.F.	1.44
1.50" thick, R11.11	S.F.	1.83
Polystyrene		
1.0" thick, R4.17	S.F.	.80
1.5" thick, R6.26	S.F.	1.04

07210.60 LOOSE FILL INSULATION

Item	Unit	Total
Blown-in type		
Fiberglass		
5" thick, R11	S.F.	.73
6" thick, R13	S.F.	.86
9" thick, R19	S.F.	1.14
Rockwool, attic application		
6" thick, R13	S.F.	.77
8" thick, R19	S.F.	.95
10" thick, R22	S.F.	1.14
12" thick, R26	S.F.	1.32
15" thick, R30	S.F.	1.60
Poured type		
Fiberglass		
1" thick, R4	S.F.	.67
2" thick, R8	S.F.	1.05
3" thick, R12	S.F.	1.45
4" thick, R16	S.F.	1.87
Mineral wool		
1" thick, R3	S.F.	.71
2" thick, R6	S.F.	1.12
3" thick, R9	S.F.	1.60
4" thick, R12	S.F.	1.87
Vermiculite or perlite		
2" thick, R4.8	S.F.	1.08
3" thick, R7.2	S.F.	1.47
4" thick, R9.6	S.F.	1.87
Masonry, poured vermiculite or perlite		
4" block	S.F.	.62
6" block	S.F.	.86
8" block	S.F.	1.17
10" block	S.F.	1.48
12" block	S.F.	1.78

07210.70 SPRAYED INSULATION

Item	Unit	Total
Foam, sprayed on		
Polystyrene		
1" thick, R4	S.F.	1.06
2" thick, R8	S.F.	1.78
Urethane		
1" thick, R4	S.F.	1.02
2" thick, R8	S.F.	1.69

07310.10 ASPHALT SHINGLES

Item	Unit	Total
Standard asphalt shingles, strip shingles		
210 lb/square	SQ.	140
235 lb/square	SQ.	150
240 lb/square	SQ.	170
260 lb/square	SQ.	220
300 lb/square	SQ.	240
385 lb/square	SQ.	320
Roll roofing, mineral surface		
90 lb	SQ.	93.50
110 lb	SQ.	140
140 lb	SQ.	150

07310.60 SLATE SHINGLES

	Unit	Total
Slate shingles		
Pennsylvania		
Ribbon	SQ.	900
Clear	SQ.	1,100
Vermont		
Black	SQ.	950
Gray	SQ.	1,000
Green	SQ.	1,050
Red	SQ.	1,650

07310.70 WOOD SHINGLES

	Unit	Total
Wood shingles, on roofs		
White cedar, #1 shingles		
4" exposure	SQ.	410
5" exposure	SQ.	340
#2 shingles		
4" exposure	SQ.	350
5" exposure	SQ.	270
Resquared and rebutted		
4" exposure	SQ.	390
5" exposure	SQ.	300
On walls		
White cedar, #1 shingles		
4" exposure	SQ.	500
5" exposure	SQ.	420
6" exposure	SQ.	350
#2 shingles		
4" exposure	SQ.	440
5" exposure	SQ.	350
6" exposure	SQ.	300
Add for fire retarding	SQ.	110

07310.80 WOOD SHAKES

	Unit	Total
Shakes, hand split, 24" red cedar, on roofs		
5" exposure	SQ.	530
7" exposure	SQ.	460
9" exposure	SQ.	410
On walls		
6" exposure	SQ.	520
8" exposure	SQ.	450
10" exposure	SQ.	400
Add for fire retarding	SQ.	74.75

07460.10 METAL SIDING PANELS

	Unit	Total
Aluminum siding panels, Corrugated		
Plain finish		
.024"	S.F.	4.83
.032"	S.F.	5.24
Painted finish		
.024"	S.F.	5.40
.032"	S.F.	5.83
Steel siding panels, Corrugated		
22 ga.	S.F.	6.38
24 ga.	S.F.	6.18

07460.50 PLASTIC SIDING

	Unit	Total
Horizontal vinyl siding, solid		
8" wide		
Standard	S.F.	3.38
Insulated	S.F.	3.65
10" wide		
Standard	S.F.	3.28
Insulated	S.F.	3.53
Vinyl moldings for doors and windows	L.F.	3.03

07460.60 PLYWOOD SIDING

	Unit	Total
Rough sawn cedar, 3/8" thick	S.F.	3.66
Fir, 3/8" thick	S.F.	2.86
Texture 1-11, 5/8" thick		
Cedar	S.F.	4.42
Fir	S.F.	3.69
Redwood	S.F.	4.51
Southern Yellow Pine	S.F.	3.38

07460.70 STEEL SIDING

	Unit	Total
Ribbed, sheets, galvanized		
22 ga.	S.F.	4.97
24 ga.	S.F.	4.73
Primed		
24 ga.	S.F.	5.42
26 ga.	S.F.	4.56

07460.80 WOOD SIDING

	Unit	Total
Beveled siding, cedar, A grade		
1/2 x 8	S.F.	6.88
3/4 x 10	S.F.	7.84
Clear		
1/2 x 6	S.F.	7.86
1/2 x 8	S.F.	7.41
3/4 x 10	S.F.	8.80
B grade		
1/2 x 6	S.F.	7.69
1/2 x 8	S.F.	28.00
3/4 x 10	S.F.	7.07
Board and batten		
Cedar		
1x6	S.F.	8.18
1x8	S.F.	7.13
1x10	S.F.	6.42
1x12	S.F.	5.77
Pine		
1x6	S.F.	4.16
1x8	S.F.	3.57
1x10	S.F.	3.28
1x12	S.F.	2.99
Redwood		
1x6	S.F.	8.64
1x8	S.F.	7.68
1x10	S.F.	7.05
1x12	S.F.	6.47
Tongue and groove		
Cedar		
1x4	S.F.	8.16
1x6	S.F.	7.81
1x8	S.F.	7.35
1x10	S.F.	7.14
Pine		
1x4	S.F.	4.63
1x6	S.F.	4.38
1x8	S.F.	4.14
1x10	S.F.	3.94
Redwood		
1x4	S.F.	8.46
1x6	S.F.	8.10
1x8	S.F.	7.77
1x10	S.F.	7.40

07510.10 BUILT-UP ASPHALT ROOFING

	Unit	Total
Built-up roofing, asphalt felt, including gravel		
2 ply	SQ.	220
3 ply	SQ.	300
4 ply	SQ.	380
Cant strip, 4" x 4"		
Treated wood	L.F.	3.86
Foamglass	L.F.	3.34
New gravel for built-up roofing, 400 lb/sq	SQ.	150

07530.10 SINGLE-PLY ROOFING

	Unit	Total
Elastic sheet roofing		
Neoprene, 1/16" thick	S.F.	3.51
PVC		
45 mil	S.F.	2.71
Flashing		
Pipe flashing, 90 mil thick		
1" pipe	EA.	46.25
Neoprene flashing, 60 mil thick strip		
6" wide	L.F.	6.36
12" wide	L.F.	10.50

07610.10 METAL ROOFING

	Unit	Total
Sheet metal roofing, copper, 16 oz,		
Batten seam	SQ.	2,150
Standing seam	SQ.	2,100
Aluminum roofing, natural finish		
Corrugated, on steel frame		
.0175" thick	SQ.	280
.0215" thick	SQ.	320
.024" thick	SQ.	360
.032" thick	SQ.	400
V-beam, on steel frame		
.032" thick	SQ.	410
.040" thick	SQ.	430
.050" thick	SQ.	500
Ridge cap, .019" thick	L.F.	5.82

07610.10 METAL ROOFING (Cont.)

	Unit	Total
Corrugated galvanized steel roofing, on steel frame		
28 ga.	SQ.	370
26 ga.	SQ.	400
24 ga.	SQ.	440
22 ga.	SQ.	470
26 ga., factory insulated with 1" polystyrene	SQ.	700
Ridge roll		
10" wide	L.F.	3.98
20" wide	L.F.	6.62

07620.10 FLASHING AND TRIM

	Unit	Total
Counter flashing		
Aluminum, .032"	S.F.	7.16
Stainless steel, .015"	S.F.	11.25
Copper		
16 oz.	S.F.	14.75
20 oz.	S.F.	16.25
24 oz.	S.F.	18.75
32 oz.	S.F.	21.75
Valley flashing		
Aluminum, .032"	S.F.	4.92
Stainless steel, .015	S.F.	8.40
Copper		
16 oz.	S.F.	12.75
20 oz.	S.F.	15.50
24 oz.	S.F.	16.75
32 oz.	S.F.	19.75
Base flashing		
Aluminum, .040"	S.F.	7.06
Stainless steel, .018"	S.F.	10.50
Copper		
16 oz.	S.F.	13.75
20 oz.	S.F.	14.25
24 oz.	S.F.	18.00
32 oz.	S.F.	21.00
Flashing and trim, aluminum		
.019" thick	S.F.	5.11
.032" thick	S.F.	5.39
.040" thick	S.F.	6.81
Neoprene sheet flashing, .060" thick	S.F.	5.48
Copper, paper backed		
2 oz.	S.F.	8.09
5 oz.	S.F.	8.89

07620.20 GUTTERS AND DOWNSPOUTS

	Unit	Total
Copper gutter and downspout		
Downspouts, 16 oz. copper		
Round		
3" dia.	L.F.	16.50
4" dia.	L.F.	19.75
Rectangular, corrugated		
2" x 3"	L.F.	16.00
3" x 4"	L.F.	18.75
Rectangular, flat surface		
2" x 3"	L.F.	18.00
3" x 4"	L.F.	24.00
Lead-coated copper downspouts		
Round		
3" dia.	L.F.	20.25
4" dia.	L.F.	24.50
Rectangular, corrugated		
2" x 3"	L.F.	20.75
3" x 4"	L.F.	24.00
Rectangular, plain		
2" x 3"	L.F.	15.50
3" x 4"	L.F.	17.50

07620.20 GUTTERS AND DOWNSPOUTS (Cont.)

	Unit	Total
Copper gutter and downspout		
Gutters, 16 oz. copper		
Half round		
4" wide	L.F.	17.00
5" wide	L.F.	20.25
Type K		
4" wide	L.F.	18.25
5" wide	L.F.	19.75
Lead-coated copper gutters		
Half round		
4" wide	L.F.	19.50
6" wide	L.F.	25.50
Type K		
4" wide	L.F.	21.00
5" wide	L.F.	26.25
Aluminum gutter and downspout		
Downspouts		
2" x 3"	L.F.	4.88
3" x 4"	L.F.	5.64
4" x 5"	L.F.	6.13
Round		
3" dia.	L.F.	5.79
4" dia.	L.F.	6.68
Gutters, stock units		
4" wide	L.F.	7.80
5" wide	L.F.	8.52
Galvanized steel gutter and downspout		
Downspouts, round corrugated		
3" dia.	L.F.	5.56
4" dia.	L.F.	6.25
5" dia.	L.F.	7.82
6" dia.	L.F.	9.13
Rectangular		
2" x 3"	L.F.	5.37
3" x 4"	L.F.	5.93
4" x 4"	L.F.	6.59
Gutters, stock units		
5" wide		
Plain	L.F.	7.69
Painted	L.F.	7.84
6" wide		
Plain	L.F.	8.73
Painted	L.F.	9.03

07810.10 PLASTIC SKYLIGHTS

	Unit	Total
Single thickness, not including mounting curb		
2' x 4'	EA.	440
4' x 4'	EA.	590
5' x 5'	EA.	800
6' x 8'	EA.	1,600
Double thickness, not including mounting curb		
2' x 4'	EA.	560
4' x 4'	EA.	700
5' x 5'	EA.	1,050
6' x 8'	EA.	1,800

07920.10 CAULKING

	Unit	Total
Caulk exterior, two component		
1/4 x 1/2	L.F.	3.20
3/8 x 1/2	L.F.	3.71
1/2 x 1/2	L.F.	4.32
Caulk interior, single component		
1/4 x 1/2	L.F.	2.92
3/8 x 1/2	L.F.	3.32
1/2 x 1/2	L.F.	3.79

08110.10 METAL DOORS

	Unit	Total
Flush hollow metal, std. duty, 20 ga., 1-3/8" thick		
2-6 x 6-8	EA.	360
2-8 x 6-8	EA.	400
3-0 x 6-8	EA.	420
1-3/4" thick		
2-6 x 6-8	EA.	420
2-8 x 6-8	EA.	440
3-0 x 6-8	EA.	470
2-6 x 7-0	EA.	450
2-8 x 7-0	EA.	470
3-0 x 7-0	EA.	490
Heavy duty, 20 ga., unrated, 1-3/4"		
2-8 x 6-8	EA.	450
3-0 x 6-8	EA.	480
2-8 x 7-0	EA.	510
3-0 x 7-0	EA.	490
3-4 x 7-0	EA.	510
18 ga., 1-3/4", unrated door		
2-0 x 7-0	EA.	480
2-4 x 7-0	EA.	480
2-6 x 7-0	EA.	480
2-8 x 7-0	EA.	520
3-0 x 7-0	EA.	530
3-4 x 7-0	EA.	540
2", unrated door		
2-0 x 7-0	EA.	530
2-4 x 7-0	EA.	530
2-6 x 7-0	EA.	530
2-8 x 7-0	EA.	570
3-0 x 7-0	EA.	590
3-4 x 7-0	EA.	600

08110.40 METAL DOOR FRAMES

	Unit	Total
Hollow metal, stock, 18 ga., 4-3/4" x 1-3/4"		
2-0 x 7-0	EA.	210
2-4 x 7-0	EA.	230
2-6 x 7-0	EA.	230
2-8 x 7-0	EA.	230
3-0 x 7-0	EA.	230
4-0 x 7-0	EA.	270
5-0 x 7-0	EA.	280
6-0 x 7-0	EA.	320
16 ga., 6-3/4" x 1-3/4"		
2-0 x 7-0	EA.	240
2-4 x 7-0	EA.	230
2-6 x 7-0	EA.	240
2-8 x 7-0	EA.	240
3-0 x 7-0	EA.	250
4-0 x 7-0	EA.	300
6-0 x 7-0	EA.	330

08210.10 WOOD DOORS

	Unit	Total
Solid core, 1-3/8" thick		
Birch faced		
2-4 x 7-0	EA.	220
2-8 x 7-0	EA.	230
3-0 x 7-0	EA.	230
3-4 x 7-0	EA.	380
2-4 x 6-8	EA.	220
2-6 x 6-8	EA.	220
2-8 x 6-8	EA.	230
3-0 x 6-8	EA.	230
Lauan faced		
2-4 x 6-8	EA.	210
2-8 x 6-8	EA.	220
3-0 x 6-8	EA.	220
3-4 x 6-8	EA.	230
Tempered hardboard faced		
2-4 x 7-0	EA.	240
2-8 x 7-0	EA.	250
3-0 x 7-0	EA.	280
3-4 x 7-0	EA.	280
Hollow core, 1-3/8" thick		
Birch faced		
2-4 x 7-0	EA.	210
2-8 x 7-0	EA.	210
3-0 x 7-0	EA.	220
3-4 x 7-0	EA.	230

08210.10 WOOD DOORS (Cont.)

	Unit	Total
Lauan faced		
2-4 x 6-8	EA.	130
2-6 x 6-8	EA.	130
2-8 x 6-8	EA.	150
3-0 x 6-8	EA.	150
3-4 x 6-8	EA.	160
Tempered hardboard faced		
2-4 x 7-0	EA.	140
2-6 x 7-0	EA.	150
2-8 x 7-0	EA.	150
3-0 x 7-0	EA.	160
3-4 x 7-0	EA.	170
Solid core, 1-3/4" thick		
Birch faced		
2-4 x 7-0	EA.	300
2-6 x 7-0	EA.	310
2-8 x 7-0	EA.	320
3-0 x 7-0	EA.	300
3-4 x 7-0	EA.	310
Lauan faced		
2-4 x 7-0	EA.	230
2-6 x 7-0	EA.	250
2-8 x 7-0	EA.	270
3-4 x 7-0	EA.	270
3-0 x 7-0	EA.	290
Tempered hardboard faced		
2-4 x 7-0	EA.	280
2-6 x 7-0	EA.	310
2-8 x 7-0	EA.	330
3-0 x 7-0	EA.	340
3-4 x 7-0	EA.	360
Hollow core, 1-3/4" thick		
Birch faced		
2-4 x 7-0	EA.	230
2-6 x 7-0	EA.	230
2-8 x 7-0	EA.	240
3-0 x 7-0	EA.	240
3-4 x 7-0	EA.	250
Lauan faced		
2-4 x 6-8	EA.	170
2-6 x 6-8	EA.	180
2-8 x 6-8	EA.	170
3-0 x 6-8	EA.	170
3-4 x 6-8	EA.	180
Tempered hardboard		
2-4 x 7-0	EA.	160
2-6 x 7-0	EA.	160
2-8 x 7-0	EA.	170
3-0 x 7-0	EA.	170
3-4 x 7-0	EA.	180
Add-on, louver	EA.	91.00
Glass	EA.	170
Exterior doors, 3-0 x 7-0 x 2-1/2", solid core, Carved		
One face	EA.	1,600
Two faces	EA.	2,150
Closet doors, 1-3/4" thick		
Bi-fold or bi-passing, includes frame and trim		
Paneled, 4-0 x 6-8	EA.	600
6-0 x 6-8	EA.	670
Louvered, 4-0 x 6-8	EA.	440
6-0 x 6-8	EA.	510
Flush, 4-0 x 6-8	EA.	350
6-0 x 6-8	EA.	420
Primed, 4-0 x 6-8	EA.	370
6-0 x 6-8	EA.	410

08210.90 WOOD FRAMES

	Unit	Total
Frame, interior, pine		
2-6 x 6-8	EA.	170
2-8 x 6-8	EA.	170
3-0 x 6-8	EA.	180
5-0 x 6-8	EA.	180
6-0 x 6-8	EA.	190
2-6 x 7-0	EA.	180
2-8 x 7-0	EA.	190
3-0 x 7-0	EA.	200
5-0 x 7-0	EA.	240
6-0 x 7-0	EA.	240

08210.90 WOOD FRAMES (Cont.)

Item	Unit	Total
Exterior, custom, with threshold, including trim		
Walnut		
3-0 x 7-0	EA.	480
6-0 x 7-0	EA.	530
Oak		
3-0 x 7-0	EA.	450
6-0 x 7-0	EA.	500
Pine		
2-4 x 7-0	EA.	240
2-6 x 7-0	EA.	240
2-8 x 7-0	EA.	250
3-0 x 7-0	EA.	250
3-4 x 7-0	EA.	270
6-0 x 7-0	EA.	360

08300.10 SPECIAL DOORS

Item	Unit	Total
Sliding glass doors		
Tempered plate glass, 1/4" thick		
6' wide		
Economy grade	EA.	1,250
Premium grade	EA.	1,400
12' wide		
Economy grade	EA.	1,800
Premium grade	EA.	2,550
Insulating glass, 5/8" thick		
6' wide		
Economy grade	EA.	1,500
Premium grade	EA.	1,900
12' wide		
Economy grade	EA.	1,950
Premium grade	EA.	2,950
1" thick		
6' wide		
Economy grade	EA.	1,850
Premium grade	EA.	2,100
12' wide		
Economy grade	EA.	2,850
Premium grade	EA.	4,050
Added costs		
Custom quality, add to material, 30%		
Tempered glass, 6' wide, add	S.F.	4.62
Residential storm door		
Minimum	EA.	260
Average	EA.	320
Maximum	EA.	650

08520.10 ALUMINUM WINDOWS

Item	Unit	Total
Jalousie		
3-0 x 4-0	EA.	420
3-0 x 5-0	EA.	470
Fixed window		
6 sf to 8 sf	S.F.	25.50
12 sf to 16 sf	S.F.	21.50
Projecting window		
6 sf to 8 sf	S.F.	52.25
12 sf to 16 sf	S.F.	43.50
Horizontal sliding		
6 sf to 8 sf	S.F.	31.75
12 sf to 16 sf	S.F.	28.25
Double hung		
6 sf to 8 sf	S.F.	45.50
10 sf to 12 sf	S.F.	39.75
Storm window, 0.5 cfm, up to		
60 u.i. (united inches)	EA.	110
70 u.i.	EA.	110
80 u.i.	EA.	120
90 u.i.	EA.	120
100 u.i.	EA.	130
2.0 cfm, up to		
60 u.i.	EA.	130
70 u.i.	EA.	130
80 u.i.	EA.	130
90 u.i.	EA.	140
100 u.i.	EA.	140

08600.10 WOOD WINDOWS

Item	Unit	Total
Double hung, 24" x 36"		
Minimum	EA.	290
Average	EA.	410
Maximum	EA.	540
24" x 48"		
Minimum	EA.	330
Average	EA.	460
Maximum	EA.	640
30" x 48"		
Minimum	EA.	340
Average	EA.	470
Maximum	EA.	680
30" x 60"		
Minimum	EA.	370
Average	EA.	570
Maximum	EA.	710
Casement, 1 leaf, 22" x 38" high		
Minimum	EA.	400
Average	EA.	480
Maximum	EA.	570
2 leaf, 50" x 50" high, Minimum	EA.	970
Average	EA.	1,250
Maximum	EA.	1,500
3 leaf, 71" x 62" high, Minimum	EA.	1,550
Average	EA.	1,600
Maximum	EA.	1,950
4 leaf, 95" x 75" high, Minimum	EA.	2,050
Average	EA.	2,350
Maximum	EA.	3,050
5 leaf, 119" x 75" high, Minimum	EA.	2,650
Average	EA.	2,850
Maximum	EA.	3,700
Picture window, fixed glass, 54" x 54" high		
Minimum	EA.	600
Average	EA.	670
Maximum	EA.	1,150
68" x 55" high		
Minimum	EA.	1,000
Average	EA.	1,200
Maximum	EA.	1,500
Sliding, 40" x 31" high		
Minimum	EA.	370
Average	EA.	550
Maximum	EA.	660
52" x 39" high		
Minimum	EA.	460
Average	EA.	660
Maximum	EA.	710
64" x 72" high		
Minimum	EA.	670
Average	EA.	1,050
Maximum	EA.	1,150
Awning windows, 34" x 21" high		
Minimum	EA.	380
Average	EA.	430
Maximum	EA.	510
40" x 21" high		
Minimum	EA.	430
Average	EA.	490
Maximum	EA.	570
48" x 27" high		
Minimum	EA.	450
Average	EA.	550
Maximum	EA.	650
60" x 36" high		
Minimum	EA.	480
Average	EA.	820
Maximum	EA.	930
Window frame, milled		
Minimum	L.F.	17.00
Average	L.F.	20.50
Maximum	L.F.	28.50

08710.10 HINGES

Item	Unit	Total
Hinges		
3 x 3 butts, steel, interior, plain bearing	PAIR	20.75
4 x 4 butts, steel, standard	PAIR	30.50
5 x 4-1/2 butts, bronze/s. steel, heavy duty	PAIR	79.25

08710.20 LOCKSETS

Item	Unit	Total
Latchset, heavy duty		
Cylindrical	EA.	230
Mortise	EA.	260
Lockset, heavy duty		
Cylindrical	EA.	350
Mortise	EA.	410
Lockset		
Privacy (bath or bedroom)	EA.	270
Entry lock	EA.	290

08710.30 CLOSERS

Item	Unit	Total
Door closers		
Standard	EA.	310
Heavy duty	EA.	350

08710.40 DOOR TRIM

Item	Unit	Total
Panic device		
Mortise	EA.	920
Vertical rod	EA.	1,300
Labeled, rim type	EA.	950
Mortise	EA.	1,200
Vertical rod	EA.	1,300

08710.60 WEATHERSTRIPPING

Item	Unit	Total
Weatherstrip, head and jamb, metal strip, neoprene bulb		
Standard duty	L.F.	8.06
Heavy duty	L.F.	9.00
Spring type		
Metal doors	EA.	190
Wood doors	EA.	240
Sponge type with adhesive backing	EA.	110
Thresholds		
Bronze	L.F.	67.25
Aluminum	L.F.	10.75
Plain	L.F.	50.50
Vinyl insert	L.F.	53.25
Aluminum with grit	L.F.	51.50
Steel		
Plain	L.F.	43.75
Interlocking	L.F.	86.25

08810.10 GLAZING

Item	Unit	Total
Sheet glass, 1/8" thick	S.F.	11.25
Plate glass, bronze or grey, 1/4" thick	S.F.	16.75
Clear	S.F.	14.50
Polished	S.F.	16.00
Plexiglass		
1/8" thick	S.F.	10.50
1/4" thick	S.F.	12.25
Float glass, clear		
3/16" thick	S.F.	11.25
1/4" thick	S.F.	11.75
3/8" thick	S.F.	20.00
Tinted glass, polished plate, twin ground		
3/16" thick	S.F.	13.50
1/4" thick	S.F.	13.75
3/8" thick	S.F.	21.00
Insulating glass, two lites, clear float glass		
1/2" thick	S.F.	22.25
5/8" thick	S.F.	26.00
3/4" thick	S.F.	30.75
7/8" thick	S.F.	33.75
1" thick	S.F.	41.75
Glass seal edge		
3/8" thick	S.F.	20.25
Tinted glass		
1/2" thick	S.F.	30.75
1" thick	S.F.	42.50
Tempered, clear		
1" thick	S.F.	60.75
Plate mirror glass		
1/4" thick		
15 sf	S.F.	16.75
Over 15 sf	S.F.	15.25

08910.10 GLAZED CURTAIN WALLS

Item	Unit	Total
Curtain wall, aluminum system, framing sections		
2" x 3"		
Jamb	L.F.	17.00
Horizontal	L.F.	17.25
Mullion	L.F.	21.25
2" x 4"		
Jamb	L.F.	23.75
Horizontal	L.F.	24.25
Mullion	L.F.	23.75
3" x 5-1/2"		
Jamb	L.F.	29.00
Horizontal	L.F.	31.25
Mullion	L.F.	29.00
4" corner mullion	L.F.	38.50
Coping sections		
1/8" x 8"	L.F.	39.75
1/8" x 9"	L.F.	40.00
1/8" x 12-1/2"	L.F.	42.75
Sill section		
1/8" x 6"	L.F.	35.25
1/8" x 7"	L.F.	35.75
1/8" x 8-1/2"	L.F.	36.25
Column covers, aluminum		
1/8" x 26"	L.F.	44.50
1/8" x 34"	L.F.	45.75
1/8" x 38"	L.F.	46.00
Doors		
Aluminum framed, standard hardware		
Narrow stile		
2-6 x 7-0	EA.	970
3-0 x 7-0	EA.	980
3-6 x 7-0	EA.	1000

	Unit	Total
09110.10 METAL STUDS		
Studs, non load bearing, galvanized		
2-1/2", 20 ga.		
12" o.c.	S.F.	1.89
16" o.c.	S.F.	1.48
25 ga.		
12" o.c.	S.F.	1.65
16" o.c.	S.F.	1.31
24" o.c.	S.F.	1.08
3-5/8", 20 ga.		
12" o.c.	S.F.	2.26
16" o.c.	S.F.	1.78
24" o.c.	S.F.	1.43
25 ga.		
12" o.c.	S.F.	1.97
16" o.c.	S.F.	1.58
24" o.c.	S.F.	1.28
4", 20 ga.		
12" o.c.	S.F.	2.34
16" o.c.	S.F.	1.84
24" o.c.	S.F.	1.48
25 ga.		
12" o.c.	S.F.	2.04
16" o.c.	S.F.	1.62
24" o.c.	S.F.	1.30
6", 20 ga.		
12" o.c.	S.F.	2.95
16" o.c.	S.F.	2.28
24" o.c.	S.F.	1.89
25 ga.		
12" o.c.	S.F.	2.53
16" o.c.	S.F.	2.02
24" o.c.	S.F.	1.63
Load bearing studs, galvanized		
3-5/8", 16 ga.		
12" o.c.	S.F.	2.95
16" o.c.	S.F.	2.55
18 ga.		
12" o.c.	S.F.	2.04
16" o.c.	S.F.	2.33
4", 16 ga.		
12" o.c.	S.F.	3.03
16" o.c.	S.F.	2.60
6", 16 ga.		
12" o.c.	S.F.	3.83
16" o.c.	S.F.	3.27
Furring		
On beams and columns		
7/8" channel	L.F.	4.28
1-1/2" channel	L.F.	4.96
On ceilings		
3/4" furring channels		
12" o.c.	S.F.	2.73
16" o.c.	S.F.	2.55
24" o.c.	S.F.	2.22
1-1/2" furring channels		
12" o.c.	S.F.	3.20
16" o.c.	S.F.	2.83
24" o.c.	S.F.	2.49
On walls		
3/4" furring channels		
12" o.c.	S.F.	2.27
16" o.c.	S.F.	2.06
24" o.c.	S.F.	1.87
1-1/2" furring channels		
12" o.c.	S.F.	2.66
16" o.c.	S.F.	2.37
24" o.c.	S.F.	2.09
09205.10 GYPSUM LATH		
Gypsum lath, 1/2" thick		
Clipped	S.Y.	10.25
Nailed	S.Y.	10.75
09205.20 METAL LATH		
Diamond expanded, galv.,2.5 lb., on walls		
Nailed	S.Y.	11.25
Wired	S.Y.	12.25
On ceilings, Nailed	S.Y.	12.25
Wired	S.Y.	13.50

	Unit	Total
09205.20 METAL LATH (Cont.)		
3.4 lb., on walls, Nailed	S.Y.	12.75
Wired	S.Y.	13.75
On ceilings, Nailed	S.Y.	13.75
Wired	S.Y.	15.00
Flat rib, 2.75 lb., on walls, Nailed	S.Y.	11.00
Wired	S.Y.	12.00
On ceilings, Nailed	S.Y.	12.00
Wired	S.Y.	13.25
3.4 lb., on walls, Nailed	S.Y.	11.75
Wired	S.Y.	12.75
On ceilings, Nailed	S.Y.	12.75
Wired	S.Y.	14.25
Stucco lath, 1.8 lb.	S.Y.	12.00
3.6 lb.	S.Y.	12.50
Paper backed		
Minimum	S.Y.	9.45
Maximum	S.Y.	14.25
09205.60 PLASTER ACCESSORIES		
Expansion joint, 3/4", 26 ga., galv.	L.F.	2.88
Plaster corner beads, 3/4", galvanized	L.F.	2.02
Casing bead, expanded flange, galvanized	L.F.	1.96
Expanded wing, 1-1/4" wide, galvanized	L.F.	2.06
Joint clips for lath	EA.	.46
Metal base, galvanized, 2-1/2" high	L.F.	2.63
Stud clips for gypsum lath	EA.	.46
Tie wire galvanized, 18 ga., 25 lb. hank	EA.	47.00
Sound deadening board, 1/4"	S.F.	1.25
09210.10 PLASTER		
Gypsum plaster, trowel finish		
2 coats, Ceilings	S.Y.	22.50
Walls	S.Y.	21.50
3 coats, Ceilings	S.Y.	31.25
Walls	S.Y.	28.50
Vermiculite plaster		
2 coats		
Ceilings	S.Y.	31.75
Walls	S.Y.	29.75
3 coats		
Ceilings	S.Y.	41.75
Walls	S.Y.	38.50
Keenes cement plaster		
2 coats		
Ceilings	S.Y.	22.50
Walls	S.Y.	20.00
3 coats		
Ceilings	S.Y.	25.25
Walls	S.Y.	22.50
On columns, add to installation, 50%	S.Y.	
Chases, fascia, & soffits, add to labor, 50%	S.Y.	
Beams, add to installation, 50%	S.Y.	
Patch holes, average size holes		
1 sf to 5 sf		
Minimum	S.F.	11.25
Average	S.F.	13.00
Maximum	S.F.	15.50
Over 5 sf		
Minimum	S.F.	7.70
Average	S.F.	9.94
Maximum	S.F.	11.25
Patch cracks		
Minimum	S.F.	4.22
Average	S.F.	5.09
Maximum	S.F.	7.70
09220.10 PORTLAND CEMENT PLASTER		
Stucco, portland, gray, 3 coat, 1" thick		
Sand finish	S.Y.	30.50
Trowel finish	S.Y.	31.50
White cement		
Sand finish	S.Y.	32.50
Trowel finish	S.Y.	34.75
Scratch coat		
For ceramic tile	S.Y.	8.04
For quarry tile	S.Y.	8.04
Portland cement plaster		
2 coats, 1/2"	S.Y.	16.00
3 coats, 7/8"	S.Y.	19.75

09250.10 GYPSUM BOARD

	Unit	Total
Drywall, plasterboard, 3/8" clipped to		
Metal furred ceiling	S.F.	.97
Columns and beams	S.F.	1.75
Walls	S.F.	.91
Nailed or screwed to		
Wood framed ceiling	S.F.	.91
Columns and beams	S.F.	1.59
Walls	S.F.	.86
1/2", clipped to		
Metal furred ceiling	S.F.	.98
Columns and beams	S.F.	1.73
Walls	S.F.	.89
Nailed or screwed to		
Wood framed ceiling	S.F.	.89
Columns and beams	S.F.	1.57
Walls	S.F.	.84
5/8", clipped to		
Metal furred ceiling	S.F.	1.06
Columns and beams	S.F.	1.91
Walls	S.F.	.98
Nailed or screwed to		
Wood framed ceiling	S.F.	1.06
Columns and beams	S.F.	1.91
Walls	S.F.	.98
Vinyl faced, clipped to metal studs		
1/2"	S.F.	1.69
5/8"	S.F.	1.64
Add for		
Fire resistant	S.F.	.11
Water resistant	S.F.	.18
Water and fire resistant	S.F.	.22
Taping and finishing joints		
Minimum	S.F.	.41
Average	S.F.	.54
Maximum	S.F.	.66
Casing bead		
Minimum	L.F.	1.75
Average	L.F.	2.03
Maximum	L.F.	3.01
Corner bead		
Minimum	L.F.	1.76
Average	L.F.	2.08
Maximum	L.F.	3.05

09310.10 CERAMIC TILE

	Unit	Total
Glazed wall tile, 4-1/4" x 4-1/4"		
Minimum	S.F.	6.13
Average	S.F.	8.13
Maximum	S.F.	18.50
Base, 4-1/4" high		
Minimum	L.F.	10.50
Average	L.F.	11.25
Maximum	L.F.	12.50
Unglazed floor tile		
Portland cem., cushion edge, face mtd		
1" x 1"	S.F.	12.50
2" x 2"	S.F.	12.50
4" x 4"	S.F.	12.00
Adhesive bed, with white grout		
1" x 1"	S.F.	11.50
4" x 4"	S.F.	11.50
Organic adhesive bed, thin set, back mounted		
1" x 1"	S.F.	11.50
2" x 2"	S.F.	12.25
For group 2 colors, add to material, 10%		
For group 3 colors, add to material, 20%		
For abrasive surface, add to material, 25%		
Unglazed wall tile, Organic adhesive, face mounted cushion edge		
1" x 1"		
Minimum	S.F.	8.03
Average	S.F.	9.53
Maximum	S.F.	12.25
2" x 2"		
Minimum	S.F.	8.23
Average	S.F.	9.13
Maximum	S.F.	12.50

09310.10 CERAMIC TILE (Cont.)

	Unit	Total
Back mounted		
1" x 1", Minimum	S.F.	8.03
Average	S.F.	9.53
Maximum	S.F.	12.25
2" x 2", Minimum	S.F.	8.23
Average	S.F.	9.13
Maximum	S.F.	12.50
For glazed finish, add to material, 25%		
For glazed mosaic, add to material, 100%		
For metallic colors, add to material, 125%		
For exterior wall use, add to total, 25%		
For exterior soffit, add to total, 25%		
For portland cement bed, add to total, 25%		
For dry set portland cement bed, add to total, 10%		
Ceramic accessories		
Towel bar, 24" long, Minimum	EA.	37.50
Average	EA.	47.00
Maximum	EA.	89.50
Soap dish, Minimum	EA.	43.25
Average	EA.	55.00
Maximum	EA.	81.00

09330.10 QUARRY TILE

	Unit	Total
Floor, 4 x 4 x 1/2"	S.F.	13.50
6 x 6 x 1/2"	S.F.	12.75
6 x 6 x 3/4"	S.F.	14.25
Wall, applied to 3/4" portland cement bed		
4 x 4 x 1/2"	S.F.	15.25
6 x 6 x 3/4"	S.F.	14.00
Cove base		
5 x 6 x 1/2" straight top	L.F.	15.00
6 x 6 x 3/4" round top	L.F.	14.50
Stair treads 6 x 6 x 3/4"	L.F.	21.50
Window sill 6 x 8 x 3/4"	L.F.	18.25
For abrasive surface, add to material, 25%		

09410.10 TERRAZZO

	Unit	Total
Floors on concrete, 1-3/4" thick, 5/8" topping		
Gray cement	S.F.	11.75
White cement	S.F.	12.00
Sand cushion, 3" thick, 5/8" top, 1/4"		
Gray cement	S.F.	13.75
White cement	S.F.	14.25
Monolithic terrazzo, 3-1/2" base slab, 5/8" topping	S.F.	10.50
Terrazzo wainscot, cast-in-place, 1/2" thick	S.F.	20.50
Base, cast in place, terrazzo cove type, 6" high	L.F.	16.25
Curb, cast in place, 6" w x 6" h, polished top	L.F.	35.75
For venetian type terrazzo, add to material, 10%		
For abrasive heavy duty terrazzo, add to material, 15%		
Divider strips		
Zinc	L.F.	1.51
Brass	L.F.	2.80
Stairs, cast-in-place, topping on concrete or metal		
1-1/2" thick treads, 12" wide	L.F.	32.00
Combined tread and riser	L.F.	74.00
Precast terrazzo, thin set		
Terrazzo tiles, non-slip surface		
9" x 9" x 1" thick	S.F.	26.25
12" x 12"		
1" thick	S.F.	27.25
1-1/2" thick	S.F.	28.50
18" x 18" x 1-1/2" thick	S.F.	35.00
24" x 24" x 1-1/2" thick	S.F.	41.75
For white cement, add to material, 10%		
For venetian type terrazzo, add to material, 25%		
Terrazzo wainscot		
12" x 12" x 1" thick	S.F.	22.25
18" x 18" x 1-1/2" thick	S.F.	30.25
Base		
6" high		
Straight	L.F.	17.25
Coved	L.F.	19.75
8" high		
Straight	L.F.	19.25
Coved	L.F.	21.75
Terrazzo curbs		
8" wide x 8" high	L.F.	55.75
6" wide x 6" high	L.F.	48.75

09410.10 TERRAZZO (Cont.)

	Unit	Total
Precast terrazzo stair treads, 12" wide		
1-1/2" thick		
Diamond pattern	L.F.	51.25
Non-slip surface	L.F.	53.50
2" thick		
Diamond pattern	L.F.	53.50
Non-slip surface	L.F.	56.75
Stair risers, 1" thick to 6" high		
Straight sections	L.F.	19.25
Cove sections	L.F.	21.75
Combined tread and riser		
Straight sections		
1-1/2" tread, 3/4" riser	L.F.	75.50
3" tread, 1" riser	L.F.	87.25
Curved sections		
2" tread, 1" riser	L.F.	94.75
3" tread, 1" riser	L.F.	97.25
Stair stringers, notched for treads and risers		
1" thick	L.F.	49.50
2" thick	L.F.	55.25
Landings, structural, nonslip		
1-1/2" thick	S.F.	43.25
3" thick	S.F.	58.50

09510.10 CEILINGS AND WALLS

	Unit	Total
Acoustical panels, suspension system not included		
Fiberglass panels		
5/8" thick		
2' x 2'	S.F.	2.12
2' x 4'	S.F.	1.72
3/4" thick		
2' x 2'	S.F.	2.56
2' x 4'	S.F.	2.32
Glass cloth faced fiberglass panels		
3/4" thick	S.F.	3.44
1" thick	S.F.	3.72
Mineral fiber panels		
5/8" thick		
2' x 2'	S.F.	1.92
2' x 4'	S.F.	1.74
3/4" thick		
2' x 2'	S.F.	2.56
2' x 4'	S.F.	2.32
Wood fiber panels		
1/2" thick		
2' x 2'	S.F.	2.48
2' x 4'	S.F.	2.30
5/8" thick		
2' x 2'	S.F.	2.65
2' x 4'	S.F.	2.47
Acoustical tiles, suspension system not included		
Fiberglass tile, 12" x 12"		
5/8" thick	S.F.	2.42
3/4" thick	S.F.	2.86
Glass cloth faced fiberglass tile		
3/4" thick	S.F.	4.48
3" thick	S.F.	5.03
Mineral fiber tile, 12" x 12"		
5/8" thick		
Standard	S.F.	1.94
Vinyl faced	S.F.	2.77
3/4" thick		
Standard	S.F.	2.33
Vinyl faced	S.F.	3.23
Ceiling suspension systems		
T bar system		
2' x 4'	S.F.	1.72
2' x 2'	S.F.	1.87
Concealed Z bar susp. system, 12" module	S.F.	2.01
For 1-1/2" carrier channels, 4' o.c., add	S.F.	.38
Carrier channel for recessed light fixtures	S.F.	.69

09550.10 WOOD FLOORING

	Unit	Total
Wood strip flooring, unfinished		
Fir floor		
C and better		
Vertical grain	S.F.	5.39
Flat grain	S.F.	5.19
Oak floor		
Minimum	S.F.	6.38
Average	S.F.	7.79
Maximum	S.F.	10.00
Maple floor		
25/32" x 2-1/4"		
Minimum	S.F.	6.14
Maximum	S.F.	7.73
33/32" x 3-1/4"		
Minimum	S.F.	8.23
Maximum	S.F.	8.95
Added costs		
For factory finish, add to material, 10%		
For random width floor, add to total, 20%		
For simulated pegs, add to total, 10%		
Wood block industrial flooring, Creosoted		
2" thick	S.F.	5.65
2-1/2" thick	S.F.	6.09
3" thick	S.F.	6.38
Parquet, 5/16", white oak		
Finished	S.F.	12.00
Unfinished	S.F.	7.20
Gym floor, 2 ply felt, 25/32" maple		
Finished, in mastic	S.F.	10.75
Over wood sleepers	S.F.	12.25
Finishing, sand, fill, finish, and wax	S.F.	2.06
Refinish sand, seal, 2 coats of polyurethane	S.F.	3.03
Clean and wax floors	S.F.	.48

09630.10 UNIT MASONRY FLOORING

	Unit	Total
Clay brick		
9 x 4-1/2 x 3" thick		
Glazed	S.F.	12.75
Unglazed	S.F.	12.25
8 x 4 x 3/4" thick		
Glazed	S.F.	12.25
Unglazed	S.F.	12.00
For herringbone pattern, add to labor, 15%		

09660.10 RESILIENT TILE FLOORING

	Unit	Total
Solid vinyl tile, 1/8" thick, 12" x 12"		
Marble patterns	S.F.	5.86
Solid colors	S.F.	7.18
Travertine patterns	S.F.	7.89
Conductive resilient flooring, vinyl tile		
1/8" thick, 12" x 12"	S.F.	8.31

09665.10 RESILIENT SHEET FLOORING

	Unit	Total
Vinyl sheet flooring		
Minimum	S.F.	4.40
Average	S.F.	6.86
Maximum	S.F.	11.50
Cove, to 6"	L.F.	3.41
Fluid applied resilient flooring, Polyurethane		
Poured in place, 3/8" thick	S.F.	15.25
Vinyl sheet goods, backed		
0.070" thick	S.F.	4.60
0.093" thick	S.F.	6.75
0.125" thick	S.F.	7.68
0.250" thick	S.F.	8.73

09678.10 RESILIENT BASE AND ACCESSORIES

	Unit	Total
Wall base, vinyl		
4" high	L.F.	2.98
6" high	L.F.	3.39

09682.10 CARPET PADDING

	Unit	Total
Carpet padding		
Foam rubber, waffle type, 0.3" thick	S.Y.	8.96
Jute padding		
Minimum	S.Y.	6.72
Average	S.Y.	8.24
Maximum	S.Y.	11.25
Sponge rubber cushion		
Minimum	S.Y.	7.49
Average	S.Y.	9.40
Maximum	S.Y.	12.50

	Unit	Total
09682.10 CARPET PADDING (Cont.)		
Carpet padding		
Urethane cushion, 3/8" thick		
Minimum	S.Y.	7.49
Average	S.Y.	8.58
Maximum	S.Y.	10.75
09685.10 CARPET		
Carpet, acrylic		
24 oz., light traffic	S.Y.	22.25
28 oz., medium traffic	S.Y.	25.50
Nylon		
15 oz., light traffic	S.Y.	28.75
28 oz., medium traffic	S.Y.	35.25
Nylon		
28 oz., medium traffic	S.Y.	34.00
35 oz., heavy traffic	S.Y.	40.25
Wool		
30 oz., medium traffic	S.Y.	52.25
36 oz., medium traffic	S.Y.	54.75
42 oz., heavy traffic	S.Y.	70.50
Carpet tile		
Foam backed		
Minimum	S.F.	4.65
Average	S.F.	5.33
Maximum	S.F.	7.87
Tufted loop or shag		
Minimum	S.F.	4.94
Average	S.F.	5.85
Maximum	S.F.	8.82
Clean and vacuum carpet		
Minimum	S.Y.	.55
Average	S.Y.	.88
Maximum	S.Y.	1.26
09905.10 PAINTING PREPARATION		
Dropcloths		
Minimum	S.F.	.06
Average	S.F.	.10
Maximum	S.F.	.12
Masking		
Paper and tape		
Minimum	L.F.	.49
Average	L.F.	.61
Maximum	L.F.	.82
Doors		
Minimum	EA.	5.89
Average	EA.	7.85
Maximum	EA.	10.50
Windows		
Minimum	EA.	5.89
Average	EA.	7.85
Maximum	EA.	10.50
Sanding		
Walls and flat surfaces		
Minimum	S.F.	.31
Average	S.F.	.39
Maximum	S.F.	.47
Doors and windows		
Minimum	EA.	7.79
Average	EA.	11.75
Maximum	EA.	15.50
Trim		
Minimum	L.F.	.58
Average	L.F.	.78
Maximum	L.F.	1.04
Puttying		
Minimum	S.F.	.73
Average	S.F.	.96
Maximum	S.F.	1.20
09910.05 EXT. PAINTING, SITEWORK		
Concrete Block		
Roller, First Coat		
Minimum	S.F.	.39
Average	S.F.	.47
Maximum	S.F.	.63
Second Coat		
Minimum	S.F.	.35
Average	S.F.	.42
Maximum	S.F.	.55

	Unit	Total
09910.05 EXT. PAINTING, SITEWORK (Cont.)		
Concrete Block, Spray, First Coat		
Minimum	S.F.	.26
Average	S.F.	.29
Maximum	S.F.	.31
Second Coat		
Minimum	S.F.	.21
Average	S.F.	.24
Maximum	S.F.	.28
Fences, Chain Link, Roller, First Coat		
Minimum	S.F.	.44
Average	S.F.	.50
Maximum	S.F.	.56
Second Coat		
Minimum	S.F.	.30
Average	S.F.	.34
Maximum	S.F.	.40
Spray, First Coat		
Minimum	S.F.	.24
Average	S.F.	.26
Maximum	S.F.	.28
Second Coat		
Minimum	S.F.	.20
Average	S.F.	.22
Maximum	S.F.	.24
Fences, Wood or Masonry, Brush, First Coat		
Minimum	S.F.	.65
Average	S.F.	.74
Maximum	S.F.	.94
Second Coat		
Minimum	S.F.	.45
Average	S.F.	.52
Maximum	S.F.	.63
Roller, First Coat		
Minimum	S.F.	.42
Average	S.F.	.47
Maximum	S.F.	.52
Second Coat		
Minimum	S.F.	.34
Average	S.F.	.38
Maximum	S.F.	.45
Spray		
First Coat		
Minimum	S.F.	.30
Average	S.F.	.34
Maximum	S.F.	.42
Second Coat		
Minimum	S.F.	.25
Average	S.F.	.28
Maximum	S.F.	.32
09910.15 EXT. PAINTING, BUILDINGS		
Decks, Wood, Stained, Brush		
First Coat		
Minimum	S.F.	.36
Average	S.F.	.39
Maximum	S.F.	.42
Second Coat		
Minimum	S.F.	.30
Average	S.F.	.31
Maximum	S.F.	.32
Roller		
First Coat		
Minimum	S.F.	.30
Average	S.F.	.31
Maximum	S.F.	.32
Second Coat		
Minimum	S.F.	.28
Average	S.F.	.29
Maximum	S.F.	.31
Spray		
First Coat		
Minimum	S.F.	.26
Average	S.F.	.27
Maximum	S.F.	.29
Second Coat		
Minimum	S.F.	.24
Average	S.F.	.25
Maximum	S.F.	.27

09910.15 EXT. PAINTING, BUILDINGS (Cont.)

Item	Unit	Total
Doors, Wood		
Brush, First Coat		
Minimum	S.F.	.85
Average	S.F.	1.07
Maximum	S.F.	1.30
Second Coat		
Minimum	S.F.	.71
Average	S.F.	.80
Maximum	S.F.	.91
Roller, First Coat		
Minimum	S.F.	.44
Average	S.F.	.52
Maximum	S.F.	.71
Second Coat		
Minimum	S.F.	.36
Average	S.F.	.39
Maximum	S.F.	.52
Spray, First Coat		
Minimum	S.F.	.26
Average	S.F.	.29
Maximum	S.F.	.34
Second Coat		
Minimum	S.F.	.23
Average	S.F.	.24
Maximum	S.F.	.27
Gutters and Downspouts		
Brush, First Coat		
Minimum	L.F.	.74
Average	L.F.	.83
Maximum	L.F.	.94
Second Coat		
Minimum	L.F.	.55
Average	L.F.	.63
Maximum	L.F.	.74
Siding, Wood		
Roller, First Coat		
Minimum	S.F.	.28
Average	S.F.	.30
Maximum	S.F.	.32
Second Coat		
Minimum	S.F.	.30
Average	S.F.	.32
Maximum	S.F.	.34
Spray, First Coat		
Minimum	S.F.	.27
Average	S.F.	.28
Maximum	S.F.	.29
Second Coat		
Minimum	S.F.	.23
Average	S.F.	.27
Maximum	S.F.	.34
Stucco		
Roller, First Coat		
Minimum	S.F.	.37
Average	S.F.	.41
Maximum	S.F.	.45
Second Coat		
Minimum	S.F.	.33
Average	S.F.	.36
Maximum	S.F.	.39
Spray, First Coat		
Minimum	S.F.	.28
Average	S.F.	.30
Maximum	S.F.	.32
Second Coat		
Minimum	S.F.	.25
Average	S.F.	.26
Maximum	S.F.	.29
Trim		
Brush, First Coat		
Minimum	L.F.	.35
Average	L.F.	.39
Maximum	L.F.	.45
Second Coat		
Minimum	L.F.	.31
Average	L.F.	.35
Maximum	L.F.	.45

09910.15 EXT. PAINTING, BUILDINGS (Cont.)

Item	Unit	Total
Walls		
Roller, First Coat		
Minimum	S.F.	.30
Average	S.F.	.30
Maximum	S.F.	.32
Second Coat		
Minimum	S.F.	.28
Average	S.F.	.29
Maximum	S.F.	.31
Spray, First Coat		
Minimum	S.F.	.17
Average	S.F.	.19
Maximum	S.F.	.22
Second Coat		
Minimum	S.F.	.16
Average	S.F.	.18
Maximum	S.F.	.20
Windows		
Brush, First Coat		
Minimum	S.F.	.89
Average	S.F.	1.05
Maximum	S.F.	1.28
Second Coat		
Minimum	S.F.	.78
Average	S.F.	.89
Maximum	S.F.	1.05

09910.25 EXT. PAINTING, MISC.

Item	Unit	Total
Shakes, Spray, First Coat		
Minimum	S.F.	.31
Average	S.F.	.33
Maximum	S.F.	.35
Second Coat		
Minimum	S.F.	.30
Average	S.F.	.31
Maximum	S.F.	.33
Shingles, Wood		
Roller, First Coat		
Minimum	S.F.	.39
Average	S.F.	.42
Maximum	S.F.	.46
Second Coat		
Minimum	S.F.	.31
Average	S.F.	.32
Maximum	S.F.	.34
Spray, First Coat		
Minimum	L.F.	.29
Average	L.F.	.30
Maximum	L.F.	.32
Second Coat		
Minimum	L.F.	.25
Average	L.F.	.26
Maximum	L.F.	.27
Shutters and Louvres		
Brush, First Coat		
Minimum	EA.	9.51
Average	EA.	12.00
Maximum	EA.	15.75
Second Coat		
Minimum	EA.	6.01
Average	EA.	7.35
Maximum	EA.	9.51
Spray, First Coat		
Minimum	EA.	3.24
Average	EA.	3.86
Maximum	EA.	4.80
Second Coat		
Minimum	EA.	2.46
Average	EA.	3.24
Maximum	EA.	3.86
Stairs, metal		
Brush, First Coat		
Minimum	S.F.	.68
Average	S.F.	.74
Maximum	S.F.	.83
Second Coat		
Minimum	S.F.	.45
Average	S.F.	.49
Maximum	S.F.	.55

09910.25 EXT. PAINTING, MISC. (Cont.)

	Unit	Total
Stairs, metal		
Spray, First Coat		
Minimum	S.F.	.38
Average	S.F.	.45
Maximum	S.F.	.48
Second Coat		
Minimum	S.F.	.31
Average	S.F.	.35
Maximum	S.F.	.41

09910.35 INT. PAINTING, BUILDINGS

	Unit	Total
Acoustical Ceiling		
Roller		
First Coat		
Minimum	S.F.	.45
Average	S.F.	.55
Maximum	S.F.	.74
Second Coat		
Minimum	S.F.	.39
Average	S.F.	.45
Maximum	S.F.	.55
Spray		
First Coat		
Minimum	S.F.	.26
Average	S.F.	.29
Maximum	S.F.	.32
Second Coat		
Minimum	S.F.	.23
Average	S.F.	.25
Maximum	S.F.	.26
Cabinets and Casework		
Brush		
First Coat		
Minimum	S.F.	.63
Average	S.F.	.68
Maximum	S.F.	.74
Second Coat		
Minimum	S.F.	.55
Average	S.F.	.59
Maximum	S.F.	.63
Spray		
First Coat		
Minimum	S.F.	.36
Average	S.F.	.41
Maximum	S.F.	.46
Second Coat		
Minimum	S.F.	.32
Average	S.F.	.33
Maximum	S.F.	.39
Ceilings		
Roller		
First Coat		
Minimum	S.F.	.32
Average	S.F.	.34
Maximum	S.F.	.36
Second Coat		
Minimum	S.F.	.29
Average	S.F.	.31
Maximum	S.F.	.32
Spray		
First Coat		
Minimum	S.F.	.23
Average	S.F.	.24
Maximum	S.F.	.26
Second Coat		
Minimum	S.F.	.20
Average	S.F.	.21
Maximum	S.F.	.23

09910.35 INT. PAINTING, BUILDINGS (Cont.)

	Unit	Total
Doors, Wood		
Brush		
First Coat		
Minimum	S.F.	.83
Average	S.F.	1.01
Maximum	S.F.	1.20
Second Coat		
Minimum	S.F.	.64
Average	S.F.	.70
Maximum	S.F.	.79
Spray		
First Coat		
Minimum	S.F.	.26
Average	S.F.	.29
Maximum	S.F.	.33
Second Coat		
Minimum	S.F.	.23
Average	S.F.	.25
Maximum	S.F.	.27
Trim		
Brush		
First Coat		
Minimum	L.F.	.35
Average	L.F.	.37
Maximum	L.F.	.42
Second Coat		
Minimum	L.F.	.30
Average	L.F.	.34
Maximum	L.F.	.42
Walls		
Roller		
First Coat		
Minimum	S.F.	.30
Average	S.F.	.30
Maximum	S.F.	.32
Second Coat		
Minimum	S.F.	.28
Average	S.F.	.29
Maximum	S.F.	.31
Spray		
First Coat		
Minimum	S.F.	.18
Average	S.F.	.20
Maximum	S.F.	.23
Second Coat		
Minimum	S.F.	.17
Average	S.F.	.19
Maximum	S.F.	.22

09955.10 WALL COVERING

	Unit	Total
Vinyl wall covering		
Medium duty	S.F.	1.49
Heavy duty	S.F.	2.48
Over pipes and irregular shapes		
Lightweight, 13 oz.	S.F.	2.37
Medium weight, 25 oz.	S.F.	2.74
Heavy weight, 34 oz.	S.F.	3.26
Cork wall covering		
1' x 1' squares		
1/4" thick	S.F.	5.63
1/2" thick	S.F.	6.83
3/4" thick	S.F.	7.55
Wall fabrics		
Natural fabrics, grass cloths		
Minimum	S.F.	2.15
Average	S.F.	2.38
Maximum	S.F.	6.28
Flexible gypsum coated wall fabric, fire resistant	S.F.	2.08
Vinyl corner guards		
3/4" x 3/4" x 8'	EA.	13.50
2-3/4" x 2-3/4" x 4'	EA.	10.25

09980.15 PAINT

	Unit	Total
Paint, enamel		
600 sf per gal.	GAL	49.50
550 sf per gal.	GAL	46.25
500 sf per gal.	GAL	33.00
450 sf per gal.	GAL	30.75
350 sf per gal.	GAL	29.75
Filler, 60 sf per gal.	GAL	35.25
Latex, 400 sf per gal.	GAL	33.00
Aluminum		
400 sf per gal.	GAL	44.00
500 sf per gal.	GAL	70.50
Red lead, 350 sf per gal.	GAL	61.50
Primer		
400 sf per gal.	GAL	29.75
300 sf per gal.	GAL	29.75
Latex base, interior, white	GAL	33.00
Sealer and varnish		
400 sf per gal.	GAL	30.75
425 sf per gal.	GAL	44.00
600 sf per gal.	GAL	57.25

10185.10 SHOWER STALLS

	Unit	Total
Shower receptors		
Precast, terrazzo		
32" x 32"	EA.	660
32" x 48"	EA.	710
Concrete		
32" x 32"	EA.	300
48" x 48"	EA.	350
Shower door, trim and hardware		
Economy, 24" wide, chrome		
Tempered glass	EA.	340
Porcelain enameled steel, flush	EA.	560
Baked enameled steel, flush	EA.	360
Aluminum, tempered glass, 48" wide,		
Sliding	EA.	700
Folding	EA.	670
Aluminum and tempered glass, molded plastic		
Complete with receptor and door		
32" x 32"	EA.	900
36" x 36"	EA.	1000
40" x 40"	EA.	1,050

10210.10 VENTS AND WALL LOUVERS

	Unit	Total
Block vent, 8"x16"x4" aluminum, w/screen,		
Mill finish	EA.	170
Standard	EA.	100
Vents w/screen, 4" deep, 8" wide, 5" high		
Modular	EA.	120
Aluminum gable louvers	S.F.	28.25
Vent screen aluminum		
4" wide, continuous	L.F.	7.28

10290.10 PEST CONTROL

	Unit	Total
Termite control		
Under slab spraying		
Minimum	S.F.	1.25
Average	S.F.	1.36
Maximum	S.F.	2.10

10350.10 FLAGPOLES

	Unit	Total
Installed in concrete base		
Fiberglass		
25' high	EA.	1,750
50' high	EA.	4,700
Aluminum		
25' high	EA.	1,750
50' high	EA.	3,700
Bonderized steel		
25' high	EA.	2,000
50' high	EA.	4,200
Freestanding tapered, fiberglass		
30' high	EA.	2,100
40' high	EA.	2,700

10800.10 BATH ACCESSORIES

	Unit	Total
Grab bar, 1-1/2" dia., stainless steel, wall mounted		
24" long	EA.	74.00
36" long	EA.	81.25
1" dia., stainless steel		
12" long	EA.	53.00
24" long	EA.	67.00
36" long	EA.	82.75
Medicine cabinet, 16 x 22		
Baked enamel, lighted	EA.	150
With mirror, lighted	EA.	230
Mirror, 1/4" plate glass, up to 10 sf	S.F.	15.50
Mirror, stainless steel frame		
18"x24"	EA.	95.75
18"x32"	EA.	110
24"x30"	EA.	120
24"x60"	EA.	410
Soap dish, stainless steel, wall mounted	EA.	170
Toilet tissue dispenser, stainless, wall mounted		
Single roll	EA.	78.50
Towel bar, stainless steel		
18" long	EA.	100
24" long	EA.	140
30" long	EA.	140
36" long	EA.	150
Toothbrush and tumbler holder	EA.	69.00

11010.10 MAINTENANCE EQUIPMENT

	Unit	Total
Vacuum cleaning system, 3 valves		
1.5 hp	EA.	1,550
2.5 hp	EA.	1,950
5 valves	EA.	2,850
7 valves	EA.	3,750

11450.10 RESIDENTIAL EQUIPMENT

	Unit	Total
Compactor, 4 to 1 compaction	EA.	1,500
Dishwasher, built-in, 2 cycles	EA.	960
4 or more cycles	EA.	2,100
Disposal, Garbage disposer	EA.	370
Heaters, electric, built-in, Ceiling type	EA.	570
Wall type		
Minimum	EA.	330
Maximum	EA.	860
Hood for range, 2-speed, vented		
30" wide	EA.	720
42" wide	EA.	1,150
Ice maker, automatic		
30 lb per day	EA.	1,900
50 lb per day	EA.	2,550
Folding access stairs, disappearing metal stair		
8' long	EA.	1,000
11' long	EA.	1,050
12' long	EA.	1,150
Wood frame, wood stair		
22" x 54" x 8'9" long	EA.	240
25" x 54" x 10' long	EA.	280
Ranges electric		
Built-in, 30", 1 oven	EA.	2,150
2 oven	EA.	2,450
Counter top, 4 burner, standard	EA.	1,300
With grill	EA.	3,000
Free standing, 21", 1 oven	EA.	1,200
30", 1 oven	EA.	2,100
2 oven	EA.	3,350
Water softener		
30 grains per gallon	EA.	1,300
70 grains per gallon	EA.	1,700

12302.10 CASEWORK

	Unit	Total
Kitchen base cabinet, standard, 24" deep, 35" high		
12"wide	EA.	250
18" wide	EA.	290
24" wide	EA.	350
27" wide	EA.	390
36" wide	EA.	460
48" wide	EA.	540
Drawer base, 24" deep, 35" high		
15"wide	EA.	310
18" wide	EA.	320
24" wide	EA.	480
27" wide	EA.	540
30" wide	EA.	620
Sink-ready, base cabinet		
30" wide	EA.	320
36" wide	EA.	330
42" wide	EA.	360
60" wide	EA.	420
Corner cabinet, 36" wide	EA.	560
Wall cabinet, 12" deep, 12" high		
30" wide	EA.	310
36" wide	EA.	320
15" high		
30" wide	EA.	350
36" wide	EA.	500
24" high		
30" wide	EA.	380
36" wide	EA.	390
30" high		
12" wide	EA.	250
18" wide	EA.	280
24" wide	EA.	300
27" wide	EA.	340
30" wide	EA.	390
36" wide	EA.	390

12302.10 CASEWORK (Cont.)

	Unit	Total
Corner cabinet, 30" high		
24" wide	EA.	430
30" wide	EA.	500
36" wide	EA.	540
Wardrobe	EA.	1,050
Vanity with top, laminated plastic		
24" wide	EA.	890
30" wide	EA.	980
36" wide	EA.	1,150
48" wide	EA.	1,300

12390.10 COUNTER TOPS

	Unit	Total
Stainless steel, counter top, w/ backsplash	S.F.	240
Acid-proof, kemrock surface	S.F.	100

12500.10 WINDOW TREATMENT

	Unit	Total
Drapery tracks, wall or ceiling mounted		
Basic traverse rod		
50 to 90"	EA.	78.25
84 to 156"	EA.	98.25
136 to 250"	EA.	130
165 to 312"	EA.	190
Traverse rod with stationary curtain rod		
30 to 50"	EA.	100
50 to 90"	EA.	120
84 to 156"	EA.	150
136 to 250"	EA.	190
Double traverse rod		
30 to 50"	EA.	120
50 to 84"	EA.	140
84 to 156"	EA.	150
136 to 250"	EA.	190

12510.10 BLINDS

	Unit	Total
Venetian blinds		
2" slats	S.F.	37.00
1" slats	S.F.	39.50

13056.10 VAULTS

	Unit	Total
Floor safes		
1.0 cf	EA.	890
1.3 cf	EA.	990

13121.10 PRE-ENGINEERED BUILDINGS

	Unit	Total
Pre-engineered metal building, 40'x100'		
14' eave height	S.F.	12.00
16' eave height	S.F.	13.75

13200.10 STORAGE TANKS

	Unit	Total
Oil storage tank, underground, single wall, no excv.		
Steel		
500 gals	EA.	3,800
1,000 gals	EA.	5,150
Fiberglass, double wall		
550 gals	EA.	10,300
1,000 gals	EA.	13,100
Above ground		
Steel, single wall		
275 gals	EA.	2,250
500 gals	EA.	5,350
1,000 gals	EA.	7,300
Fill cap	EA.	180
Vent cap	EA.	180
Level indicator	EA.	250

14410.10 PERSONNEL LIFTS

	Unit	Total
Electrically operated, 1 or 2 person lift		
With attached foot platforms		
3 stops	EA.	10,200
Residential stair climber, per story	EA.	5,300

15100.10 SPECIALTIES

Item	Unit	Total
Wall penetration, Concrete wall, 6" thick		
2" dia.	EA.	14.50
4" dia.	EA.	22.00
12" thick		
2" dia.	EA.	20.00
4" dia.	EA.	31.25

15120.10 BACKFLOW PREVENTERS

Item	Unit	Total
Backflow preventer, flanged, cast iron, with valves		
3" pipe	EA.	3,650
4" pipe	EA.	4,600
Threaded		
3/4" pipe	EA.	720
2" pipe	EA.	1,250

15140.11 PIPE HANGERS, LIGHT

Item	Unit	Total
A band, black iron, 1/2"	EA.	5.39
1"	EA.	5.63
1-1/4"	EA.	5.93
1-1/2"	EA.	6.37
2"	EA.	6.91
2-1/2"	EA.	8.12
3"	EA.	9.24
4"	EA.	10.75
Copper, 1/2"	EA.	6.02
3/4"	EA.	6.44
1"	EA.	6.44
1-1/4"	EA.	6.75
1-1/2"	EA.	7.30
2"	EA.	7.90
2-1/2"	EA.	10.75
3"	EA.	11.75
4"	EA.	13.00
2 hole clips, galvanized, 3/4"	EA.	4.36
1"	EA.	4.54
1-1/4"	EA.	4.77
1-1/2"	EA.	5.02
2"	EA.	5.35
2-1/2"	EA.	6.03
3"	EA.	6.74
4"	EA.	9.05
Perforated strap, 3/4"		
Galvanized, 20 ga.	L.F.	3.48
Copper, 22 ga.	L.F.	3.71
J-Hooks, 1/2"	EA.	3.52
3/4"	EA.	3.58
1"	EA.	3.74
1-1/4"	EA.	3.85
1-1/2"	EA.	3.94
2"	EA.	3.97
3"	EA.	4.27
4"	EA.	4.35
PVC coated hangers, galvanized, 28 ga.		
1-1/2" x 12"	EA.	5.36
2" x 12"	EA.	5.77
3" x 12"	EA.	6.27
4" x 12"	EA.	6.82
Copper, 30 ga.		
1-1/2" x 12"	EA.	6.04
2" x 12"	EA.	6.69
3" x 12"	EA.	7.27
4" x 12"	EA.	7.90
Wire hook hangers, Black wire, 1/2" x		
4"	EA.	3.50
6"	EA.	3.73
Copper wire hooks, 1/2" x		
4"	EA.	3.66
6"	EA.	3.90

15240.10 VIBRATION CONTROL

Item	Unit	Total
Vibration isolator, in-line, stainless connector		
1/2"	EA.	130
3/4"	EA.	150
1"	EA.	150
1-1/4"	EA.	190
1-1/2"	EA.	210
2"	EA.	260
2-1/2"	EA.	360
3"	EA.	420
4"	EA.	520

15290.10 DUCTWORK INSULATION

Item	Unit	Total
Fiberglass duct insulation, plain blanket		
1-1/2" thick	S.F.	.98
2" thick	S.F.	1.30
With vapor barrier		
1-1/2" thick	S.F.	1.01
2" thick	S.F.	1.33
Rigid with vapor barrier		
2" thick	S.F.	3.37

15410.05 C.I. PIPE, ABOVE GROUND

Item	Unit	Total
No hub pipe		
1-1/2" pipe	L.F.	12.75
2" pipe	L.F.	12.50
3" pipe	L.F.	16.25
4" pipe	L.F.	23.50
No hub fittings, 1-1/2" pipe		
1/4 bend	EA.	29.50
1/8 bend	EA.	28.00
Sanitary tee	EA.	43.00
Sanitary cross	EA.	47.50
Plug	EA.	4.91
Coupling	EA.	17.50
Wye	EA.	46.25
Tapped tee	EA.	36.75
P-trap	EA.	34.50
Tapped cross	EA.	39.00
2" pipe		
1/4 bend	EA.	34.75
1/8 bend	EA.	32.75
Sanitary tee	EA.	55.00
Sanitary cross	EA.	64.75
Plug	EA.	4.91
Coupling	EA.	15.50
Wye	EA.	64.50
Double wye	EA.	71.50
2x1-1/2" wye & 1/8 bend	EA.	63.00
Double wye & 1/8 bend	EA.	71.50
Test tee less 2" plug	EA.	37.25
Tapped tee		
2"x2"	EA.	41.00
2"x1-1/2"	EA.	40.00
P-trap		
2"x2"	EA.	39.50
Tapped cross		
2"x1-1/2"	EA.	45.75
3" pipe		
1/4 bend	EA.	44.75
1/8 bend	EA.	42.50
Sanitary tee	EA.	55.75
3"x2" sanitary tee	EA.	54.00
3"x1-1/2" sanitary tee	EA.	54.75
Sanitary cross	EA.	87.75
3x2" sanitary cross	EA.	83.75
Plug	EA.	7.28
Coupling	EA.	17.75
Wye	EA.	70.00
3x2" wye	EA.	65.25
Double wye	EA.	88.75
3x2" double wye	EA.	83.00
3x2" wye & 1/8 bend	EA.	61.50
3x1-1/2" wye & 1/8 bend	EA.	61.50
Double wye & 1/8 bend	EA.	88.75
3x2" double wye & 1/8 bend	EA.	83.00
3x2" reducer	EA.	35.00
Test tee, less 3" plug	EA.	50.25
Plug	EA.	7.28
3x3" tapped tee	EA.	75.50
3x2" tapped tee	EA.	55.00
3x1-1/2" tapped tee	EA.	51.50
P-trap	EA.	63.50
3x2" tapped cross	EA.	61.25
3x1-1/2" tapped cross	EA.	59.50
Closet flange, 3-1/2" deep	EA.	36.00
4" pipe, 1/4 bend	EA.	51.00
1/8 bend	EA.	45.75
Sanitary tee	EA.	77.75
4x3" sanitary tee	EA.	75.75
4x2" sanitary tee	EA.	71.50

15410.05 C.I. PIPE, ABOVE GROUND (Cont.)

	Unit	Total
4" pipe, 1/4 bend	EA.	51.00
Sanitary cross	EA.	130
4x3" sanitary cross	EA.	120
4x2" sanitary cross	EA.	110
Plug	EA.	11.25
Coupling	EA.	17.25
Wye	EA.	81.75
4x3" wye	EA.	77.75
4x2" wye	EA.	70.75
Double wye	EA.	140
4x3" double wye	EA.	110
4x2" double wye	EA.	100
Wye & 1/8 bend	EA.	92.75
4x3" wye & 1/8 bend	EA.	81.50
4x2" wye & 1/8 bend	EA.	74.75
Double wye & 1/8 bend	EA.	170
4x3" double wye & 1/8 bend	EA.	130
4x2" double wye & 1/8 bend	EA.	130
4x3" reducer	EA.	41.75
4x2" reducer	EA.	41.75
Test tee, less 4" plug	EA.	63.75
Plug	EA.	11.25
4x2" tapped tee	EA.	55.00
4x1-1/2" tapped tee	EA.	52.25
P-trap	EA.	87.75
4x2" tapped cross	EA.	74.25
4x1-1/2" tapped cross	EA.	64.75
Closet flange, 3" deep	EA.	53.50
8" deep	EA.	89.25

15410.06 C.I. PIPE, BELOW GROUND

	Unit	Total
No hub pipe		
1-1/2" pipe	L.F.	11.00
2" pipe	L.F.	11.50
3" pipe	L.F.	14.75
4" pipe	L.F.	19.50
Fittings, 1-1/2", 1/4 bend	EA.	26.75
1/8 bend	EA.	25.25
Plug	EA.	4.91
Wye	EA.	37.50
Wye & 1/8 bend	EA.	31.50
P-trap	EA.	33.00
2", 1/4 bend	EA.	30.75
1/8 bend	EA.	29.25
Plug	EA.	4.91
Double wye	EA.	58.75
Wye & 1/8 bend	EA.	45.00
Double wye & 1/8 bend	EA.	73.50
P-trap	EA.	35.50
3", 1/4 bend	EA.	38.50
1/8 bend	EA.	36.25
Plug	EA.	7.28
Wye	EA.	57.25
3x2" wye	EA.	52.50
Wye & 1/8 bend	EA.	61.00
Double wye & 1/8 bend	EA.	92.25
3x2" double wye & 1/8 bend	EA.	79.25
3x2" reducer	EA.	31.50
P-trap	EA.	57.25
4", 1/4 bend	EA.	44.75
1/8 bend	EA.	39.50
Plug	EA.	11.25
Wye	EA.	69.00
4x3" wye	EA.	65.00
4x2" wye	EA.	58.00
Double wye	EA.	130
4x3" double wye	EA.	99.25
4x2" double wye	EA.	93.50
Wye & 1/8 bend	EA.	80.00
4x3" wye & 1/8 bend	EA.	68.75
4x2" wye & 1/8 bend	EA.	62.00
Double wye & 1/8 bend	EA.	160
4x3" double wye & 1/8 bend	EA.	120
4x2" double wye & 1/8 bend	EA.	120
4x3" reducer	EA.	35.50
4x2" reducer	EA.	35.50

15410.10 COPPER PIPE

	Unit	Total
Type "K" copper, 1/2"	L.F.	6.06
3/4"	L.F.	9.77
1"	L.F.	12.25
DWV, copper, 1-1/4"	L.F.	13.75
1-1/2"	L.F.	17.00
2"	L.F.	21.50
3"	L.F.	35.25
4"	L.F.	59.25
6"	L.F.	220
Refrigeration tubing, copper, sealed		
1/8"	L.F.	3.27
3/16"	L.F.	3.50
1/4"	L.F.	3.80
Type "L" copper, 1/4"	L.F.	3.48
3/8"	L.F.	4.38
1/2"	L.F.	4.90
3/4"	L.F.	6.81
1"	L.F.	9.34
Type "M" copper, 1/2"	L.F.	4.03
3/4"	L.F.	5.47
1"	L.F.	7.76
Type "K" tube, coil, 1/4" x 60'	EA.	120
1/2" x 60'	EA.	260
1/2" x 100'	EA.	430
3/4" x 60'	EA.	480
3/4" x 100'	EA.	800
1" x 60'	EA.	630
1" x 100'	EA.	1,050
Type "L" tube, coil, 1/4" x 60'	EA.	130
3/8" x 60'	EA.	210
1/2" x 60'	EA.	280
1/2" x 100'	EA.	460
3/4" x 60'	EA.	440
3/4" x 100'	EA.	740
1" x 60'	EA.	640
1" x 100'	EA.	1,050

15410.11 COPPER FITTINGS

	Unit	Total
Coupling, with stop		
1/4"	EA.	21.50
3/8"	EA.	25.75
1/2"	EA.	27.75
5/8"	EA.	33.50
3/4"	EA.	36.25
1"	EA.	40.25
Reducing coupling		
1/4" x 1/8"	EA.	27.00
3/8" x 1/4"	EA.	29.50
1/2" x		
3/8"	EA.	32.75
1/4"	EA.	33.25
1/8"	EA.	33.50
3/4" x		
3/8"	EA.	38.50
1/2"	EA.	37.75
1" x		
3/8"	EA.	46.25
1" x 1/2"	EA.	46.00
1" x 3/4"	EA.	44.75
Slip coupling		
1/4"	EA.	21.25
1/2"	EA.	25.75
3/4"	EA.	33.50
1"	EA.	39.75
Coupling with drain		
1/2"	EA.	40.25
3/4"	EA.	48.25
1"	EA.	56.00
Reducer		
3/8" x 1/4"	EA.	27.25
1/2" x 3/8"	EA.	26.75
3/4" x		
1/4"	EA.	32.50
3/8"	EA.	32.75
1/2"	EA.	32.75
1" x		
1/2"	EA.	37.50
3/4"	EA.	36.00

15410.11 COPPER FITTINGS (Cont.)

Item	Unit	Total
Female adapters		
1/4"	EA.	31.50
3/8"	EA.	35.25
1/2"	EA.	34.25
3/4"	EA.	39.00
1"	EA.	45.25
Increasing female adapters		
1/8" x		
3/8"	EA.	31.50
1/2"	EA.	31.00
1/4" x 1/2"	EA.	33.50
3/8" x 1/2"	EA.	35.25
1/2" X		
3/4"	EA.	38.50
1"	EA.	46.25
3/4" X		
1"	EA.	50.75
1-1/4"	EA.	62.25
1" x		
1-1/4"	EA.	64.00
1-1/2"	EA.	66.75
Reducing female adapters		
3/8" x 1/4"	EA.	34.25
1/2" x		
1/4"	EA.	36.25
3/8"	EA.	36.25
3/4" x 1/2"	EA.	41.75
1" x		
1/2"	EA.	54.50
3/4"	EA.	50.50
Female fitting adapters		
1/2"	EA.	40.25
3/4"	EA.	43.25
3/4" x 1/2"	EA.	47.00
1"	EA.	50.75
Male adapters		
1/4"	EA.	39.00
3/8"	EA.	33.50
Increasing male adapters		
3/8" x 1/2"	EA.	35.25
1/2" x		
3/4"	EA.	37.25
1"	EA.	45.00
3/4" x		
1"	EA.	46.25
1-1/4"	EA.	50.25
1" x 1-1/4"	EA.	52.25
Reducing male adapters		
1/2" x		
1/4"	EA.	40.00
3/8"	EA.	38.50
3/4" x 1/2"	EA.	41.00
1" x		
1/2"	EA.	58.50
3/4"	EA.	53.75
Fitting x male adapters		
1/2"	EA.	44.25
3/4"	EA.	49.50
1"	EA.	51.75
90 ells		
1/8"	EA.	26.50
1/4"	EA.	27.75
3/8"	EA.	31.00
1/2"	EA.	31.75
3/4"	EA.	34.50
1"	EA.	40.00
Reducing 90 ell		
3/8" x 1/4"	EA.	33.25
1/2" x		
1/4"	EA.	38.25
3/8"	EA.	38.25
3/4" x 1/2"	EA.	38.75
1" x		
1/2"	EA.	45.75
3/4"	EA.	45.00

15410.11 COPPER FITTINGS (Cont.)

Item	Unit	Total
Street ells, copper		
1/4"	EA.	30.00
3/8"	EA.	31.75
1/2"	EA.	32.25
3/4"	EA.	35.50
1"	EA.	42.50
Female, 90 ell		
1/2"	EA.	31.75
3/4"	EA.	34.50
1"	EA.	40.00
Female increasing, 90 ell		
3/8" x 1/2"	EA.	39.50
1/2" x		
3/4"	EA.	38.75
1"	EA.	47.00
3/4" x 1"	EA.	46.75
1" x 1-1/4"	EA.	71.50
Female reducing, 90 ell		
1/2" x 3/8"	EA.	43.50
3/4" x 1/2"	EA.	46.25
1" x		
1/2"	EA.	54.00
3/4"	EA.	55.75
Male, 90 ell		
1/4"	EA.	34.25
3/8"	EA.	38.50
1/2"	EA.	36.25
3/4"	EA.	44.50
1"	EA.	48.50
Male, increasing 90 ell		
1/2" x		
3/4"	EA.	50.00
1"	EA.	69.00
3/4" x 1"	EA.	68.50
1" x 1-1/4"	EA.	67.75
Male, reducing 90 ell		
1/2" x 3/8"	EA.	41.75
3/4" x 1/2"	EA.	51.50
1" x		
1/2"	EA.	70.75
3/4"	EA.	69.00
Drop ear ells		
1/2"	EA.	37.75
Female drop ear ells		
1/2"	EA.	37.75
1/2" x 3/8"	EA.	43.00
3/4"	EA.	52.75
Female flanged sink ell		
1/2"	EA.	43.50
45 ells		
1/4"	EA.	30.25
3/8"	EA.	32.75
45 street ell		
1/4"	EA.	31.00
3/8"	EA.	35.25
1/2"	EA.	32.75
3/4"	EA.	35.50
1"	EA.	42.75
Tee		
1/8"	EA.	29.50
1/4"	EA.	29.75
3/8"	EA.	32.00
Caps		
1/4"	EA.	25.50
3/8"	EA.	29.50
Test caps		
1/2"	EA.	31.50
3/4"	EA.	33.25
1"	EA.	36.00
Flush bushing		
1/4" x 1/8"	EA.	26.25
1/2" x		
1/4"	EA.	33.00
3/8"	EA.	32.75
3/4" x		
3/8"	EA.	36.50
1/2"	EA.	36.00

15410.11 COPPER FITTINGS (Cont.)

	Unit	Total
Flush bushing		
1" x		
1/2"	EA.	40.75
3/4"	EA.	40.00
Female flush bushing		
1/2" x		
1/2" x 1/8"	EA.	36.00
1/4"	EA.	36.25
Union		
1/4"	EA.	57.00
3/8"	EA.	72.50
Female		
1/2"	EA.	46.25
3/4"	EA.	47.75
Male		
1/2"	EA.	47.50
3/4"	EA.	54.50
1"	EA.	82.50
45 degree wye		
1/2"	EA.	51.50
3/4"	EA.	62.00
1"	EA.	74.50
1" x 3/4" x 3/4"	EA.	90.00
Twin ells		
1" x 3/4" x 3/4"	EA.	48.75
1" x 1" x 1"	EA.	48.75
90 union ells, male		
1/2"	EA.	53.25
3/4"	EA.	69.75
1"	EA.	90.25
DWV fittings, coupling with stop		
1-1/4"	EA.	41.50
1-1/2"	EA.	45.00
1-1/2" x 1-1/4"	EA.	48.75
2"	EA.	49.75
2" x 1-1/4"	EA.	53.00
2" x 1-1/2"	EA.	53.00
3"	EA.	68.25
3" x 1-1/2"	EA.	92.25
3" x 2"	EA.	90.25
4"	EA.	120
Slip coupling		
1-1/2"	EA.	48.50
2"	EA.	52.75
3"	EA.	72.75
90 ells		
1-1/2"	EA.	50.50
1-1/2" x 1-1/4"	EA.	71.75
2"	EA.	63.00
2" x 1-1/2"	EA.	85.75
3"	EA.	110
4"	EA.	260
Street, 90 elbows		
1-1/2"	EA.	54.00
2"	EA.	74.75
3"	EA.	140
4"	EA.	280
Female, 90 elbows		
1-1/2"	EA.	53.75
2"	EA.	70.50
Male, 90 elbows		
1-1/2"	EA.	65.50
2"	EA.	96.50
90 with side inlet		
3" x 3" x 1"	EA.	130
3" x 3" x 1-1/2"	EA.	140
3" x 3" x 2"	EA.	140
45 ells		
1-1/4"	EA.	46.25
1-1/2"	EA.	46.75
2"	EA.	60.25
3"	EA.	92.00
4"	EA.	240
Street, 45 ell		
1-1/2"	EA.	52.00
2"	EA.	64.75
3"	EA.	120

15410.11 COPPER FITTINGS (Cont.)

	Unit	Total
60 ell		
1-1/2"	EA.	59.50
2"	EA.	79.50
3"	EA.	140
22-1/2 ell		
1-1/2"	EA.	64.00
2"	EA.	73.75
3"	EA.	110
11-1/4 ell		
1-1/2"	EA.	66.50
2"	EA.	80.75
3"	EA.	130
Wye		
1-1/4"	EA.	79.00
1-1/2"	EA.	85.00
2"	EA.	100
2" x 1-1/2" x 1-1/2"	EA.	110
2" x 1-1/2" x 2"	EA.	120
2" x 1-1/2" x 2"	EA.	120
3"	EA.	200
3" x 3" x 1-1/2"	EA.	180
3" x 3" x 2"	EA.	180
4"	EA.	360
4" x 4" x 2"	EA.	270
4" x 4" x 3"	EA.	270
Sanitary tee		
1-1/4"	EA.	58.00
1-1/2"	EA.	65.50
2"	EA.	72.50
2" x 1-1/2" x 1-1/2"	EA.	91.00
2" x 1-1/2" x 2"	EA.	92.25
2" x 2" x 1-1/2"	EA.	70.75
3"	EA.	160
3" x 3" x 1-1/2"	EA.	140
3" x 3" x 2"	EA.	140
4"	EA.	360
4" x 4" x 3"	EA.	310
Female sanitary tee		
1-1/2"	EA.	90.75
Long turn tee		
1-1/2"	EA.	90.50
2"	EA.	160
3" x 1-1/2"	EA.	200
Double wye		
1-1/2"	EA.	120
2"	EA.	180
2" x 2" x 1-1/2" x 1-1/2"	EA.	150
3"	EA.	270
3" x 3" x 1-1/2" x 1-1/2"	EA.	270
3" x 3" x 2" x 2"	EA.	270
4" x 4" x 1-1/2" x 1-1/2"	EA.	290
Double sanitary tee		
1-1/2"	EA.	91.50
2"	EA.	160
2" x 2" x 1-1/2"	EA.	150
3"	EA.	190
3" x 3" x 1-1/2" x 1-1/2"	EA.	230
3" x 3" x 2" x 2"	EA.	200
4" x 4" x 1-1/2" x 1-1/2"	EA.	390
Long		
2" x 1-1/2"	EA.	180
Twin elbow		
1-1/2"	EA.	110
2"	EA.	150
2" x 1-1/2" x 1-1/2"	EA.	140
Spigot adapter, manoff		
1-1/2" x 2"	EA.	84.00
1-1/2" x 3"	EA.	93.50
2"	EA.	63.50
2" x 3"	EA.	94.00
2" x 4"	EA.	120
3"	EA.	130
3" x 4"	EA.	190
4"	EA.	180

15410.11 COPPER FITTINGS (Cont.)

	Unit	Total
No-hub adapters		
1-1/2" x 2"	EA.	66.00
2"	EA.	67.00
2" x 3"	EA.	100
3"	EA.	100
3" x 4"	EA.	160
4"	EA.	170
Fitting reducers		
1-1/2" x 1-1/4"	EA.	48.25
2" x 1-1/2"	EA.	56.25
3" x 1-1/2"	EA.	94.00
3" x 2"	EA.	89.50
Slip joint (Desanco)		
1-1/4"	EA.	52.50
1-1/2"	EA.	55.50
1-1/2" x 1-1/4"	EA.	56.25
Street x slip joint (Desanco)		
1-1/2"	EA.	59.50
1-1/2" x 1-1/4"	EA.	61.00
Flush bushing		
1-1/2" x 1-1/4"	EA.	50.50
2" x 1-1/2"	EA.	61.75
3" x 1-1/2"	EA.	88.50
3" x 2"	EA.	88.50
Male hex trap bushing		
1-1/4" x 1-1/2"	EA.	54.00
1-1/2"	EA.	51.50
1-1/2" x 2"	EA.	58.00
2"	EA.	56.25
Round trap bushing		
1-1/2"	EA.	53.50
2"	EA.	57.00
Female adapter		
1-1/4"	EA.	53.75
1-1/2"	EA.	65.75
1-1/2" x 2"	EA.	110
2"	EA.	78.00
2" x 1-1/2"	EA.	100
3"	EA.	200
Fitting x female adapter		
1-1/2"	EA.	75.25
2"	EA.	89.75
Male adapters		
1-1/4"	EA.	51.50
1-1/4" x 1-1/2"	EA.	71.75
1-1/2"	EA.	56.00
1-1/2" x 2"	EA.	110
2"	EA.	70.50
2" x 1-1/2"	EA.	110
3"	EA.	200
Male x slip joint adapters		
1-1/2" x 1-1/4"	EA.	66.25
Dandy cleanout		
1-1/2"	EA.	87.75
2"	EA.	99.25
3"	EA.	260
End cleanout, flush pattern		
1-1/2" x 1"	EA.	68.50
2" x 1-1/2"	EA.	77.00
3" x 2-1/2"	EA.	130
Copper caps		
1-1/2"	EA.	48.75
2"	EA.	59.75
Closet flanges		
3"	EA.	95.75
4"	EA.	140
Drum traps, with cleanout		
1-1/2" x 3" x 6"	EA.	210
P-trap, swivel, with cleanout		
1-1/2"	EA.	150
P-trap, solder union		
1-1/2"	EA.	82.50
2"	EA.	120
With cleanout		
1-1/2"	EA.	87.00
2"	EA.	130
2" x 1-1/2"	EA.	130

15410.11 COPPER FITTINGS (Cont.)

	Unit	Total
Swivel joint, with cleanout		
1-1/2" x 1-1/4"	EA.	100
1-1/2"	EA.	120
2" x 1-1/2"	EA.	140
Estabrook TY, with inlets		
3", with 1-1/2" inlet	EA.	180
Fine thread adapters		
1/2"	EA.	34.25
1/2" x 1/2" IPS	EA.	34.75
1/2" x 3/4" IPS	EA.	37.25
1/2" x male	EA.	33.25
1/2" x female	EA.	35.75
Copper pipe fittings		
1/2"		
90 deg ell	EA.	15.25
45 deg ell	EA.	15.75
Tee	EA.	20.00
Cap	EA.	7.90
Coupling	EA.	15.00
Union	EA.	23.25
3/4"		
90 deg ell	EA.	18.75
45 deg ell	EA.	19.25
Tee	EA.	26.25
Cap	EA.	9.32
Coupling	EA.	17.50
Union	EA.	29.25
1"		
90 deg ell	EA.	28.50
45 deg ell	EA.	30.75
Tee	EA.	37.50
Cap	EA.	14.00
Coupling	EA.	26.25
Union	EA.	35.75

15410.14 BRASS I.P.S. FITTINGS

	Unit	Total
Fittings, iron pipe size, 45 deg ell		
1/8"	EA.	34.25
1/4"	EA.	34.25
3/8"	EA.	37.75
1/2"	EA.	40.50
3/4"	EA.	46.25
1"	EA.	58.00
90 deg ell		
1/8"	EA.	33.75
1/4"	EA.	33.75
3/8"	EA.	37.25
1/2"	EA.	40.00
3/4"	EA.	43.25
1"	EA.	54.00
90 deg ell, reducing		
1/4" x 1/8"	EA.	35.50
3/8" x 1/8"	EA.	39.00
3/8" x 1/4"	EA.	39.00
1/2" x 1/4"	EA.	41.75
1/2" x 3/8"	EA.	41.75
3/4" x 1/2"	EA.	48.25
1" x 3/8"	EA.	57.00
1" x 1/2"	EA.	57.00
1" x 3/4"	EA.	57.00
Street ell, 45 deg		
1/2"	EA.	41.75
3/4"	EA.	48.25
90 deg		
1/8"	EA.	35.50
1/4"	EA.	35.50
3/8"	EA.	39.00
1/2"	EA.	41.75
3/4"	EA.	45.75
1"	EA.	52.00
Tee, 1/8"	EA.	34.00
1/4"	EA.	34.00
3/8"	EA.	37.50
1/2"	EA.	40.25
3/4"	EA.	45.00
1"	EA.	53.00

15410.14 BRASS I.P.S. FITTINGS (Cont.)

Item	Unit	Total
Tee, reducing, 3/8" x		
1/4"	EA.	41.00
1/2"	EA.	41.00
1/2" x		
1/4"	EA.	43.75
3/8"	EA.	43.75
3/4"	EA.	46.00
3/4" x		
1/4"	EA.	47.50
1/2"	EA.	47.50
1"	EA.	63.00
1" x		
1/2"	EA.	64.75
3/4"	EA.	64.75
Tee, reducing		
1/2" x 3/8" x 1/2"	EA.	42.50
3/4" x 1/2" x 1/2"	EA.	49.25
3/4" x 1/2" x 3/4"	EA.	48.25
1" x 1/2" x 1/2"	EA.	63.75
1" x 1/2" x 3/4"	EA.	63.75
1" x 3/4" x 1/2"	EA.	70.25
1" x 3/4" x 3/4"	EA.	63.75
Union		
1/8"	EA.	49.00
1/4"	EA.	49.00
3/8"	EA.	52.50
1/2"	EA.	55.25
3/4"	EA.	66.00
1"	EA.	79.25
Brass face bushing		
3/8" x 1/4"	EA.	36.50
1/2" x 3/8"	EA.	39.25
3/4" x 1/2"	EA.	42.75
1" x 3/4"	EA.	52.25
Hex bushing, 1/4" x 1/8"	EA.	30.50
1/2" x		
1/4"	EA.	36.25
3/8"	EA.	36.25
5/8" x		
1/8"	EA.	36.25
1/4"	EA.	36.25
3/4" x		
1/8"	EA.	40.25
1/4"	EA.	40.25
3/8"	EA.	39.25
1/2"	EA.	39.25
1" x		
1/4"	EA.	44.75
3/8"	EA.	44.75
1/2"	EA.	44.00
3/4"	EA.	44.00
Caps, 1/8"	EA.	30.00
1/4"	EA.	30.50
3/8"	EA.	34.00
1/2"	EA.	36.75
3/4"	EA.	38.50
1"	EA.	45.50
Couplings, 1/8"	EA.	30.75
1/4"	EA.	30.75
3/8"	EA.	34.25
1/2"	EA.	37.00
3/4"	EA.	41.00
1"	EA.	48.00
Couplings, reducing, 1/4" x 1/8"	EA.	32.00
3/8" x		
1/8"	EA.	35.50
1/4"	EA.	35.50
1/2" x		
1/8"	EA.	40.00
1/4"	EA.	38.75
3/8"	EA.	38.75
3/4" x		
1/4"	EA.	45.00
3/8"	EA.	42.75
1/2"	EA.	42.75
1" x		
1/2"	EA.	47.00
3/4"	EA.	47.00

15410.14 BRASS I.P.S. FITTINGS (Cont.)

Item	Unit	Total
Square head plug, solid		
1/8"	EA.	30.75
1/4"	EA.	30.75
3/8"	EA.	34.25
1/2"	EA.	37.00
3/4"	EA.	39.75
Cored		
1/2"	EA.	35.75
3/4"	EA.	38.50
1"	EA.	44.25
Countersunk		
1/2"	EA.	37.75
3/4"	EA.	39.50
Locknut		
3/4"	EA.	38.50
1"	EA.	42.00
Close standard red nipple, 1/8"	EA.	26.50
1/8" x		
1-1/2"	EA.	28.25
2"	EA.	28.50
2-1/2"	EA.	29.25
3"	EA.	29.75
3-1/2"	EA.	30.75
4"	EA.	31.25
4-1/2"	EA.	31.50
5"	EA.	32.00
5-1/2"	EA.	33.25
6"	EA.	33.75
1/4" x close	EA.	28.50
1/4" x		
1-1/2"	EA.	30.50
2"	EA.	31.00
2-1/2"	EA.	31.25
3"	EA.	31.50
3-1/2"	EA.	32.50
4"	EA.	32.75
4-1/2"	EA.	33.25
5"	EA.	33.50
5-1/2"	EA.	34.50
6"	EA.	34.75
3/8" x close	EA.	32.00
3/8" x		
1-1/2"	EA.	32.75
2"	EA.	33.25
2-1/2"	EA.	34.50
3"	EA.	35.75
3-1/2"	EA.	36.50
4"	EA.	39.00
4-1/2"	EA.	39.25
5"	EA.	40.00
5-1/2"	EA.	40.75
6"	EA.	42.50
1/2" x close	EA.	36.25
1/2" x		
1-1/2"	EA.	36.75
2"	EA.	38.25
2-1/2"	EA.	39.25
3"	EA.	40.50
3-1/2"	EA.	41.50
4"	EA.	42.00
4-1/2"	EA.	42.75
5"	EA.	43.00
5-1/2"	EA.	43.50
6"	EA.	44.75
7-1/2"	EA.	73.00
8"	EA.	73.00
3/4" x close	EA.	47.25
3/4" x		
1-1/2"	EA.	40.75
2"	EA.	42.00
2-1/2"	EA.	43.00
3"	EA.	43.75
3-1/2"	EA.	45.00
4"	EA.	45.75
4-1/2"	EA.	46.75
5"	EA.	47.25
5-1/2"	EA.	49.25
6"	EA.	50.00
1" x close	EA.	46.25

15410.14 BRASS I.P.S. FITTINGS (Cont.)

Item	Unit	Total
1" x 2"	EA.	51.75
2-1/2"	EA.	52.00
3"	EA.	52.75
3-1/2"	EA.	53.50
4"	EA.	55.25
4-1/2"	EA.	55.50
5"	EA.	59.00
5-1/2"	EA.	59.75
6"	EA.	62.25

15410.15 BRASS FITTINGS

Item	Unit	Total
Compression fittings, union		
3/8"	EA.	13.75
1/2"	EA.	16.00
5/8"	EA.	17.00
Union elbow		
3/8"	EA.	12.75
1/2"	EA.	13.75
5/8"	EA.	14.75
Union tee		
3/8"	EA.	13.25
1/2"	EA.	14.50
5/8"	EA.	15.50
Male connector		
3/8"	EA.	12.75
1/2"	EA.	12.25
5/8"	EA.	12.00
Female connector		
3/8"	EA.	12.50
1/2"	EA.	13.00
5/8"	EA.	13.50
Brass flare fittings, union		
3/8"	EA.	12.00
1/2"	EA.	12.75
5/8"	EA.	12.75
90 deg elbow union		
3/8"	EA.	13.75
1/2"	EA.	16.25
5/8"	EA.	19.25
Three way tee		
3/8"	EA.	20.75
1/2"	EA.	22.25
5/8"	EA.	26.00
Cross		
3/8"	EA.	31.00
1/2"	EA.	41.50
5/8"	EA.	63.00
Sleeve		
1/8"	EA.	12.50
1/4"	EA.	12.25
5/16"	EA.	12.50
3/8"	EA.	12.50
1/2"	EA.	12.50
5/8"	EA.	12.75
Tee		
1/4"	EA.	20.50
5/16"	EA.	22.00
Male tee		
5/16" x 1/8"	EA.	23.75
Female union, 1/8" x 1/8"	EA.	16.75
1/4" x 3/8"	EA.	18.25
3/8" x 1/4"	EA.	17.75
3/8" x 1/2"	EA.	18.25
5/8" x 1/2"	EA.	22.25
Male union, 1/4"		
1/4" x 1/4"	EA.	16.75
3/8"	EA.	17.25
1/2"	EA.	18.00
5/16" x		
1/8"	EA.	16.75
1/4"	EA.	17.00
3/8"	EA.	18.00
3/8" x		
1/8"	EA.	17.00
1/4"	EA.	17.25
1/2"	EA.	17.75
5/8" x		
3/8"	EA.	21.25
1/2"	EA.	20.75

15410.15 BRASS FITTINGS (Cont.)

Item	Unit	Total
Female elbow, 1/4" x 1/4"	EA.	21.00
5/16" x		
1/8"	EA.	21.50
1/4"	EA.	22.50
3/8" x		
3/8"	EA.	20.75
1/2"	EA.	20.00
Male elbow, 1/8" x 1/8"	EA.	21.00
3/16" x 1/4"	EA.	20.75
1/4" x 1/8"	EA.	19.50
1/4"	EA.	19.75
3/8"	EA.	19.50
5/16" x 1/8"	EA.	19.50
1/4"	EA.	20.00
3/8"	EA.	21.00
3/8" x 1/8"	EA.	19.50
1/4"	EA.	20.25
3/8"	EA.	19.50
1/2"	EA.	20.25
1/2" x 1/4"	EA.	25.00
3/8"	EA.	24.50
1/2"	EA.	24.00
5/8" x 3/8"	EA.	25.00
1/2"	EA.	25.25
3/4"	EA.	30.00
Union, 1/8"	EA.	19.50
3/16"	EA.	19.50
1/4"	EA.	19.25
5/16"	EA.	19.50
3/8"	EA.	19.75
Reducing union, 3/8" x 1/4"	EA.	23.00
5/8" x		
3/8"	EA.	24.25
1/2"	EA.	24.75

15410.17 CHROME PLATED FITTINGS

Item	Unit	Total
Fittings		
90 ell, 3/8"	EA.	42.75
1/2"	EA.	50.75
45 ell, 3/8"	EA.	50.75
1/2"	EA.	62.00
Tee, 3/8"	EA.	54.50
1/2"	EA.	61.00
Fittings, Coupling, 3/8"	EA.	36.75
1/2"	EA.	36.75
Union, 3/8"	EA.	50.75
1/2"	EA.	52.00
Tee, 1/2" x 3/8" x 3/8"	EA.	61.00
1/2" x 3/8" x 1/2"	EA.	61.75

15410.30 PVC/CPVC PIPE

Item	Unit	Total
PVC schedule 40		
1/2" pipe	L.F.	3.07
3/4" pipe	L.F.	3.49
1" pipe	L.F.	3.96
1-1/4" pipe	L.F.	4.55
1-1/2" pipe	L.F.	5.55
2" pipe	L.F.	6.54
2-1/2" pipe	L.F.	8.60
3" pipe	L.F.	10.50
4" pipe	L.F.	14.00
Fittings, 1/2"		
90 deg ell	EA.	8.16
45 deg ell	EA.	8.34
Tee	EA.	9.28
Reducing insert	EA.	10.75
Threaded	EA.	8.87
Male adapter	EA.	10.75
Female adapter	EA.	8.19
Coupling	EA.	8.05
Union	EA.	16.25
Cap	EA.	10.75
Flange	EA.	20.50
3/4"		
90 deg elbow	EA.	10.75
45 deg elbow	EA.	11.25
Tee	EA.	13.00
Reducing insert	EA.	9.25
Threaded	EA.	11.00

15410.30 PVC/CPVC PIPE (Cont.)

Item	Unit	Total
1"		
90 deg elbow	EA.	13.00
45 deg elbow	EA.	13.50
Tee	EA.	14.75
Reducing insert	EA.	13.00
Threaded	EA.	14.75
Male adapter	EA.	16.00
Female adapter	EA.	16.00
Coupling	EA.	15.75
Union	EA.	26.50
Cap	EA.	13.00
Flange	EA.	29.00
1-1/4"		
90 deg elbow	EA.	19.00
45 deg elbow	EA.	19.25
Tee	EA.	22.25
Reducing insert	EA.	21.50
Threaded	EA.	22.25
Female adapter	EA.	21.50
Coupling	EA.	21.50
Union	EA.	38.00
Cap	EA.	21.50
Flange	EA.	33.00
1-1/2"		
90 deg elbow	EA.	19.00
45 deg elbow	EA.	19.75
Tee	EA.	22.75
Reducing insert	EA.	21.50
Threaded	EA.	22.50
Male adapter	EA.	21.75
Female adapter	EA.	21.75
Coupling	EA.	21.50
Union	EA.	49.50
Cap	EA.	21.50
Flange	EA.	45.25
2"		
90 deg elbow	EA.	23.00
45 deg elbow	EA.	23.75
Tee	EA.	27.75
Reducing insert	EA.	26.75
Threaded	EA.	27.25
Male adapter	EA.	26.25
Female adapter	EA.	26.25
Coupling	EA.	26.00
Union	EA.	64.00
Cap	EA.	26.00
Flange	EA.	53.75
2-1/2"		
90 deg elbow	EA.	46.25
45 deg elbow	EA.	49.50
Tee	EA.	50.75
Reducing insert	EA.	44.00
Threaded	EA.	45.50
Male adapter	EA.	46.00
Female adapter	EA.	45.25
Coupling	EA.	44.00
Union	EA.	85.25
Cap	EA.	42.50
Flange	EA.	71.75
3"		
90 deg elbow	EA.	59.50
45 deg elbow	EA.	62.00
Tee	EA.	69.00
Reducing insert	EA.	55.25
Threaded	EA.	56.25
Male adapter	EA.	57.50
Female adapter	EA.	56.25
Coupling	EA.	56.00
Union	EA.	97.25
Cap	EA.	55.25
Flange	EA.	80.25

15410.30 PVC/CPVC PIPE (Cont.)

Item	Unit	Total
4"		
90 deg elbow	EA.	76.25
45 deg elbow	EA.	80.75
Tee	EA.	90.25
Reducing insert	EA.	70.50
Threaded	EA.	73.00
Male adapter	EA.	69.50
Female adapter	EA.	70.00
Coupling	EA.	68.25
Union	EA.	120
Cap	EA.	70.75
Flange	EA.	100
PVC schedule 80 pipe		
1-1/2" pipe	L.F.	5.99
2" pipe	L.F.	7.30
3" pipe	L.F.	12.25
4" pipe	L.F.	15.50
Fittings, 1-1/2"		
90 deg elbow	EA.	27.25
45 deg elbow	EA.	35.25
Tee	EA.	53.75
Reducing insert	EA.	24.75
Threaded	EA.	25.50
Male adapter	EA.	28.50
Female adapter	EA.	29.25
Coupling	EA.	29.75
Union	EA.	47.50
Cap	EA.	25.25
Flange	EA.	41.75
2"		
90 deg elbow	EA.	32.50
45 deg elbow	EA.	43.50
Tee	EA.	67.25
Reducing insert	EA.	30.50
Threaded	EA.	30.50
Male adapter	EA.	35.50
Female adapter	EA.	39.75
2-1/2"		
90 deg elbow	EA.	57.50
45 deg elbow	EA.	78.50
Tee	EA.	82.50
Reducing insert	EA.	49.00
Threaded	EA.	51.50
Male adapter	EA.	51.75
Female adapter	EA.	62.50
Coupling	EA.	51.50
Union	EA.	87.25
Cap	EA.	53.75
Flange	EA.	70.50
3"		
90 deg elbow	EA.	68.25
45 deg elbow	EA.	100.00
Tee	EA.	100
Reducing insert	EA.	68.00
Threaded	EA.	75.50
Male adapter	EA.	66.00
Female adapter	EA.	78.25
Coupling	EA.	66.00
Union	EA.	110
Cap	EA.	70.50
Flange	EA.	83.50
4"		
90 deg elbow	EA.	110
45 deg elbow	EA.	150
Tee	EA.	120
Reducing insert	EA.	84.50
Threaded	EA.	98.75
Male adapter	EA.	87.50
Coupling	EA.	80.00
Union	EA.	120
Cap	EA.	85.00
Flange	EA.	76.75
CPVC schedule 40		
1/2" pipe	L.F.	3.18
3/4" pipe	L.F.	3.62
1" pipe	L.F.	4.27
1-1/4" pipe	L.F.	4.98
1-1/2" pipe	L.F.	5.74
2" pipe	L.F.	6.92

15410.30 PVC/CPVC PIPE (Cont.)

Item	Unit	Total
Fittings, CPVC, schedule 80		
1/2", 90 deg ell	EA.	9.58
Tee	EA.	20.75
3/4", 90 deg ell	EA.	10.50
Tee	EA.	25.75
1", 90 deg ell	EA.	14.00
Tee	EA.	27.75
1-1/4", 90 deg ell	EA.	19.75
Tee	EA.	26.75
1-1/2", 90 deg ell	EA.	26.50
Tee	EA.	32.75
2", 90 deg ell	EA.	27.75
Tee	EA.	35.00

15410.33 ABS DWV PIPE

Item	Unit	Total
Schedule 40 ABS		
1-1/2" pipe	L.F.	4.32
2" pipe	L.F.	5.08
3" pipe	L.F.	7.81
4" pipe	L.F.	11.00
Fittings, 1/8 bend		
1-1/2"	EA.	14.00
2"	EA.	18.00
3"	EA.	27.00
4"	EA.	36.00
Tee, sanitary, 1-1/2"	EA.	23.25
2"	EA.	28.50
3"	EA.	41.75
4"	EA.	58.75
Tee, sanitary reducing		
2 x 1-1/2 x 1-1/2	EA.	28.25
2 x 1-1/2 x 2	EA.	29.25
2 x 2 x 1-1/2	EA.	31.50
3 x 3 x 1-1/2	EA.	37.25
3 x 3 x 2	EA.	42.25
4 x 4 x 1-1/2	EA.	58.75
4 x 4 x 2	EA.	62.75
4 x 4 x 3	EA.	63.75
Wye		
1-1/2"	EA.	21.25
2"	EA.	30.00
3"	EA.	43.00
4"	EA.	65.00
Reducer		
2 x 1-1/2	EA.	17.75
3 x 1-1/2	EA.	27.25
3 x 2	EA.	26.25
4 x 2	EA.	36.00
4 x 3	EA.	36.25
P-trap		
1-1/2"	EA.	26.50
2"	EA.	30.75
3"	EA.	57.75
4"	EA.	94.25
Double sanitary, tee		
1-1/2"	EA.	30.25
2"	EA.	39.25
3"	EA.	61.75
4"	EA.	88.25
Long sweep, 1/4 bend		
1-1/2"	EA.	15.25
2"	EA.	19.00
3"	EA.	29.75
4"	EA.	47.75
Wye, standard		
1-1/2"	EA.	24.50
2"	EA.	30.00
3"	EA.	43.25
4"	EA.	65.00
Wye, reducing		
2 x 1-1/2 x 1-1/2	EA.	27.75
2 x 2 x 1-1/2	EA.	31.50
4 x 4 x 2	EA.	53.25
4 x 4 x 3	EA.	61.00

15410.33 ABS DWV PIPE (Cont.)

Item	Unit	Total
Double wye		
1-1/2"	EA.	33.25
2"	EA.	41.25
3"	EA.	65.50
4"	EA.	110
2 x 2 x 1-1/2 x 1-1/2	EA.	41.25
3 x 3 x 2 x 2	EA.	60.50
4 x 4 x 3 x 3	EA.	100
Combination wye and 1/8 bend		
1-1/2"	EA.	26.75
2"	EA.	32.00
3"	EA.	46.75
4"	EA.	71.25
2 x 2 x 1-1/2	EA.	31.00
3 x 3 x 1-1/2	EA.	46.00
3 x 3 x 2	EA.	41.50
4 x 4 x 2	EA.	59.50
4 x 4 x 3	EA.	64.25

15410.80 STEEL PIPE

Item	Unit	Total
Black steel, extra heavy pipe, threaded		
1/2" pipe	L.F.	5.05
3/4" pipe	L.F.	5.81
Fittings, malleable iron, threaded, 1/2" pipe		
90 deg ell	EA.	23.75
45 deg ell	EA.	25.00
Tee	EA.	34.25
Reducing tee	EA.	38.75
Cap	EA.	15.00
Coupling	EA.	28.25
Union	EA.	36.00
Nipple, 4" long	EA.	23.50
3/4" pipe		
90 deg ell	EA.	24.25
45 deg ell	EA.	36.75
Tee	EA.	35.75
Reducing tee	EA.	29.25
Cap	EA.	16.00
Coupling	EA.	24.75
Union	EA.	38.00
Nipple, 4" long	EA.	23.75
Cast iron fittings, 1/2" pipe		
90 deg. ell	EA.	24.75
45 deg. ell	EA.	29.25
Tee	EA.	36.50
Reducing tee	EA.	41.50
3/4" pipe		
90 deg. ell	EA.	25.00
45 deg. ell	EA.	26.25
Tee	EA.	37.75
Reducing tee	EA.	40.00

15410.82 GALVANIZED STEEL PIPE

Item	Unit	Total
Galvanized pipe		
1/2" pipe	L.F.	9.66
3/4" pipe	L.F.	12.25
90 degree ell, 150 lb malleable iron, galvanized		
1/2"	EA.	14.50
3/4"	EA.	18.50
45 degree ell, 150 lb m.i., galv.		
1/2"	EA.	16.00
3/4"	EA.	20.50
Tees, straight, 150 lb m.i., galv.		
1/2"	EA.	18.50
3/4"	EA.	22.75
Tees, reducing, out, 150 lb m.i., galv.		
1/2"	EA.	20.75
3/4"	EA.	23.75
Couplings, straight, 150 lb m.i., galv.		
1/2"	EA.	15.25
3/4"	EA.	17.25
Couplings, reducing, 150 lb m.i., galv		
1/2"	EA.	15.75
3/4"	EA.	17.50
Caps, 150 lb m.i., galv.		
1/2"	EA.	8.56
3/4"	EA.	9.66
Unions, 150 lb m.i., galv.		
1/2"	EA.	28.75
3/4"	EA.	32.75

15410.82 GALVANIZED STEEL PIPE (Cont.)

Item	Unit	Total
Nipples, galvanized steel, 4" long		
1/2"	EA.	11.25
3/4"	EA.	12.75
90 degree reducing ell, 150 lb m.i., galv.		
3/4" x 1/2"	EA.	16.00
1" x 3/4"	EA.	19.00
Square head plug (C.I.)		
1/2"	EA.	9.23
3/4"	EA.	13.00

15430.23 CLEANOUTS

Item	Unit	Total
Cleanout, wall		
2"	EA.	250
3"	EA.	330
4"	EA.	350
Floor		
2"	EA.	240
3"	EA.	300
4"	EA.	320

15430.25 HOSE BIBBS

Item	Unit	Total
Hose bibb, 1/2"	EA.	29.50
3/4"	EA.	30.00

15430.60 VALVES

Item	Unit	Total
Gate valve, 125 lb, bronze, soldered		
1/2"	EA.	43.75
3/4"	EA.	49.25
Threaded, 1/4", 125 lb	EA.	57.25
1/2"		
125 lb	EA.	55.75
150 lb	EA.	66.25
300 lb	EA.	100
3/4"		
125 lb	EA.	61.25
150 lb	EA.	74.25
300 lb	EA.	120
Check valve, bronze, soldered, 125 lb		
1/2"	EA.	69.25
3/4"	EA.	82.00
Threaded, 1/2", 125 lb	EA.	83.00
150 lb	EA.	78.75
200 lb	EA.	81.00
3/4", 125 lb	EA.	71.00
150 lb	EA.	97.00
200 lb	EA.	110
Vertical check valve, bronze, 125 lb, threaded		
1/2"	EA.	96.00
3/4"	EA.	130
Globe valve, bronze, soldered, 125 lb		
1/2"	EA.	83.75
3/4"	EA.	100
Threaded, 1/2", 125 lb	EA.	81.00
150 lb	EA.	100
300 lb	EA.	170
3/4", 125 lb	EA.	110
150 lb	EA.	120
300 lb	EA.	200
Ball valve, bronze, 250 lb, threaded, 1/2"	EA.	43.00
3/4"	EA.	52.25
Angle valve, bronze, 150 lb, threaded, 1/2"	EA.	110
3/4"	EA.	140
Balancing valve, meter connections, circuit setter		
1/2"	EA.	110
3/4"	EA.	110
Balancing valve, straight type, 1/2"	EA.	46.75
3/4"	EA.	51.50
Angle type, 1/2"	EA.	54.50
3/4"	EA.	66.00
Square head cock, 125 lb, bronze body		
1/2"	EA.	38.00
3/4"	EA.	45.50
Radiator temp control valve, with control and sensor		
1/2" valve	EA.	160
Pressure relief valve, 1/2", bronze		
Low pressure	EA.	52.50
High pressure	EA.	57.25

15430.60 VALVES (Cont.)

Item	Unit	Total
Pressure and temperature relief valve		
Bronze, 3/4"	EA.	120
Cast iron, 3/4"		
High pressure	EA.	73.00
Temperature relief	EA.	90.00
Pressure & temp relief valve	EA.	100
Pressure reducing valve, bronze, threaded, 250 lb		
1/2"	EA.	210
3/4"	EA.	210
Solar water temperature regulating valve		
3/4"	EA.	690
Tempering valve, threaded		
3/4"	EA.	370
Thermostatic mixing valve, threaded, 1/2"	EA.	140
3/4"	EA.	140
Sweat connection, 1/2"	EA.	150
3/4"	EA.	190
Mixing valve, sweat connection, 1/2"	EA.	94.25
3/4"	EA.	96.75
Liquid level gauge, aluminum body		
3/4"	EA.	380
4125 psi, pvc body, 3/4"	EA.	450
150 psi, crs body, 3/4"	EA.	360
175 psi, bronze body, 1/2"	EA.	710

15430.65 VACUUM BREAKERS

Item	Unit	Total
Vacuum breaker, atmospheric, threaded connection		
3/4"	EA.	70.25
Anti-siphon, brass, 3/4"	EA.	74.00

15430.68 STRAINERS

Item	Unit	Total
Strainer, Y pattern, 125 psi, cast iron body, threaded		
3/4"	EA.	33.50
250 psi, brass body, threaded, 3/4"	EA.	54.25
Cast iron body, threaded, 3/4"	EA.	42.00

15430.70 DRAINS, ROOF & FLOOR

Item	Unit	Total
Floor drain, cast iron, w/ cast iron top, 2"	EA.	200
3"	EA.	200
4"	EA.	370
Roof drain, cast iron, 2"	EA.	280
3"	EA.	290
4"	EA.	350

15430.80 TRAPS

Item	Unit	Total
Bucket trap, threaded, 3/4"	EA.	250
Inverted bucket steam trap, threaded, 3/4"	EA.	290
With stainless interior		
1/2"	EA.	200
3/4"	EA.	220
Brass interior, 3/4"	EA.	320
Cast steel body, threaded, high temperature		
3/4"	EA.	770
Float trap, 15 psi		
3/4"	EA.	220
Float and thermostatic trap, 15 psi		
3/4"	EA.	230
Steam trap, cast iron body, threaded, 125 psi		
3/4"	EA.	270
Thermostatic trap, low pressure, angle type, 25 psi		
1/2"	EA.	110
3/4"	EA.	160
Cast iron body, threaded, 125 psi		
3/4"	EA.	200

15440.10 BATHS

Item	Unit	Total
Bath tub, 5' long, Minimum	EA.	740
Average	EA.	1,450
Maximum	EA.	3,250
6' long, Minimum	EA.	800
Average	EA.	1,500
Maximum	EA.	4,000
Square tub, whirlpool, 4'x4', Minimum	EA.	2,100
Average	EA.	3,150
Maximum	EA.	8,600
5'x5', Minimum	EA.	2,100
Average	EA.	3,150
Maximum	EA.	8,750
6'x6', Minimum	EA.	2,500
Average	EA.	3,850
Maximum	EA.	10,000

	Unit	Total
15440.10 BATHS (Cont.)		
For trim and rough-in, Minimum	EA.	400
Average	EA.	590
Maximum	EA.	1,400
15440.12 DISPOSALS & ACCESSORIES		
Continuous feed, Minimum	EA.	190
Average	EA.	350
Maximum	EA.	600
Batch feed, 1/2 hp, Minimum	EA.	400
Average	EA.	700
Maximum	EA.	1,150
Hot water dispenser, Minimum	EA.	320
Average	EA.	470
Maximum	EA.	720
Epoxy finish faucet	EA.	410
Lock stop assembly	EA.	140
Mounting gasket	EA.	58.25
Tailpipe gasket	EA.	52.25
Stopper assembly	EA.	85.50
Switch assembly, on/off	EA.	130
Tailpipe gasket washer	EA.	31.75
Stop gasket	EA.	36.75
Tailpipe flange	EA.	31.00
Tailpipe	EA.	41.75
15440.15 FAUCETS		
Kitchen, Minimum	EA.	180
Average	EA.	350
Maximum	EA.	440
Bath, Minimum	EA.	180
Average	EA.	360
Maximum	EA.	520
Lavatory, domestic, Minimum	EA.	190
Average	EA.	400
Maximum	EA.	610
Washroom, Minimum	EA.	210
Average	EA.	400
Maximum	EA.	660
Handicapped, Minimum	EA.	240
Average	EA.	510
Maximum	EA.	770
Shower, Minimum	EA.	210
Average	EA.	440
Maximum	EA.	660
For trim and rough-in		
Minimum	EA.	200
Average	EA.	270
Maximum	EA.	510
15440.18 HYDRANTS		
Wall hydrant		
8" thick	EA.	460
12" thick	EA.	550
15440.20 LAVATORIES		
Lavatory, counter top, porcelain enamel on cast iron		
Minimum	EA.	310
Average	EA.	440
Maximum	EA.	730
Wall hung, china		
Minimum	EA.	380
Average	EA.	460
Maximum	EA.	980
Handicapped		
Minimum	EA.	580
Average	EA.	710
Maximum	EA.	1,150
For trim and rough-in		
Minimum	EA.	370
Average	EA.	580
Maximum	EA.	770
15440.30 SHOWERS		
Shower, fiberglass, 36"x34"x84"		
Minimum	EA.	1,000
Average	EA.	1,400
Maximum	EA.	1,750
Steel, 1 piece, 36"x36"		
Minimum	EA.	970
Average	EA.	1,400
Maximum	EA.	1,550

	Unit	Total
15440.30 SHOWERS (Cont.)		
Receptor, molded stone, 36"x36"		
Minimum	EA.	430
Average	EA.	680
Maximum	EA.	1,100
For trim and rough-in		
Minimum	EA.	500
Average	EA.	710
Maximum	EA.	1,050
15440.40 SINKS		
Service sink, 24"x29"		
Minimum	EA.	790
Average	EA.	1000
Maximum	EA.	1,450
Kitchen sink, single, stainless steel, single bowl		
Minimum	EA.	400
Average	EA.	470
Maximum	EA.	790
Double bowl		
Minimum	EA.	470
Average	EA.	570
Maximum	EA.	930
Porcelain enamel, cast iron, single bowl		
Minimum	EA.	320
Average	EA.	410
Maximum	EA.	620
Double bowl		
Minimum	EA.	430
Average	EA.	600
Maximum	EA.	860
Mop sink, 24"x36"x10"		
Minimum	EA.	600
Average	EA.	730
Maximum	EA.	990
Washing machine box		
Minimum	EA.	330
Average	EA.	460
Maximum	EA.	620
For trim and rough-in		
Minimum	EA.	500
Average	EA.	750
Maximum	EA.	970
15440.60 WATER CLOSETS		
Water closet flush tank, floor mounted		
Minimum	EA.	480
Average	EA.	860
Maximum	EA.	1,300
Handicapped		
Minimum	EA.	580
Average	EA.	980
Maximum	EA.	1,900
For trim and rough-in		
Minimum	EA.	360
Average	EA.	460
Maximum	EA.	640
15440.70 WATER HEATERS		
Water heater, electric, 6 gal	EA.	510
10 gal	EA.	520
15 gal	EA.	510
20 gal	EA.	700
30 gal	EA.	720
40 gal	EA.	770
52 gal	EA.	880
Oil fired		
20 gal	EA.	1,600
50 gal	EA.	2,450
15450.40 STORAGE TANKS		
Hot water storage tank, cement lined		
10 gallon	EA.	700
70 gallon	EA.	1,850

	Unit	Total
15555.10 BOILERS		
Cast iron, gas fired, hot water		
115 mbh	EA.	4,600
175 mbh	EA.	5,300
235 mbh	EA.	6,350
Steam		
115 mbh	EA.	4,850
175 mbh	EA.	5,650
235 mbh	EA.	6,500
Electric, hot water		
115 mbh	EA.	5,850
175 mbh	EA.	6,350
235 mbh	EA.	7,050
Steam		
115 mbh	EA.	7,050
175 mbh	EA.	8,400
235 mbh	EA.	9,050
Oil fired, hot water		
115 mbh	EA.	5,050
175 mbh	EA.	6,200
235 mbh	EA.	8,200
Steam		
115 mbh	EA.	5,050
175 mbh	EA.	6,200
235 mbh	EA.	7,750
15610.10 FURNACES		
Electric, hot air		
40 mbh	EA.	1,100
60 mbh	EA.	1,200
80 mbh	EA.	1,300
100 mbh	EA.	1,450
125 mbh	EA.	1,650
Gas fired hot air		
40 mbh	EA.	1,100
60 mbh	EA.	1,200
80 mbh	EA.	1,350
100 mbh	EA.	1,400
125 mbh	EA.	1,500
Oil fired hot air		
40 mbh	EA.	1,400
60 mbh	EA.	2,100
80 mbh	EA.	2,150
100 mbh	EA.	2,200
125 mbh	EA.	2,250
15670.10 CONDENSING UNITS		
Air cooled condenser, single circuit		
3 ton	EA.	1,750
5 ton	EA.	2,700
With low ambient dampers, 3 ton	EA.	2,050
5 ton	EA.	3,100
15780.20 ROOFTOP UNITS		
Packaged, single zone rooftop unit, with roof curb		
2 ton	EA.	4,350
3 ton	EA.	4,550
4 ton	EA.	5,050
15830.10 RADIATION UNITS		
Baseboard radiation unit		
1.7 mbh/lf	L.F.	110
2.1 mbh/lf	L.F.	140
15830.70 UNIT HEATERS		
Steam unit heater, horizontal		
12,500 btuh, 200 cfm	EA.	640
17,000 btuh, 300 cfm	EA.	810
15855.10 AIR HANDLING UNITS		
Air handling unit, medium pressure, single zone		
1500 cfm	EA.	4,400
3000 cfm	EA.	5,950
Rooftop air handling units		
4950 cfm	EA.	12,200
7370 cfm	EA.	15,500
15870.20 EXHAUST FANS		
Belt drive roof exhaust fans		
640 cfm, 2618 fpm	EA.	1,150
940 cfm, 2604 fpm	EA.	1,450

	Unit	Total
15890.10 METAL DUCTWORK		
Rectangular duct		
Galvanized steel		
Minimum	Lb.	6.47
Average	Lb.	7.93
Maximum	Lb.	12.00
Aluminum		
Minimum	Lb.	14.50
Average	Lb.	18.25
Maximum	Lb.	24.25
Fittings		
Minimum	EA.	27.75
Average	EA.	41.75
Maximum	EA.	77.50
15890.30 FLEXIBLE DUCTWORK		
Flexible duct, 1.25" fiberglass		
5" dia.	L.F.	6.38
6" dia.	L.F.	7.09
7" dia.	L.F.	8.15
8" dia.	L.F.	8.60
10" dia.	L.F.	10.75
12" dia.	L.F.	11.75
Flexible duct connector, 3" wide fabric	L.F.	12.50
15910.10 DAMPERS		
Horizontal parallel aluminum backdraft damper		
12" x 12"	EA.	70.25
16" x 16"	EA.	74.25
15940.10 DIFFUSERS		
Ceiling diffusers, round, baked enamel finish		
6" dia.	EA.	57.00
8" dia.	EA.	69.50
10" dia.	EA.	74.25
12" dia.	EA.	88.00
Rectangular		
6x6"	EA.	59.50
9x9"	EA.	78.00
12x12"	EA.	99.75
15x15"	EA.	120
18x18"	EA.	140
15940.40 REGISTERS AND GRILLES		
Lay in flush mounted, perforated face, return		
6x6/24x24	EA.	73.00
8x8/24x24	EA.	73.00
9x9/24x24	EA.	77.25
10x10/24x24	EA.	81.25
12x12/24x24	EA.	81.25
Rectangular, ceiling return, single deflection		
10x10	EA.	60.00
12x12	EA.	64.75
14x14	EA.	72.25
16x8	EA.	64.75
16x16	EA.	64.75
Wall, return air register		
12x12	EA.	63.75
16x16	EA.	86.75
18x18	EA.	99.75
Ceiling, return air grille		
6x6	EA.	48.50
8x8	EA.	59.50
10x10	EA.	67.75
Ceiling, exhaust grille, aluminum egg crate		
6x6	EA.	39.75
8x8	EA.	43.75
10x10	EA.	45.75
12x12	EA.	57.00

16050.30 BUS DUCT

	Unit	Total
Bus duct, 100a, plug-in		
10', 600v	EA.	510
With ground	EA.	710
Circuit breakers, with enclosure		
1 pole		
15a-60a	EA.	380
70a-100a	EA.	440
2 pole		
15a-60a	EA.	530
70a-100a	EA.	630
Circuit breaker, adapter cubicle		
225a	EA.	5,300
400a	EA.	6,200
Fusible switches, 240v, 3 phase, 30a	EA.	660
60a	EA.	820
100a	EA.	1,100
200a	EA.	1,850

16110.20 CONDUIT SPECIALTIES

	Unit	Total
Rod beam clamp, 1/2"	EA.	9.85
Hanger rod		
3/8"	L.F.	4.18
1/2"	L.F.	6.88
All thread rod		
1/4"	L.F.	2.58
3/8"	L.F.	3.34
1/2"	L.F.	4.46
5/8"	L.F.	7.30
Hanger channel, 1-1/2"		
No holes	EA.	6.34
Holes	EA.	7.33
Channel strap		
1/2"	EA.	4.87
3/4"	EA.	5.31
Conduit penetrations, roof and wall, 8" thick		
1/2"	EA.	44.00
3/4"	EA.	44.00
1"	EA.	57.00
Threaded rod couplings		
1/4"	EA.	4.95
3/8"	EA.	5.02
1/2"	EA.	5.22
5/8"	EA.	6.10
3/4"	EA.	6.35
Hex nuts		
1/4"	EA.	3.72
3/8"	EA.	3.80
1/2"	EA.	4.08
5/8"	EA.	4.67
3/4"	EA.	5.04
Square nuts		
1/4"	EA.	3.70
3/8"	EA.	3.83
3/8"	EA.	4.02
5/8"	EA.	4.16
3/4"	EA.	4.62
Flat washers		
1/4"	EA.	.16
3/8"	EA.	.22
1/2"	EA.	.30
5/8"	EA.	.60
3/4"	EA.	.85
Lockwashers		
1/4"	EA.	.10
3/8"	EA.	.17
1/2"	EA.	.21
5/8"	EA.	.36
3/4"	EA.	.60

16110.21 ALUMINUM CONDUIT

	Unit	Total
Aluminum conduit		
1/2"	L.F.	4.15
3/4"	L.F.	5.44
1"	L.F.	7.18
90 deg. elbow		
1/2"	EA.	29.00
3/4"	EA.	38.75
1"	EA.	51.25

16110.21 ALUMINUM CONDUIT (Cont.)

	Unit	Total
Coupling		
1/2"	EA.	7.25
3/4"	EA.	9.82
1"	EA.	13.00

16110.22 EMT CONDUIT

	Unit	Total
EMT conduit		
1/2"	L.F.	2.77
3/4"	L.F.	3.98
1"	L.F.	5.44
90 deg. elbow		
1/2"	EA.	12.25
3/4"	EA.	13.50
1"	EA.	17.50
Connector, steel compression		
1/2"	EA.	8.20
3/4"	EA.	9.89
1"	EA.	11.75
Coupling, steel, compression		
1/2"	EA.	7.39
3/4"	EA.	8.54
1"	EA.	10.75
1 hole strap, steel		
1/2"	EA.	3.06
3/4"	EA.	3.11
1"	EA.	3.26
Connector, steel set screw		
1/2"	EA.	6.38
3/4"	EA.	7.24
1"	EA.	8.88
Insulated throat		
1/2"	EA.	6.85
3/4"	EA.	8.02
1"	EA.	10.00
Connector, die cast set screw		
1/2"	EA.	5.11
3/4"	EA.	5.72
1"	EA.	7.04
Insulated throat		
1/2"	EA.	6.10
3/4"	EA.	7.25
1"	EA.	9.47
Coupling, steel set screw		
1/2"	EA.	5.15
3/4"	EA.	6.32
1"	EA.	8.48
Diecast set screw		
1/2"	EA.	3.66
3/4"	EA.	4.15
1"	EA.	5.01
1 hole malleable straps		
1/2"	EA.	3.22
3/4"	EA.	3.37
1"	EA.	3.70
EMT to rigid compression coupling		
1/2"	EA.	11.50
3/4"	EA.	13.25
1"	EA.	20.25
Set screw couplings		
1/2"	EA.	8.27
3/4"	EA.	8.85
1"	EA.	13.00
Set screw offset connectors		
1/2"	EA.	9.68
3/4"	EA.	10.50
1"	EA.	16.50
Compression offset connectors		
1/2"	EA.	11.25
3/4"	EA.	12.50
1"	EA.	18.00
Type "LB" set screw condulets		
1/2"	EA.	28.25
3/4"	EA.	35.50
1"	EA.	49.50
Type "T" set screw condulets		
1/2"	EA.	36.00
3/4"	EA.	47.25
1"	EA.	58.75

16110.22 EMT CONDUIT (Cont.)

	Unit	Total
Type "C" set screw condulets		
1/2"	EA.	30.25
3/4"	EA.	36.75
1"	EA.	50.75
Type "LL" set screw condulets		
1/2"	EA.	30.25
3/4"	EA.	36.25
1"	EA.	50.50
Type "LR" set screw condulets		
1/2"	EA.	30.25
3/4"	EA.	36.25
1"	EA.	50.50
Type "LB" compression condulets		
1/2"	EA.	49.25
3/4"	EA.	77.50
1"	EA.	89.25
Type "T" compression condulets		
1/2"	EA.	66.25
3/4"	EA.	81.50
1"	EA.	120
Condulet covers		
1/2"	EA.	10.50
3/4"	EA.	11.00
1"	EA.	11.75
Clamp type entrance caps		
1/2"	EA.	27.00
3/4"	EA.	32.00
1"	EA.	41.50
Slip fitter type entrance caps		
1/2"	EA.	24.50
3/4"	EA.	29.25
1"	EA.	38.25

16110.23 FLEXIBLE CONDUIT

	Unit	Total
Flexible conduit, steel, 3/8"	L.F.	2.91
1/2	L.F.	3.01
3/4"	L.F.	4.03
1"	L.F.	5.09
Flexible conduit, liquid tight		
3/8"	L.F.	4.25
1/2"	L.F.	4.52
3/4"	L.F.	6.08
1"	L.F.	7.72
Connector, straight		
3/8"	EA.	9.25
1/2"	EA.	9.50
3/4"	EA.	11.25
1"	EA.	15.75
Straight insulated throat connectors		
3/8"	EA.	13.00
1/2"	EA.	13.00
3/4"	EA.	16.50
1"	EA.	20.00
90 deg connectors		
3/8"	EA.	16.50
1/2"	EA.	16.50
3/4"	EA.	22.00
1"	EA.	31.50
90 degree insulated throat connectors		
3/8"	EA.	17.75
1/2"	EA.	17.75
3/4"	EA.	23.50
1"	EA.	34.00
Flexible aluminum conduit		
3/8"	L.F.	2.60
1/2"	L.F.	2.68
3/4"	L.F.	3.57
1"	L.F.	4.21
Connector, straight		
3/8"	EA.	8.49
1/2"	EA.	9.01
3/4"	EA.	9.67
1"	EA.	16.25
Straight insulated throat connectors		
3/8"	EA.	7.66
1/2"	EA.	8.99
3/4"	EA.	9.16
1"	EA.	14.00

16110.23 FLEXIBLE CONDUIT (Cont.)

	Unit	Total
90 deg connectors		
3/8"	EA.	12.50
1/2"	EA.	14.00
3/4"	EA.	16.00
1"	EA.	22.25
90 deg insulated throat connectors		
3/8"	EA.	13.00
1/2"	EA.	14.25
3/4"	EA.	17.00
1"	EA.	23.25

16110.24 GALVANIZED CONDUIT

	Unit	Total
Galvanized rigid steel conduit		
1/2"	L.F.	5.99
3/4"	L.F.	7.03
1"	L.F.	9.25
1-1/4"	L.F.	12.75
1-1/2"	L.F.	14.50
2"	L.F.	17.75
90 degree ell		
1/2"	EA.	26.50
3/4"	EA.	31.25
1"	EA.	41.25
1-1/4"	EA.	51.00
1-1/2"	EA.	59.75
2"	EA.	72.50
Couplings, with set screws		
1/2"	EA.	7.95
3/4"	EA.	10.00
1"	EA.	15.00
1-1/4"	EA.	23.00
1-1/2"	EA.	29.25
2"	EA.	56.00
Split couplings		
1/2"	EA.	17.25
3/4"	EA.	22.50
1"	EA.	26.50
1-1/4"	EA.	35.50
1-1/2"	EA.	44.75
2"	EA.	81.00
Erickson couplings		
1/2"	EA.	36.25
3/4"	EA.	41.25
1"	EA.	55.00
1-1/4"	EA.	83.25
1-1/2"	EA.	96.75
2"	EA.	140
Seal fittings		
1/2"	EA.	61.50
3/4"	EA.	72.50
1"	EA.	91.00
1-1/4"	EA.	110
1-1/2"	EA.	130
2"	EA.	160
Entrance fitting, (weather head), threaded		
1/2"	EA.	39.25
3/4"	EA.	45.00
1"	EA.	52.50
1-1/4"	EA.	67.00
1-1/2"	EA.	84.00
2"	EA.	110
Locknuts		
1/2"	EA.	3.76
3/4"	EA.	3.80
1"	EA.	3.94
1-1/4"	EA.	4.09
1-1/2"	EA.	5.10
2"	EA.	5.49
Plastic conduit bushings		
1/2"	EA.	9.22
3/4"	EA.	11.00
1"	EA.	14.50
1-1/4"	EA.	17.00
1-1/2"	EA.	19.50
2"	EA.	25.75

16110.24 GALVANIZED CONDUIT (Cont.)

	Unit	Total
Conduit bushings, steel		
1/2"	EA.	9.36
3/4"	EA.	11.00
1"	EA.	14.50
1-1/4"	EA.	17.25
1-1/2"	EA.	20.00
2"	EA.	26.50
Pipe cap		
1/2"	EA.	4.13
3/4"	EA.	4.18
1"	EA.	4.55
1-1/4"	EA.	7.39
1-1/2"	EA.	8.34
2"	EA.	8.67
Threaded couplings		
1/2"	EA.	5.47
3/4"	EA.	6.57
1"	EA.	9.18
1-1/4"	EA.	10.75
1-1/2"	EA.	12.50
2"	EA.	14.75
Threadless couplings		
1/2"	EA.	13.75
3/4"	EA.	15.75
1"	EA.	19.25
1-1/4"	EA.	24.00
1-1/2"	EA.	30.25
2"	EA.	40.25
Threadless connectors		
1/2"	EA.	10.25
3/4"	EA.	14.00
1"	EA.	18.25
1-1/4"	EA.	27.25
1-1/2"	EA.	38.75
2"	EA.	62.00
Setscrew connectors		
1/2"	EA.	8.26
3/4"	EA.	9.89
1"	EA.	12.75
1-1/4"	EA.	18.50
1-1/2"	EA.	24.50
2"	EA.	41.75
Clamp type entrance caps		
1/2"	EA.	30.50
3/4"	EA.	37.25
1"	EA.	45.75
1-1/4"	EA.	52.25
1-1/2"	EA.	73.75
2"	EA.	87.50
"LB" condulets		
1/2"	EA.	31.75
3/4"	EA.	39.00
1"	EA.	49.25
1-1/4"	EA.	66.00
1-1/2"	EA.	83.50
2"	EA.	120
"T" condulets		
1/2"	EA.	39.50
3/4"	EA.	46.25
1"	EA.	57.75
1-1/4"	EA.	72.75
1-1/2"	EA.	87.00
2"	EA.	120
"X" condulets		
1/2"	EA.	49.75
3/4"	EA.	55.00
1"	EA.	72.75
1-1/4"	EA.	85.75
1-1/2"	EA.	100
2"	EA.	170
Blank steel condulet covers		
1/2"	EA.	9.89
3/4"	EA.	10.50
1"	EA.	11.75
1-1/4"	EA.	14.50
1-1/2"	EA.	14.75
2"	EA.	18.75

16110.24 GALVANIZED CONDUIT (Cont.)

	Unit	Total
Solid condulet gaskets		
1/2"	EA.	5.84
3/4"	EA.	6.03
1"	EA.	6.41
1-1/4"	EA.	9.24
1-1/2"	EA.	9.43
2"	EA.	9.87
One-hole malleable straps		
1/2"	EA.	3.23
3/4"	EA.	3.38
1"	EA.	3.61
1-1/4"	EA.	5.08
1-1/2"	EA.	5.31
2"	EA.	6.98
One-hole steel straps		
1/2"	EA.	2.95
3/4"	EA.	2.99
1"	EA.	3.09
1-1/4"	EA.	3.90
1-1/2"	EA.	4.02
2"	EA.	4.16
Grounding locknuts		
1/2"	EA.	7.79
3/4"	EA.	8.34
1"	EA.	9.51
1-1/4"	EA.	10.50
1-1/2"	EA.	10.50
2"	EA.	12.75
Insulated grounding metal bushings		
1/2"	EA.	15.00
3/4"	EA.	18.00
1"	EA.	20.75
1-1/4"	EA.	27.00
1-1/2"	EA.	33.50
2"	EA.	40.75

16110.25 PLASTIC CONDUIT

	Unit	Total
PVC conduit, schedule 40, 1/2"	L.F.	2.85
3/4"	L.F.	3.02
1"	L.F.	4.11
1-1/4"	L.F.	4.59
1-1/2"	L.F.	5.63
2"	L.F.	6.21
Couplings, 1/2"	EA.	3.99
3/4"	EA.	4.08
1"	EA.	4.36
1-1/4"	EA.	5.29
1-1/2"	EA.	5.69
2"	EA.	6.15
90 degree elbows, 1/2"	EA.	8.79
3/4"	EA.	10.50
1"	EA.	11.75
1-1/4"	EA.	14.25
1-1/2"	EA.	19.00
2"	EA.	23.25
Terminal adapters, 1/2"	EA.	7.76
3/4"	EA.	8.14
1"	EA.	8.39
1-1/4"	EA.	13.00
1-1/2"	EA.	13.50
2"	EA.	14.25
LB conduit body, 1/2"	EA.	19.00
3/4"	EA.	20.50
1	EA.	21.25
1-1/4"	EA.	33.75
1-1/2"	EA.	36.00
2"	EA.	47.00
PVC cement, 1 pint	EA.	15.00
1 quart	EA.	22.00

16110.27 PLASTIC COATED CONDUIT

	Unit	Total
Rigid steel conduit, plastic coated		
1/2"	L.F.	9.39
3/4"	L.F.	11.00
1"	L.F.	14.50
1-1/4"	L.F.	18.25
1-1/2"	L.F.	22.25
2"	L.F.	27.75

16110.27 PLASTIC COATED CONDUIT (Cont.)

	Unit	Total
90 degree elbows		
1/2"	EA.	45.00
3/4"	EA.	51.00
1"	EA.	59.00
1-1/4"	EA.	69.25
1-1/2"	EA.	85.25
2"	EA.	110
Couplings		
1/2"	EA.	10.75
3/4"	EA.	12.50
1"	EA.	15.50
1-1/4"	EA.	18.00
1-1/2"	EA.	23.50
2"	EA.	28.75
1 hole conduit straps		
3/4"	EA.	14.75
1"	EA.	15.00
1-1/4"	EA.	21.00
1-1/2"	EA.	22.00
2"	EA.	30.00

16110.28 STEEL CONDUIT

	Unit	Total
Intermediate metal conduit (IMC)		
1/2"	L.F.	4.18
3/4"	L.F.	5.35
1"	L.F.	7.34
1-1/4"	L.F.	9.07
1-1/2"	L.F.	11.75
2"	L.F.	14.25
90 degree ell		
1/2"	EA.	33.25
3/4"	EA.	38.25
1"	EA.	52.25
1-1/4"	EA.	66.25
1-1/2"	EA.	78.25
2"	EA.	100
Couplings		
1/2"	EA.	7.37
3/4"	EA.	8.90
1"	EA.	12.50
1-1/4"	EA.	15.00
1-1/2"	EA.	18.25
2"	EA.	22.00

16110.35 SURFACE MOUNTED RACEWAY

	Unit	Total
Single Raceway		
3/4" x 17/32" Conduit	L.F.	4.52
Mounting Strap	EA.	4.25
Connector	EA.	4.40
Elbow		
45 degree	EA.	11.25
90 degree	EA.	5.99
internal	EA.	6.62
external	EA.	6.39
Switch	EA.	48.25
Utility Box	EA.	41.75
Receptacle	EA.	52.00
3/4" x 21/32" Conduit	L.F.	4.75
Mounting Strap	EA.	4.50
Connector	EA.	4.53
Elbow		
45 degree	EA.	13.00
90 degree	EA.	6.16
internal	EA.	7.08
external	EA.	7.08
Switch	EA.	48.25
Utility Box	EA.	41.75
Receptacle	EA.	52.00

16120.41 ALUMINUM CONDUCTORS

	Unit	Total
Type XHHW, stranded aluminum, 600v		
#8	L.F.	.67
#6	L.F.	.77
#4	L.F.	.98
#2	L.F.	1.21
1/0	L.F.	1.70
2/0	L.F.	2.03
3/0	L.F.	2.45
4/0	L.F.	2.69

16120.41 ALUMINUM CONDUCTORS (Cont.)

	Unit	Total
Type S.E.U. cable		
#8/3	L.F.	3.26
#6/3	L.F.	3.48
#4/3	L.F.	4.38
#2/3	L.F.	5.25
#1/3	L.F.	6.29
1/0-3	L.F.	6.86
2/0-3	L.F.	7.60
3/0-3	L.F.	9.85
4/0-3	L.F.	10.25
Type S.E.R. cable with ground		
#8/3	L.F.	3.79
#6/3	L.F.	4.50

16120.43 COPPER CONDUCTORS

	Unit	Total
Copper conductors, type THW, solid		
#14	L.F.	.42
#12	L.F.	.57
#10	L.F.	.74
THHN-THWN, solid		
#14	L.F.	.42
#12	L.F.	.57
#10	L.F.	.74
Stranded		
#14	L.F.	.42
#12	L.F.	.57
#10	L.F.	.74
#8	L.F.	1.11
#6	L.F.	1.50
#4	L.F.	2.07
#2	L.F.	2.75
#1	L.F.	3.38
1/0	L.F.	4.08
2/0	L.F.	5.06
3/0	L.F.	6.34
4/0	L.F.	7.70
Bare stranded wire		
#8	L.F.	1.04
#6	L.F.	1.50
#4	L.F.	1.94
#2	L.F.	2.75
#1	L.F.	3.46
Type "BX" solid armored cable		
#14/2	L.F.	2.69
#14/3	L.F.	3.43
#14/4	L.F.	4.19
#12/2	L.F.	2.93
#12/3	L.F.	3.68
#12/4	L.F.	4.54
#10/2	L.F.	3.91
#10/3	L.F.	4.94
#10/4	L.F.	6.67
Steel type, metal clad cable, solid, with ground		
#14/2	L.F.	2.03
#14/3	L.F.	2.57
#14/4	L.F.	3.17
#12/2	L.F.	2.20
#12/3	L.F.	3.04
#12/4	L.F.	3.85
#10/2	L.F.	3.21
#10/3	L.F.	4.20
#10/4	L.F.	5.80

16120.47 SHEATHED CABLE

	Unit	Total
Non-metallic sheathed cable		
Type NM cable with ground		
#14/2	L.F.	1.37
#12/2	L.F.	1.60
#10/2	L.F.	2.00
#8/2	L.F.	2.62
#6/2	L.F.	3.65
#14/3	L.F.	2.26
#12/3	L.F.	2.55
#10/3	L.F.	2.97
#8/3	L.F.	3.72
#6/3	L.F.	4.82
#4/3	L.F.	8.12
#2/3	L.F.	11.25

16120.47 SHEATHED CABLE (Cont.)

Item	Unit	Total
Type U.F. cable with ground		
#14/2	L.F.	1.49
#12/2	L.F.	1.88
#14/3	L.F.	1.92
#12/3	L.F.	2.30
Type S.F.U. cable, 3 conductor		
#8	L.F.	3.50
#6	L.F.	4.80
Type SER cable, 4 conductor		
#6	L.F.	6.32
#4	L.F.	8.01
Flexible cord, type STO cord		
#18/2	L.F.	.93
#18/3	L.F.	1.10
#18/4	L.F.	1.46
#16/2	L.F.	1.02
#16/3	L.F.	.94
#16/4	L.F.	1.22
#14/2	L.F.	1.50
#14/3	L.F.	1.48
#14/4	L.F.	1.79
#12/2	L.F.	1.88
#12/3	L.F.	1.57
#12/4	L.F.	2.15
#10/2	L.F.	2.30
#10/3	L.F.	2.29
#10/4	L.F.	3.30

16130.40 BOXES

Item	Unit	Total
Round cast box, type SEH		
1/2"	EA.	44.75
3/4"	EA.	50.00
SEHC		
1/2"	EA.	48.75
3/4"	EA.	54.00
SEHL		
1/2"	EA.	49.25
3/4"	EA.	55.75
SEHT		
1/2"	EA.	56.25
3/4"	EA.	62.00
SEHX		
1/2"	EA.	64.25
3/4"	EA.	72.50
Blank cover	EA.	15.00
1/2", hub cover	EA.	14.75
Cover with gasket	EA.	17.75
Rectangle, type FS boxes		
1/2"	EA.	35.00
3/4"	EA.	39.50
1"	EA.	47.50
FSA		
1/2"	EA.	43.25
3/4"	EA.	45.75
FSC		
1/2"	EA.	36.25
3/4"	EA.	42.50
1"	EA.	51.50
FSL		
1/2"	EA.	43.00
3/4"	EA.	46.75
FSR		
1/2"	EA.	43.75
3/4"	EA.	48.00
FSS		
1/2"	EA.	36.25
3/4"	EA.	41.00
FSLA		
1/2"	EA.	32.50
3/4"	EA.	37.25
FSCA		
1/2"	EA.	47.75
3/4"	EA.	50.75
FSCC		
1/2"	EA.	42.50
3/4"	EA.	56.75

16130.40 BOXES (Cont.)

Item	Unit	Total
FSCT, 1/2"	EA.	42.50
3/4"	EA.	53.25
1"	EA.	55.00
FST, 1/2"	EA.	56.25
3/4"	EA.	61.25
FSX, 1/2"	EA.	67.50
3/4"	EA.	73.50
FSCD boxes, 1/2"	EA.	63.50
3/4"	EA.	72.25
Rectangle, type FS, 2 gang boxes		
1/2"	EA.	46.75
3/4"	EA.	51.00
1"	EA.	59.50
FSC, 2 gang boxes, 1/2"	EA.	48.00
3/4"	EA.	54.25
1"	EA.	67.00
FSS, 2 gang boxes, 3/4"	EA.	52.75
FS, tandem boxes		
1/2"	EA.	52.75
3/4"	EA.	56.75
FSC, tandem boxes		
1/2"	EA.	61.25
3/4"	EA.	66.75
FS, three gang boxes		
3/4"	EA.	67.50
1"	EA.	75.00
FSS, three gang boxes, 3/4"	EA.	81.75
Weatherproof cast aluminum boxes, 1 gang, 3 outlets		
1/2"	EA.	35.00
3/4"	EA.	42.75
2 gang, 3 outlets		
1/2"	EA.	48.25
3/4"	EA.	51.25
1 gang, 4 outlets		
1/2"	EA.	55.50
3/4"	EA.	64.25
2 gang, 4 outlets		
1/2"	EA.	56.00
3/4"	EA.	65.00
1 gang, 5 outlets		
1/2"	EA.	61.25
3/4"	EA.	68.25
2 gang, 5 outlets		
1/2"	EA.	68.75
3/4"	EA.	77.75
2 gang, 6 outlets		
1/2"	EA.	80.00
3/4"	EA.	84.75
2 gang, 7 outlets		
1/2"	EA.	91.75
3/4"	EA.	100
Weatherproof & type FS box covers, blank, 1 gang	EA.	13.25
Tumbler switch, 1 gang	EA.	16.25
1 gang, single recept	EA.	14.00
Duplex recept	EA.	15.25
Despard	EA.	15.25
Red pilot light	EA.	33.50
SW and		
Single recept	EA.	24.50
Duplex recept	EA.	22.75
2 gang		
Blank	EA.	16.00
Tumbler switch	EA.	17.00
Single recept	EA.	17.00
Duplex recept	EA.	17.00
3 gang		
Blank	EA.	21.25
Tumbler switch	EA.	23.00
4 gang		
Tumbler switch	EA.	29.00
Box covers		
Surface	EA.	29.75
Sealing	EA.	31.25
Dome	EA.	37.75
1/2" nipple	EA.	44.25
3/4" nipple	EA.	45.25

16130.60 PULL AND JUNCTION BOXES

	Unit	Total
4"		
Octagon box	EA.	11.75
Box extension	EA.	10.50
Plaster ring	EA.	7.62
Cover blank	EA.	5.73
Square box	EA.	13.50
Box extension	EA.	9.40
Plaster ring	EA.	7.06
Cover blank	EA.	5.68
Switch and device boxes		
2 gang	EA.	24.25
3 gang	EA.	36.25
4 gang	EA.	49.00
Device covers		
2 gang	EA.	17.00
3 gang	EA.	17.50
4 gang	EA.	22.00
Handy box	EA.	12.00
Extension	EA.	7.93
Switch cover	EA.	6.19
Switch box with knockout	EA.	16.25
Weatherproof cover, spring type	EA.	16.75
Cover plate, dryer receptacle 1 gang plastic	EA.	8.81
For 4" receptacle, 2 gang	EA.	10.00
Duplex receptacle cover plate, plastic	EA.	4.97
4", vertical bracket box, 1-1/2" with		
RMX clamps	EA.	17.75
BX clamps	EA.	18.50
4", octagon device cover		
1 switch	EA.	8.69
1 duplex recept	EA.	8.69
4", octagon swivel hanger box, 1/2" hub	EA.	16.25
3/4" hub	EA.	17.75
4" octagon adjustable bar hangers		
18-1/2"	EA.	9.10
26-1/2"	EA.	9.61
With clip		
18-1/2"	EA.	7.66
26-1/2"	EA.	8.16
4", square face bracket boxes, 1-1/2"		
RMX	EA.	19.25
BX	EA.	20.00
4" square to round plaster rings	EA.	7.25
2 gang device plaster rings	EA.	7.35
Surface covers		
1 gang switch	EA.	6.95
2 gang switch	EA.	7.01
1 single recept	EA.	8.33
1 20a twist lock recept	EA.	9.36
1 30a twist lock recept	EA.	10.75
1 duplex recept	EA.	6.77
2 duplex recept	EA.	6.77
Switch and duplex recept	EA.	8.47
4" plastic round boxes, ground straps		
Box only	EA.	12.25
Box w/clamps	EA.	16.50
Box w/16" bar	EA.	21.00
Box w/24" bar	EA.	22.50
4" plastic round box covers		
Blank cover	EA.	5.49
Plaster ring	EA.	6.29
4" plastic square boxes		
Box only	EA.	11.75
Box w/clamps	EA.	16.00
Box w/hanger	EA.	20.00
Box w/nails and clamp	EA.	21.00
4" plastic square box covers		
Blank cover	EA.	5.45
1 gang ring	EA.	5.72
2 gang ring	EA.	6.32
Round ring	EA.	5.89

16130.80 RECEPTACLES

	Unit	Total
Contractor grade duplex receptacles, 15a 120v		
Duplex	EA.	15.75
125 volt, 20a, duplex, standard grade	EA.	26.25
Ground fault interrupter type	EA.	59.75
250 volt, 20a, 2 pole, single, ground type	EA.	34.25
120/208v, 4 pole, single receptacle, twist lock		
20a	EA.	48.50
50a	EA.	70.00
125/250v, 3 pole, flush receptacle		
30a	EA.	45.00
50a	EA.	50.75
60a	EA.	100
Dryer receptacle, 250v, 30a/50a, 3 wire	EA.	39.00
Clock receptacle, 2 pole, grounding type	EA.	26.25
125v, 20a single recept. grounding type		
Standard grade	EA.	27.25
125/250v, 3 pole, 3 wire surface recepts		
30a	EA.	41.25
50a	EA.	43.50
60a	EA.	74.25
Cord set, 3 wire, 6' cord		
30a	EA.	39.25
50a	EA.	46.50
125/250v, 3 pole, 3 wire cap		
30a	EA.	46.50
50a	EA.	61.25
60a	EA.	73.75

16199.10 UTILITY POLES & FITTINGS

	Unit	Total
Wood pole, creosoted		
25'	EA.	620
30'	EA.	750
Treated, wood preservative, 6"x6"		
8'	EA.	130
10'	EA.	200
12'	EA.	210
14'	EA.	290
16'	EA.	330
18'	EA.	390
20'	EA.	460
Aluminum, brushed, no base		
8'	EA.	730
10'	EA.	870
15'	EA.	960
20'	EA.	1,150
25'	EA.	1,500
Steel, no base		
10'	EA.	870
15'	EA.	970
20'	EA.	1,250
25'	EA.	1,450
Concrete, no base		
13'	EA.	1,300
16'	EA.	1,750
18'	EA.	2,150
25'	EA.	2,550

16350.10 CIRCUIT BREAKERS

	Unit	Total
Load center circuit breakers, 240v		
1 pole, 10-60a	EA.	34.25
2 pole		
10-60a	EA.	67.00
70-100a	EA.	170
110-150a	EA.	300
Load center, G.F.I. breakers, 240v		
1 pole, 15-30a	EA.	160
Tandem breakers, 240v		
1 pole, 15-30a	EA.	59.75
2 pole, 15-30a	EA.	95.25

16365.10 FUSES

	Unit	Total
Fuse, one-time, 250v		
30a	EA.	6.08
60a	EA.	7.82
100a	EA.	21.25

16395.10 GROUNDING

Item	Unit	Total
Ground rods, copper clad, 1/2" x		
6'	EA.	62.25
8'	EA.	72.00
5/8" x		
6'	EA.	71.25
8'	EA.	96.50
Ground rod clamp		
5/8"	EA.	14.75
Ground rod couplings		
1/2"	EA.	18.25
5/8"	EA.	22.75
Ground rod, driving stud		
1/2"	EA.	16.00
5/8"	EA.	17.75
Ground rod clamps, #8-2 to		
1" pipe	EA.	23.75
2" pipe	EA.	29.75

16430.20 METERING

Item	Unit	Total
Outdoor wp meter sockets, 1 gang, 240v, 1 phase		
Includes sealing ring, 100a	EA.	150
150a	EA.	190
200a	EA.	210
Die cast hubs, 1-1/4"	EA.	29.25
1-1/2"	EA.	30.25
2"	EA.	32.00

16470.10 PANELBOARDS

Item	Unit	Total
Indoor load center, 1 phase 240v main lug only		
30a - 2 spaces	EA.	170
100a - 8 spaces	EA.	260
150a - 16 spaces	EA.	450
200a - 24 spaces	EA.	750
200a - 42 spaces	EA.	810
Main circuit breaker		
100a - 8 spaces	EA.	470
100a - 16 spaces	EA.	520
150a - 16 spaces	EA.	740
150a - 24 spaces	EA.	850
200a - 24 spaces	EA.	830
200a - 42 spaces	EA.	1,100
120/208v, flush, 3 ph., 4 wire, main only		
100a		
12 circuits	EA.	1,300
20 circuits	EA.	1,750
30 circuits	EA.	2,400
225a		
30 circuits	EA.	2,500
42 circuits	EA.	3,150

16490.10 SWITCHES

Item	Unit	Total
Photo electric switches		
1000 watt		
105-135v	EA.	85.25
Dimmer switch and switch plate		
600w	EA.	52.75
Time clocks with skip, 40a, 120v		
SPST	EA.	150
Contractor grade wall switch 15a, 120v		
Single pole	EA.	13.25
Three way	EA.	17.25
Four way	EA.	29.00
Specification grade toggle switches, 20a, 120-277v		
Single pole	EA.	17.75
Double pole	EA.	29.50
3 way	EA.	27.00
4 way	EA.	49.25
Combination switch & pilot light, single pole	EA.	33.50
3 way	EA.	40.00
Combination switch & receptacle, single pole	EA.	38.75
3 way	EA.	42.75
Switch plates, plastic ivory		
1 gang	EA.	6.07
2 gang	EA.	8.01
3 gang	EA.	9.89
4 gang	EA.	13.75
5 gang	EA.	15.25
6 gang	EA.	17.25

16490.10 SWITCHES (Cont.)

Item	Unit	Total
Stainless steel		
1 gang	EA.	8.87
2 gang	EA.	11.50
3 gang	EA.	15.50
4 gang	EA.	21.75
5 gang	EA.	25.00
6 gang	EA.	30.00
Brass		
1 gang	EA.	11.50
2 gang	EA.	20.00
3 gang	EA.	28.25
4 gang	EA.	32.75
5 gang	EA.	39.50
6 gang	EA.	46.75

16510.05 INTERIOR LIGHTING

Item	Unit	Total
Recessed fluorescent fixtures, 2'x2'		
2 lamp	EA.	120
4 lamp	EA.	150
Surface mounted incandescent fixtures		
40w	EA.	160
75w	EA.	160
100w	EA.	170
150w	EA.	210
Pendant		
40w	EA.	140
75w	EA.	150
100w	EA.	170
150w	EA.	180
Contractor grade recessed down lights		
100 watt housing only	EA.	140
150 watt housing only	EA.	170
100 watt trim	EA.	94.00
150 watt trim	EA.	130
Recessed incandescent fixtures		
40w	EA.	260
75w	EA.	270
100w	EA.	280
150w	EA.	290
Light track single circuit		
2'	EA.	78.25
4'	EA.	85.75
8'	EA.	140
12'	EA.	210
Fittings and accessories		
Dead end	EA.	27.00
Starter kit	EA.	40.25
Conduit feed	EA.	32.00
Straight connector	EA.	29.50
Center feed	EA.	41.00
L-connector	EA.	32.00
T-connector	EA.	39.50
X-connector	EA.	49.50
Cord and plug	EA.	42.50
Rigid corner	EA.	56.75
Flex connector	EA.	46.50
2 way connector	EA.	110
Spacer clip	EA.	5.13
Grid box	EA.	19.00
T-bar clip	EA.	5.91
Utility hook	EA.	17.00
Fixtures, square		
R-20	EA.	53.25
R-30	EA.	77.00
40w flood	EA.	120
40w spot	EA.	120
100w flood	EA.	130
100w spot	EA.	110
Mini spot	EA.	51.25
Mini flood	EA.	110
Quartz, 500w	EA.	250
R-20 sphere	EA.	82.50
R-30 sphere	EA.	48.25
R-20 cylinder	EA.	61.25
R-30 cylinder	EA.	69.25
R-40 cylinder	EA.	70.25
R-30 wall wash	EA.	110
R-40 wall wash	EA.	130

16510.10 LIGHTING INDUSTRIAL

	Unit	Total
Surface mounted fluorescent, wrap around lens		
1 lamp	EA.	140
2 lamps	EA.	200
Wall mounted fluorescent		
2-20w lamps	EA.	120
2-30w lamps	EA.	140
2-40w lamps	EA.	150
Strip fluorescent		
4'		
1 lamp	EA.	90.75
2 lamps	EA.	100
8'		
1 lamp	EA.	120
2 lamps	EA.	160
Compact fluorescent		
2-7w	EA.	220
2-13w	EA.	280

16670.10 LIGHTNING PROTECTION

	Unit	Total
Lightning protection		
Copper point, nickel plated, 12'		
1/2" dia.	EA.	120
5/8" dia.	EA.	120

16750.20 SIGNALING SYSTEMS

	Unit	Total
Contractor grade doorbell chime kit		
Chime	EA.	110
Door button	EA.	27.75

16850.10 ELECTRIC HEATING

	Unit	Total
Baseboard heater		
2', 375w	EA.	110
3', 500w	EA.	120
4', 750w	EA.	140
5', 935w	EA.	170
6', 1125w	EA.	200
7', 1310w	EA.	230
8', 1500w	EA.	260
9', 1680w	EA.	290
10', 1875w	EA.	340
Unit heater, wall mounted		
750w	EA.	280
1500w	EA.	340
Thermostat		
Integral	EA.	73.25
Line voltage	EA.	74.25
Electric heater connection	EA.	19.50
Fittings		
Inside corner	EA.	52.75
Outside corner	EA.	55.00
Receptacle section	EA.	56.00
Blank section	EA.	62.50
Radiant ceiling heater panels		
500w	EA.	360
750w	EA.	390
Unit heater thermostat	EA.	87.75
Mounting bracket	EA.	100
Relay	EA.	110

16910.40 CONTROL CABLE

	Unit	Total
Control cable, 600v, #14 THWN, PVC jacket		
2 wire	L.F.	.92
4 wire	L.F.	1.30

Part Three

Metro Area Multipliers

The costs presented in this Costbook attempt to represent national averages. Costs, however, vary among regions, states and even between adjacent localities. In order to more closely approximate the probable costs for specific locations throughout the U. S., this table of Metro Area Multipliers is provided. These adjustment factors are used to modify costs obtained from this book to help account for regional variations of construction costs and to provide a more accurate estimate for specific areas. The factors are formulated by comparing costs in a specific area to the costs presented in this Costbook. An example of how to use these factors is shown below. Whenever local current costs are known, whether material prices or labor rates, they should be used when more accuracy is required.

Cost Obtained from Costbook Pages	X	Metro Area Multiplier / Divided by 100	=	**Adjusted Cost**

For example, a project estimated to cost $1,000,000 using the Costbook can be adjusted to more closely approximate the cost in Los Angeles where the Multiplier is 119:

$$1{,}000{,}000 \times \frac{119}{100} = \mathbf{1{,}190{,}000}$$

State	City	Multiplier
AK	ANCHORAGE	132
AL	ANNISTON	81
	AUBURN	82
	BIRMINGHAM	82
	DECATUR	84
	DOTHAN	83
	FLORENCE	84
	GADSDEN	82
	HUNTSVILLE	84
	MOBILE	86
	MONTGOMERY	81
	OPELIKA	82
	TUSCALOOSA	81
AR	FAYETTEVILLE	79
	FORT SMITH	79
	JONESBORO	78
	LITTLE ROCK	82
	NORTH LITTLE ROCK	82
	PINE BLUFF	80
	ROGERS	79
	SPRINGDALE	79
	TEXARKANA	79
AZ	FLAGSTAFF	94
	MESA	94
	PHOENIX	95
	TUCSON	93
	YUMA	94
CA	BAKERSFIELD	116
	CHICO	118
	FAIRFIELD	120
	FRESNO	118
	LODI	117
	LONG BEACH	119
	LOS ANGELES	119
	MERCED	118
	MODESTO	114
	NAPA	120
	OAKLAND	124
	ORANGE COUNTY	118
	PARADISE	114
	PORTERVILLE	116
	REDDING	114
	RIVERSIDE	116
	SACRAMENTO	118
	SALINAS	120
	SAN BERNARDINO	116
	SAN DIEGO	117
	SAN FRANCISCO	129
	SAN JOSE	126
	SAN LUIS OBISPO	113
	SANTA BARBARA	116
	SANTA CRUZ	120
	SANTA ROSA	121
	STOCKTON	117
	TULARE	118

State	City	Multiplier
CA	VALLEJO	120
	VENTURA	116
	VISALIA	118
	WATSONVILLE	118
	YOLO	118
	YUBA CITY	118
CO	BOULDER	103
	COLORADO SPRINGS	100
	DENVER	101
	FORT COLLINS	110
	GRAND JUNCTION	99
	GREELEY	108
	LONGMONT	103
	LOVELAND	110
	PUEBLO	105
CT	BRIDGEPORT	113
	DANBURY	113
	HARTFORD	112
	MERIDEN	113
	NEW HAVEN	113
	NEW LONDON	110
	NORWALK	117
	NORWICH	110
	STAMFORD	117
	WATERBURY	112
DC	WASHINGTON	105
DE	DOVER	105
	NEWARK	106
	WILMINGTON	106
FL	BOCA RATON	80
	BRADENTON	80
	CAPE CORAL	78
	CLEARWATER	81
	DAYTONA BEACH	75
	FORT LAUDERDALE	83
	FORT MYERS	78
	FORT PIERCE	81
	FORT WALTON BEACH	76
	GAINESVILLE	80
	JACKSONVILLE	78
	LAKELAND	78
	MELBOURNE	75
	MIAMI	81
	NAPLES	79
	OCALA	79
	ORLANDO	77
	PALM BAY	75
	PANAMA CITY	77
	PENSACOLA	76
	PORT ST. LUCIE	81
	PUNTA GORDA	78
	SARASOTA	80
	ST. PETERSBURG	80
	TALLAHASSEE	75
	TAMPA	80

METRO AREA MULTIPLIERS

State	City	Multiplier
FL	TITUSVILLE	75
	WEST PALM BEACH	80
	WINTER HAVEN	78
GA	ALBANY	86
	ATHENS	89
	ATLANTA	92
	AUGUSTA	86
	COLUMBUS	79
	MACON	83
	SAVANNAH	87
HI	HONOLULU	138
IA	CEDAR FALLS	91
	CEDAR RAPIDS	102
	DAVENPORT	106
	DES MOINES	104
	DUBUQUE	95
	IOWA CITY	97
	SIOUX CITY	91
	WATERLOO	91
ID	BOISE CITY	102
	POCATELLO	102
IL	BLOOMINGTON	113
	CHAMPAIGN	109
	CHICAGO	125
	DECATUR	107
	KANKAKEE	113
	NORMAL	113
	PEKIN	111
	PEORIA	111
	ROCKFORD	113
	SPRINGFIELD	108
	URBANA	109
IN	BLOOMINGTON	102
	ELKHART	96
	EVANSVILLE	99
	FORT WAYNE	100
	GARY	107
	GOSHEN	96
	INDIANAPOLIS	103
	KOKOMO	101
	LAFAYETTE	101
	MUNCIE	101
	SOUTH BEND	102
	TERRE HAUTE	100
KS	KANSAS CITY	120
	LAWRENCE	109
	TOPEKA	96
	WICHITA	87
KY	LEXINGTON	91
	LOUISVILLE	102
	OWENSBORO	101
LA	ALEXANDRIA	89
	BATON ROUGE	93
	BOSSIER CITY	90
	HOUMA	93
LA	LAFAYETTE	91
	LAKE CHARLES	93
	MONROE	89
	NEW ORLEANS	95
	SHREVEPORT	90
MA	BARNSTABLE	124
	BOSTON	128
	BROCKTON	118
	FITCHBURG	120
	LAWRENCE	121
	LEOMINSTER	120
	LOWELL	124
	NEW BEDFORD	118
	PITTSFIELD	118
	SPRINGFIELD	119
	WORCESTER	120
	YARMOUTH	124
MD	BALTIMORE	95
	CUMBERLAND	98
	HAGERSTOWN	90
ME	AUBURN	87
	BANGOR	87
	LEWISTON	87
	PORTLAND	88
MI	ANN ARBOR	119
	BATTLE CREEK	111
	BAY CITY	116
	BENTON HARBOR	111
	DETROIT	120
	EAST LANSING	117
	FLINT	116
	GRAND RAPIDS	112
	HOLLAND	112
	JACKSON	107
	KALAMAZOO	111
	LANSING	117
	MIDLAND	115
	MUSKEGON	112
	SAGINAW	116
MN	DULUTH	107
	MINNEAPOLIS	112
	ROCHESTER	107
	ST. CLOUD	105
	ST. PAUL	112
MO	COLUMBIA	114
	JOPLIN	103
	KANSAS CITY	118
	SPRINGFIELD	96
	ST. JOSEPH	117
	ST. LOUIS	115
MS	BILOXI	79
	GULFPORT	79
	HATTIESBURG	79
	JACKSON	79
	PASCAGOULA	79

METRO AREA MULTIPLIERS

State	City	Multiplier
MT	BILLINGS	96
	GREAT FALLS	90
	MISSOULA	91
NC	ASHEVILLE	73
	CHAPEL HILL	79
	CHARLOTTE	82
	DURHAM	81
	FAYETTEVILLE	75
	GOLDSBORO	80
	GREENSBORO	81
	GREENVILLE	79
	HICKORY	72
	HIGH POINT	81
	JACKSONVILLE	72
	LENOIR	72
	MORGANTON	72
	RALEIGH	80
	ROCKY MOUNT	72
	WILMINGTON	72
	WINSTON SALEM	77
ND	BISMARCK	84
	FARGO	98
	GRAND FORKS	81
NE	LINCOLN	84
	OMAHA	91
NH	MANCHESTER	106
	NASHUA	106
	PORTSMOUTH	111
NJ	ATLANTIC CITY	126
	BERGEN	129
	BRIDGETON	125
	CAPE MAY	125
	HUNTERDON	128
	JERSEY CITY	130
	MIDDLESEX	129
	MILLVILLE	125
	MONMOUTH	129
	NEWARK	129
	OCEAN	130
	PASSAIC	130
	SOMERSET	128
	TRENTON	128
	VINELAND	125
NM	ALBUQUERQUE	91
	LAS CRUCES	91
	SANTA FE	91
NV	LAS VEGAS	109
	RENO	97
NY	ALBANY	119
	BINGHAMTON	116
	BUFFALO	118
	DUTCHESS COUNTY	119
	ELMIRA	118
	GLENS FALLS	120
	JAMESTOWN	112

State	City	Multiplier
NY	NASSAU	137
	NEW YORK	148
	NEWBURGH	119
	NIAGARA FALLS	121
	ROCHESTER	118
	ROME	109
	SCHENECTADY	119
	SUFFOLK	137
	SYRACUSE	118
	TROY	119
	UTICA	109
OH	AKRON	112
	CANTON	107
	CINCINNATI	105
	CLEVELAND	114
	COLUMBUS	115
	DAYTON	115
	ELYRIA	114
	HAMILTON	105
	LIMA	115
	LORAIN	114
	MANSFIELD	115
	MASSILLON	107
	MIDDLETOWN	115
	SPRINGFIELD	109
	STEUBENVILLE	115
	TOLEDO	109
	WARREN	111
	YOUNGSTOWN	111
OK	ENID	86
	LAWTON	86
	OKLAHOMA CITY	85
	TULSA	80
OR	ASHLAND	109
	CORVALLIS	112
	EUGENE	112
	MEDFORD	109
	PORTLAND	114
	SALEM	112
	SPRINGFIELD	112
PA	ALLENTOWN	118
	ALTOONA	110
	BETHLEHEM	118
	CARLISLE	113
	EASTON	118
	ERIE	112
	HARRISBURG	113
	HAZLETON	118
	JOHNSTOWN	104
	LANCASTER	93
	LEBANON	115
	PHILADELPHIA	134
	PITTSBURGH	116
	READING	119
	SCRANTON	116

METRO AREA MULTIPLIERS

State	City	Multiplier
PA	SHARON	112
	STATE COLLEGE	98
	WILKES BARRE	116
	WILLIAMSPORT	97
	YORK	113
PR	MAYAGUEZ	73
	PONCE	74
	SAN JUAN	75
RI	PROVIDENCE	122
SC	AIKEN	89
	ANDERSON	71
	CHARLESTON	76
	COLUMBIA	76
	FLORENCE	73
	GREENVILLE	76
	MYRTLE BEACH	73
	NORTH CHARLESTON	81
	SPARTANBURG	73
	SUMTER	76
SD	RAPID CITY	81
	SIOUX FALLS	85
TN	CHATTANOOGA	84
	CLARKSVILLE	83
	JACKSON	83
	JOHNSON CITY	83
	KNOXVILLE	80
	MEMPHIS	84
	NASHVILLE	83
TX	ABILENE	88
	AMARILLO	92
	ARLINGTON	87
	AUSTIN	89
	BEAUMONT	88
	BRAZORIA	88
	BROWNSVILLE	73
	BRYAN	86
	COLLEGE STATION	86
	CORPUS CHRISTI	84
	DALLAS	89
	DENISON	87
	EDINBURG	73
	EL PASO	81
	FORT WORTH	87
	GALVESTON	93
	HARLINGEN	73
	HOUSTON	88
	KILLEEN	77
	LAREDO	78
	LONGVIEW	78
	LUBBOCK	91
	MARSHALL	87
	MCALLEN	73
	MIDLAND	87
	MISSION	73
	ODESSA	87
	PORT ARTHUR	88
	SAN ANGELO	87
	SAN ANTONIO	90
TX	SAN BENITO	73
	SAN MARCOS	89
	SHERMAN	87
	TEMPLE	77
	TEXARKANA	79
	TEXAS CITY	93
	TYLER	84
	VICTORIA	74
	WACO	77
	WICHITA FALLS	87
UT	OGDEN	95
	OREM	93
	PROVO	93
	SALT LAKE CITY	92
VA	CHARLOTTESVILLE	86
	LYNCHBURG	83
	NEWPORT NEWS	88
	NORFOLK	91
	PETERSBURG	78
	RICHMOND	90
	ROANOKE	76
	VIRGINIA BEACH	91
VT	BURLINGTON	97
WA	BELLEVUE	119
	BELLINGHAM	111
	BREMERTON	113
	EVERETT	117
	KENNEWICK	101
	OLYMPIA	113
	PASCO	100
	RICHLAND	101
	SEATTLE	119
	SPOKANE	98
	TACOMA	116
	YAKIMA	104
WI	APPLETON	113
	BELOIT	117
	EAU CLAIRE	113
	GREEN BAY	112
	JANESVILLE	117
	KENOSHA	118
	LA CROSSE	114
	MADISON	116
	MILWAUKEE	118
	NEENAH	113
	OSHKOSH	113
	RACINE	118
	SHEBOYGAN	112
	WAUKESHA	118
	WAUSAU	113
WV	CHARLESTON	113
	HUNTINGTON	113
	PARKERSBURG	113
	WHEELING	113
WY	CASPER	85
	CHEYENNE	85

A

B

C

D

T

U

V

W

Y